Chicago Quarterly Review Books

Chicago & San Francisco

My Postwar Life

**New Writings from Japan
and Okinawa**

Elizabeth McKenzie
Editor

with a Foreword by
Karen Tei Yamashita

For correspondence, updates and further information
about this book, visit Chicago Quarterly Review Books at
www.chicagoquarterlyreviewbooks.com
email: editor@chicagoquarterlyreviewbooks.com

Design by Hillary Geller
Printed in the United States of America.

10 9 8 7 6 5 4 3 2 1

Library of Congress Control Number: 2011918414

ISBN-10: 0984778802
ISBN-13: 978-0-9847788-0-5

Published by
Chicago Quarterly Review Books
Chicago & San Francisco

*The title of this book is taken
from Ben Takara's poem* Gama.

*Names of Japanese persons
throughout this work
appear in western form, family
name last.*

Table of Contents

Foreword

Memories of the Future in the Long Postwar
(Apsara in Twilight)

Although in Japan it is tomorrow, symbolically, at 8:15 in the morning of August 6, 2011, this writing begins. In the muted space of zero gravity, light years over ground zero, a dancer choreographs the celestial movements of floating apsara. The absence of sound is surreal and deafening, though an uncanny serendipity awaits me in a twilight concert of the poly-symphonic registers of composer Mizuno Shuko. Natsu (Summer), *in its compounding dissonance, then fills space. The program notes date the composition, 1988. During the entirety of that year, the emperor Hirohito lay dying, and the then mayor of Nagasaki spoke the unspeakable, suggesting that the healing of reconciliation might begin with an apology. In the relentless sauna of summer, there occurs the languid return to furusato to awaken and to be blessed by the spirits of the dead, to light the multiplying lanterns that skim across waters in a milky way.*

How many ways to remember? How many ways to forget? How many ways to re-member? How many ways to dis-member? A poet meditates across a walking earthscape. Earth walking. A sacred communion of solitude in the lap of nature. At the end of the trail, the poet may disappear, may disappear into a gama of memories and emerge with a prayer, or he may leave his footprint in lava, then plunge into the volcano of his desire, an apsara cradling his fall. He may recede into the jungle of a brutalizing war and emerge with the memory of lost love. Or in surviving that war, find a poetess to inscribe the watercolors of those lost years. He may, through a sheet of rain, see the vestiges of an erased self. Or through a veil of tears, a former life.

The writer recalls the past as a dreamscape. In the dream, the writer dangles a newborn through the din of a high-rise window like a gift to urbanity. The baby may be a tossed bomb to flatten the already superflat, cartooned commercialism, Godzilla returned to firebomb Tokyo and 66 other cities across the archipelago. The manga rears its furious body to implicate the deleted story, to forage in the rubble for the dead, or to reverse the patriarchal gaze. And though reconstituted as heroine-centered, youthful fantasy continues to desire the lore of the nimble warrior. Yet beware; perhaps the story is karmic and circular, a karmascape from which there is no escape. The writer recalls the future.

The writer recalls the past as a wordscape. What were the names for mother, grandmother, aunt? Appa, anna, obaa. In the wordscape, images are attached to a deep and original language without which there can be no memory. Translation can only transfer an approximation, the fuzzy form of eccentricity or derangement attached to women attached to soldiers attached to war perceived through the eyes of a starving youth or a lonely inquisitive child. The writer proposes a memory of women in twilight, akou-kurou. The writer recalls the names of his great grandmothers, traces his maternal lineages into an American landscape. The nineteenth century with its imperial beginnings augurs our stories—immigrant intentions, dreams of empire, the fateful collision with war. The writer invokes the name of her grandmother, a physician called to Nagasaki's ultimate disaster, to trace a love story made urgent and a life given meaning by cruel necessity, but ultimately by war.

The war haunts everything. It is the blot that names: Zainichi, hibakusha, Okinawan, nisei, renunciant, POW, comfort woman, Merikan, juri. War's occupation will control and censor every outcome, will obliterate the aftermath of starvation, black markets, and prostitution, will reinstate the zaibatsu and create an economic miracle and subservient ally. The artists and writers here were and are the born-into recipients of all this. This is their memory. This is their failure to memory.

The photographer recreates again and again the shuttered blast of the unutterable event, the superimposed shadow of life obliterated, the stopped watch at the precise moment. The work of the camera is his atonement. Now, Google Earth can zoom you headlong into Natori and the nearby Fukushima TEPCO nuclear power plant. The precision of time is likely known exactly, and your computer mouse can pull like a lampshade across your screen the before and after March 11, 2:45 pm satellite images. An earthscape slips into deathscape. You see in a swipe the ethereal clouds on those powder-blue boxes that masked the four nuclear reactors turn to debris and structural shells, and you cannot but recall in those precarious remains the forms of four boxed atomic domes. The irony of the puffy clouds drifting over domes like the ceiling of a child's room infuriates. You feel no atonement.

Time folds 66 years. Out of wreckage, the stone face of an angel is rescued from Nagasaki's Urakami Cathedral and buried as a totem beneath the rubble rebuilt as ramshackle shelter. A surviving woman lives there until her death. Upon her death, the face of the angel is revealed, and the apsara flutters heavenward. It is transcendence longed for.

11:02 am
August 9, 2011

Karen Tei Yamashita
Santa Cruz, California

I fell in love with Japanese literature preparing for a trip with my parents in the seventies. Academic librarians were on the move in those days, because they were sharing ideas about the future and books and how to organize them, and because my father was this kind of librarian at UCLA we were having Nigerian and Fijian and Australian and other assorted librarians over for dinner, and if we were going to Japan it meant the librarians there were ready to entertain us as well. My father checked out a canonical stack for me before we left—Ibuse, Endo, Soseki, Osamu, Oe. Library automation was the subject in those days, every book to be indexed in phlegm-colored, boulder-sized computers about to bury the card catalogues in an unstoppable avalanche, but upon our arrival in Kyoto, business with our hosts meant feasts with sake for the grownups and a milky, suspect drink for us kids called Calpis. Without meaning any harm, those librarians took us to a family bath, and my sister and I hid in the dressing room, sobbing as our parents dragged us in for a fascinating *cultural experience.* I remember what we had to shed; my sister's nylon smiling cat-head blouse spilled to the floor like a victim. Our mother said the librarians had spent a week's salary taking us around so we should be grateful whatever happened, and so we were. In our hotel, I was reading a New Directions paperback of Mishima's *Death in Midsummer.* I didn't understand what the young couple had to do for money in "Three Million Yen."

My readings led me into a house-of-mirrors Japan, constructed by writers rather than politics or geography, mysteriously ethereal yet earthy. There was a quality of expressive opacity to these writings; I couldn't tell if this was due to the once-removed quality of translation or to some distinctly Japanese habit of mind.

Keijiro Suga, Professor at Meiji University, recognizes "translational poetics" in his essay "Translation, Exophony, Omniphony:"

A language is not fully alive when translated into another. Half-dead, it gives a new life to the host language. Its original meaning becomes distorted and somewhat obscure, but at the same time the translated form is charged with an aura of discovery and excitement in a new environment.

Maybe in this "distorted" language I found something approximating my own struggles with expression, of needing to translate my own mind through the act of writing. In my early efforts I mimicked that slightly skewed opacity as a tool for accessing what felt like the real "me" in narrative form, as if coaxing a skittish spirit through hypnotic means.

This identification with Japan and its translated literature continues. Recently I've enjoyed the cheerful strangeness of Yoko Tawada, the matter-of-fact brutality of Natsuo Kirino, the twisted fury of poet Kaneko Mitsuharu, the slyness of Shotaro Yasuoka, and the stark realism of Kenji Nakagami. Haruki Murakami remains a favorite, book after book. I have three new novels sitting on my desk: Yo Hemmi's *Gush,* Hiromi Kawakami's *Manazuru,* and Choukitsu Kurumatani's *The Paradise Bird Tattoo (or, Attempted Double-Suicide),* variously billed as "bizarre," "surreal and grotesque," and "quietly reflective and bitterly gritty." I'm eager to see how it's been done.

I'm also looking forward to sitting down with *Manoa's* new issue *Living Spirit: Literature and Resurgence in Okinawa,* devoted to Okinawan writers including Shun Medoruma, Tami Sakiyama, Eiki Matayoshi and Ben Takara. In his Editor's Note, Katsunori Yamazato, Professor at University of the Ryukyus, writes:

> *Okinawan writing has been largely marginalized or subsumed in the larger category of Japanese literature. Okinawan litera-ture, however, is not a subordinate category but a literature with its own history, traditions, and sensibilities. It stands on an equal basis with Japanese and other world literatures.*

In the spirit of demarginalizing Okinawan literature, and of celebrating its resurgence, we pull it from under the umbrella of Japanese literature in our title to stand freely on its own.

In 2010, in Japan on a Japan–U.S. Friendship Commission fellow-ship with my husband and children, I researched the long shadow of the war for a novel. And though I wasn't in the loop with librarians anymore, we were meeting people equally concerned with books who helped us assemble material for the journal I co-edit, *Chicago Quarterly Review.* Poets, fiction writers, politicians, photographers, playwrights, activists and academics kindly offered their creations to this project; soon it was clear we had more

—

The Ryukyu islands, generally referred to as Okinawa, were unified under the inde-pendent Ryukyu kingdom in 1429. Invaded in 1609 by the Satsuma clan of south-ern Kyushu, the Ryukyus were annexed by Meiji Japan in 1879. Many Okinawans resented Japanese rule. After invading Okinawa in 1945 in the bloodiest land battle of the Pacific war, the U.S. assumed control over the ter-ritory. Okinawa was returned to Japan in 1972, though there remains a major U.S. mi-litary base to this day.

than a simple issue on our hands. And so this becomes the first anthology to be published by Chicago Quarterly Review Books.

Many pieces in this volume were translated for the first time for us. "Don't Arrogate, Hiroshima," a controversial essay by former Nagasaki Mayor Hitoshi Motoshima to oppose the World Heritage designation for the Hiroshima Peace Memorial in 1996, appears in English here for the first time, as does the poetry of Okinawan activist Ben Takara, in whose poem "Gama" we found our thematic base and book's title, "Park City," a play about Hiroshima's latent memories by experimental playwright Masataka Matsuda, a story and essay on Okinawan language by Tami Sakiyama, an essay on the *fin de siècle* Japanese working student in America by Takayuki Tatsumi, an essay by Mari Kotani on Yaoi culture, and poetry by Korean Kim Shi-Jong, born and educated under Japanese rule. The diary of Noboru Tokuda, soldier in the Imperial Army, appears with special thanks to Mineo and Sanae Tokuda of Kyoto for befriending us and sharing this personal object.

Translators Carl Nommensen, Kyoko Nommensen, Kyoko Yoshida, James Dorsey, Ikue Kina, Ryuta Imafuku, Joel Klotz and Sakae Fujita have made this possible.

Master photographer Shomei Tomatsu's retrospective, *Hues and Textures of Nagasaki,* was published in 2010 by the Nagasaki Prefectural Art Museum and provides us with fourteen of Tomatsu's iconic photographs. Ryuta Imafuku's accompanying essay, "Nagasaki. And Scattered Islets of Time," previously translated by Waku Miller for the retrospective, explores many of the postwar themes which thread through this collection.

Some of the writings have been translated by the authors, such as the wistful work of Katsunori Yamazato ("The Silver Motorcycle") and Keijiro Suga ("Walking"). Other pieces were written in English by Japanese writers: Goro Takano's surreal story "Blast," Kentaro Yamaki's yearning wartime story "Last Time I Saw You," new writer Iona Sugihara's story "Small Fish." After the devastation in northeastern Japan in March of 2011, Hiroshi Fukurai, Professor at the University of California, Santa Cruz, wrote about the destruction of his hometown Natori in "Disaster Memories."

Others pieces are by English speakers with a variety of connections to Japan. "Superflat Tokyo," by bi-national writer and cultural critic Roland Kelts, compares the megalopolis to the artistic vision of Takashi Murakami, who coined the term "superflat" to describe the shallow emptiness of postwar Japanese consumer society. Christopher Yohmei Blasdel, artistic director at the International House in Tokyo, writes about the tragic disappearance in Japan of American poet Craig Arnold in "An Exchange for Fire." Stewart Wachs, Associate Editor of *Kyoto Journal,* writes in "Dream Corridor" about a nearly supernatural call to spend his life in Japan. "The Deleted Line" from Canadian writer Deni Y. Bechard's forthcoming story collection *An Opera of War* revolves around a Tokyo editor's unraveling after he removes important language from a textbook about the devastation in Okinawa during the war.

"The Atomic Survivors: A Jungian Contribution" comes from analyst Janice Nakao, Director of Social Work for the Japanese American Service Committee of Chicago. Stephen Woodhams' "The Emperor and the Mayor" concerns our meeting with former Mayor Hitoshi Motoshima in Nagasaki and delves into the knotty history of the mayor's near assassination and peace activism. "The Art of Passing Through Walls" is excerpted from a novel in both Japanese and English by prolific writer-translators Leza Lowitz and Shogo Oketani, about a young Japanese American ninja's first visit to her ancestral home in Aomori.

The inclusion of Setsuko Ishiguro, who choreographs zero gravity dances for Japanese astronauts, was a happy accident: we sat beside her on a train in Italy, this book already in the works. The photo she showed us of her unlikely achievement seemed fated to end up here.

In the words of Paul Yamazaki, co-founder of *Reading the World,* a collaboration between publishers and independent bookstores to promote literature in translation:

> *We are lost in a vast sea of literature unknown to us. The barriers of language have left us rudderless in the midst of the marvelous. To become familiar with the stories and storytellers from other parts of our planet... is a key component of being a citizen in the world today.*

When I learned that the fellowship I had received was founded by a payment from the Japanese government to the United States at the time of the reversion of Okinawa to Japan in 1972, I felt strongly moved, as if a tentacle of our fraught and complicated history with Japan and Okinawa had brushed my own cheek, and that whatever would come of my time there, it should be worthy of this legacy.

The shared mission of producing this collection with the writers and translators whose work appears in it has been richly rewarding. The instincts must have been contagious that led my father and his fellow librarians to joyfully convene at great distances over the gathering and availability and future of books.

Elizabeth McKenzie

My Postwar Life
New Writings from Japan and Okinawa

—
fig. 1
A wristwatch recovered from the rubble of the atomic blast
(Nagasaki Atomic Bomb Museum, 1961)

Nagasaki. And Scattered Islets of Time
Ryuta Imafuku

Hues and Textures of Nagasaki
Shomei Tomatsu

Time: Suspended

That defining moment is really the only place to begin: the moment indicated by the hands on a wristwatch, stopped forever at 11:02 a.m., the time that the atomic bomb went off. A shot of that watch (fig. 1) is among the photographs that Shomei Tomatsu took during his first visit to Nagasaki, in 1961. The watch and other personal effects emerged from the rubble and ashes in the Uenomachi district, about 700 meters from ground zero. A dial for seconds on the lower part of the face is damaged, and the hand is gone. Miraculously, the hour and minute hands survived the blast. They retained the decisive instant with starkly mechanical precision, which riveted the photographer's eye.

Tomatsu's photo of the watch invokes "Nagasaki time," arrested in the instant of the nuclear explosion. It expresses concisely the indelible, historical fact of that instant. The photo enables us to continue contemplating the conflagration wrought of a single point in human history. It enables us to return repeatedly to that fateful instant by means of contemplation, to come to a full stop atop the significance of that instant, to dare to imagine the unspeakable tragedy unleashed in that instant—a carnage of unprecedented swiftness, which extinguished the heartbeats of tens of thousands in the blink of an eye.

The continuity of life and the inexorable flow of history belie the time stoppage symbolized by the watch in Tomatsu's photo. Thus does the image captured on film evoke all the more powerfully the extraordinary circumstances of its singular moment. We attribute a similar singularity to other moments: to Japan's "2.26" (February 26, 1936), when fanatical young officers in the Imperial Army mutinied in the name of the emperor; to Korea's "4-3" (April 3, 1948), when interfactional strife, which would ultimately claim some 20,000 lives, erupted on the island of Jeju; and, more recently, to the United States' "9/11" (September 11, 2001), when suicide hijackers crashed passenger airliners into the World Trade Center in New York City and into the Pentagon near Washington, D.C.

Several historic watersheds, such as the examples cited, have earned a nomenclature that catalogs them in memory by month and day. That Nagasaki's moment commanded greater specificity than month and day, that it commanded cataloging by hour and minute, is testimony to the immensity of the nuclear violence perpetrated in that instant.

The suspended time indicated by the watch in Tomatsu's photo is doubly emblematic. Along with denoting Nagasaki's moment, it heralds the beginning of Tomatsu's photographic journey in the city—a sojourn of recording Nagasaki, of committing the city to memory through photographs. The fateful encounter spawned a photographer's critical commentary on postwar Japanese history. It launched Tomatsu on a personal quest, even before he was fully conscious of its significance.

Tomatsu had become entirely conscious of his mission when he published his first book of photographs, which he titled *11:02 Nagasaki* (1966). And the tragic moment remained central to his Nagasaki photography, as in the 1990 exhibition Weathering Time and in the 1995 book *Nagasaki, 11:02 a.m., August 9, 1945*. Tomatsu's half-century photographic exploration of Nagasaki, which began with the encounter with the watch, yields a continuing accumulation of insight for us to witness.

Time: Dangling

The watch stopped at 11:02 quietly permeates the past and the present—Nagasaki's and ours—as physical evidence of an undiminished trauma. In the immobility of its hands is a powerful antidote to the fading and lapse of memory. The visual image of that mute and immobile timepiece is, simultaneously, a powerful reminder that time stops for no one. It reminds us that the current phase of history—the "present"—could never come to a standstill. It reminds us, too, that the catastrophe that began with the detonation of the atomic bomb at 11:02 did not end there.

A lasting agony appears in the stationary face of the watch, evincing an undying misery, a stifling suppression, a persistent contradiction. Tomatsu inserts himself between the frozen moment and the unceasing advance of Nagasaki's everyday existence. And in the disconnect between stasis, on the one hand, and passage, on the other, he takes to the field of photographic struggle. Tomatsu wrote in the 1961 essay "*Genkokei* [Primal Scene]":

> *Nagasaki has two timeframes: the time forever stopped 16 years ago at 11:02 a.m. on August 9 and the subsequent span, dated from that moment, complete with all the change that it has enveloped. The deaths of the victims are a link between those two timeframes.*

—
fig. 2
Tsuyo Kataoka
(Motoharamachi, 1961)

Casting a shadow over Nagasaki's "subsequent span" have been the deaths, one by one, of the surviving victims. Each death confirms anew the horror unleashed by the 11:02 blast and, in merging Nagasaki's "two time-frames," exposes the callousness of time. The victims succumb to a fate that was, in dangling time, unavoidable, and they return quietly—inevitably—to that moment at 11:02 a.m. on August 9, 1945. Their reprieve extended, that is, through Nagasaki's "subsequent span," only to return to the starting point of that span.

Fulfilling fate is, in a sense, a positive exercise. Along with suspending time, the 11:02 wristwatch has imparted the will to impel the life of Nagasaki onward into the future. It has demonstrated the potential for life to retain a sanctity while continuing in the aftermath of a tragic moment. Tomatsu soon acquired in Nagasaki a powerful commitment to recording and communicating the life that unfolded there before his eyes (fig. 2).

The moment denoted by "11:02" ceased being simply a tragedy frozen in time. It became the origin of a new sort of linkage among human life. In turning all to ashes, the nuclear event engendered from out of the ruins, as was required, a new order, a new sensibility, a new value system. The ruins of time blanketed the rubble that the city had approached and asserted new adaptations on the works resident there. Tomatsu was too alert to miss the ruins inherent to every living individual. Those ruins, anything but fossilized tragedy, manifested as a creative energy born of the pulsing life of flesh and bones. Tomatsu recalls in the essay *"Genkokei"* coming to terms with the ruins:

> I had regarded ruins only as the product of the deterioration
> of a city. What I learned [in Nagasaki] was that ruins also exist
> inside people.

We detect an affirmative element in Tomatsu's recollection. The victims and their families found their way through the ruins of sickness and suffering, bounded by death and terror, and Tomatsu documented and continues to document their progress (fig. 3). Glowing in his photographs is a beauty suggestive of a flower, name unknown. Somewhere amid the changing seasons, the flower has begun to bloom on the periphery of the stark ruins.

Time dangles, does away with stock notions of human relations. New ties arise from the ruins of daily life, and victims and photographer assert the commonality of an extended family. Springing forth from that familial atmosphere is a reassuring warmth where we might otherwise have expected a cold emptiness. That pervasive spirit renders the victims and the nuclear artifacts continuously visible. Thus are they discernible even in Tomatsu's snapshot-like photographs in which they do not appear overtly.

—
fig. 3
Shizuka Urakawa
(Sakamotomachi, 1961)

—
fig. 4
Bamboo stalks imprinted by the atomic blast with the images of surrounding stalks and leaves
(Nagasaki Atomic Bomb Museum, 1961)

Time: Cauterizing

In the mechanics of a photograph, time appears as light. Creating a photographic image is ordinarily a matter of exposing silver halide film or a charge-coupled device for a few hundredths or a few tenths of a second. An equivalence between time and light becomes instinctive for any photographer. An astonishingly similar equivalence is evident in some of Nagasaki's nuclear artifacts. Especially well known is a photograph taken by Eiichi Matsumoto a month after the bombing.

Matsumoto's photo portrays the silhouettes of a ladder and a human figure on the wooden wall of the army headquarters in Nagasaki. The atomic blast burned off the tar coating on the wall except where the shapes of the soldier and his ladder intervened. Gruesome optics etched the silhouettes on the wall as a photographic negative.

Nagasaki's nuclear tragedy yielded numerous relics like the silhouettes on the wall of the army headquarters. Tomatsu saw a lot of them in the archives at the Nagasaki International Cultural Center (now the Nagasaki Atomic Bomb Museum), and the photos and physical specimens must have impressed on him the photographic character of the atomic blast. Tomatsu's preoccupation with Nagasaki time and his concern with light became two sides of the same photographic coin.

Tomatsu took his memorable photo of photo-etched bamboo (fig. 4) during his first visit to Nagasaki. The photo is of large stalks of bamboo onto which the blast has edged photonegative images of surrounding stalks and leaves. Tomatsu's strong feeling for his subject is readily apparent in the subtle angles of the bamboo stalks, in the lacelike silhouettes of the leaves and stalks, and in the pitch-black background.

Taking close-up photographs of relics in a museum 16 years after the fact is hardly equivalent to witnessing the bombing itself. Nor is it merely a matter of cataloging physical specimens. Rather, Tomatsu is exploring a medium for converting time into light. And by rendering his findings photographically, he directs our gaze to the metaphysical aspect of the synthesis of images.

The "cauterized time" expressed by the nuclear artifacts exerted a lasting hold on the photographer. As Tomatsu walked about Nagasaki and photographed scenes of daily life, the flash of the explosion was ever present. He recorded something of that flash in the fleeting instant of each shot, in each batting of an eye, in each split-second exposure.

We encounter throughout Tomatsu's Nagasaki oeuvre a richly compassionate, carefully moderated approach to human and inanimate subjects. That approach would seem to reflect a sensitive ethic rooted in a subconscious sense of photographic responsibility. The photographer apparently senses alarming parallels between the repetitive "violence" of the rendering of images inside his camera and the transformational violence of the atomic blast. And he addresses that concern in each photograph that he takes.

Time: Discovered, Regenerative

The death in July 2000 of Nagasaki resident Moto Watanabe at the age of 85 occasioned a startling discovery. Watanabe lived in the Uenomachi district. Her house was near the Urakami Cathedral, a Nagasaki landmark that had been largely destroyed in the atomic blast and which had been rebuilt after the war. Watanabe had built her house from debris gathered at the blast site.

What startled the friends and family members who came to sort Watanabe's belongings was what they found under the house. Unremarkably, Watanabe had assembled a simple stone bin for storing sweet potatoes, a staple food in Nagasaki. What was remarkable was what she had secretly saved beside the bin: a large section of a stained glass window and the head from the sculpture of an angel, both apparently salvaged from the ruins of the cathedral.

Tomatsu had struck up a friendship with Watanabe on his first visit to Nagasaki, and the two had remained close over the years. The photographer was astounded at the discovery of his friend's hidden and utterly unsuspected trove. Everything about the trove and its discovery propelled Tomatsu further in his inquiry into the workings of time.

The angel's head, rediscovered after more than half a century out of sight, suggests especially interesting parallels with Tomatsu's work. Photos of sculptures of angels and saints toppled by the atomic blast (fig. 5) are the best-known works in Tomatsu's earliest Nagasaki photography. Among those works are brutally arresting images of sculptures of angels and Jesus from which the heads have been blasted away. The blast that wrought horrific violence on humans wrought a similar violence on stone-sculpted objects of Catholic devotion. And the beheaded sculptures conjure notions of flesh torn from the corporeal being of Nagasaki (fig. 6). Tomatsu's images reverberate with awareness of Nagasaki's Christian history, which dates from the arrival of missionaries in the sixteenth century.

Discovered beneath the floor of the late Watanabe's house, the angel's head was the rediscovery of another time, a jolting shift in the fabric of history. Tomatsu took the head back to the site of the house after wreckers had demolished the structure. He placed it amid the rubble and photographed it again. The head had miraculously restored what had been painfully missing in his earlier photographs of headless sculptures. The revelatory 1961 photos of headless sculptures were reborn in 2000 with the photographing of the head from under Watanabe's house. Two points in time transcended a gulf of contradictions and came together as one (fig. 7, catalog no. 208).

We can also regard the event as a summons: a time summoned from the past as a witness. Watanabe's faith and Tomatsu's photographic mediation beg the question, "What happened back then?" The question, more than mere testimony from the past, resounds into the present and addresses us in the frame of will and intent.

—
fig. 5
Statues of angels and saints destroyed in the atomic blast
(Urakami Cathedral, 1961)

—
fig. 6
The bomb-damaged statue of an angel
(Urakami Cathedral, 1961)

fig. 7
The head of a statue of an
angel from Urakami
Cathedral found under Moto
Watanabe's house and
photographed at the former
site of the house
(Uenomachi, 2000)

Watanabe never revealed to anyone why she had kept the angel's head under her floor. We can well imagine, however, the desperation that prevailed in the immediate aftermath of the bombing. We can contemplate how the religious faith invested in a stone figure could have meshed with the will to survive. And we can see how Watanabe, happening upon the head in the rubble, might have elected to install it under her makeshift house.

The faith-shaped actions of Watanabe and others preserved, unobserved, the scattered holy figures of the Urakami Cathedral. Time coalesces in those survivors' legacy, summoned forth, and conveys the essence of the victims' struggle.

As notable as the head safeguarded by Watanabe is the section of stained glass that she secreted away. On its discovery, Tomatsu promptly photographed the glass atop a stone in front of Watanabe's house (catalog no. 6). That, too, documented a rediscovery of time. The red and the blue of the stained glass are less evocative of despair, however, than of an oddly pure sense of hope.

Tomatsu reshot several artifacts in preparation for this exhibition, including Watanabe's stained glass. He rephotographed it in light filtered through the stained glass of the rebuilt Urakami Cathedral. None of the resultant photographs ended up as part of the exhibition, but they are vintage Tomatsu: linking disparate times, transpositioning reborn light, reaffirming the present in reference to the equivalence of light and time. Disparate times manifest in the gleaming spectra of the photographs. The photographer, steered by Nagasaki's beacon, has finally arrived at the scattered islets of time that are his destiny.

Time: Contact; Time: Interference

Multiple timeframes coexist in Nagasaki, unfolding in a pattern suggestive of scattered islets. Tomatsu folds those archipelagic times onto each other in a scintillating approach to criticism. That approach first took shape definitively in 2000 in his large exhibition Nagasaki Mandala.

The 2000 exhibition included a troubling shot (fig. 8) of specimen jars that contained organs removed from victims killed in the atomic blast and preserved in formalin. The jars rest, neatly arranged, on sheets of English-language newspaper spread on a floor, and Tomatsu has photographed them from above. His composition could conceivably suggest an aerial view of Nagasaki as seen from the aircraft that dropped the atomic bomb.

Tomatsu has, in other words, turned his critical imagination to a present-day incarnation of the blast site and has brought together times from different points in history. He propagates a subtly nuanced interference between the times, accompanied by a delicate wavering. The exceedingly critical and philosophical stance on view in this photo is representative of his work in recent years.

—
catalog no. 6
Stained Glass
The atomic blast fused panes of stained glass into the mass seen in this photo. Moto Watanabe kept the glass under the floor of her house, where it was discovered after her death. Watanabe's survivors donated it to Urakami Cathedral. (Uenomachi, 2000)

—
fig. 8
Specimen jars that hold organs removed from victims killed in the atomic blast
(Atomic Bomb Disease Institute, Nagasaki University, 2000)

In the present exhibition, Tomatsu has turned to digital photography throughout. That has permitted him to go to greater extremes in combining disparate times. Especially notable is his new rendering of the bamboo imprinted with leafy patterns by heat waves from the atomic blast. Tomatsu ventured out to the bamboo grove in Nagasaki's Nameshi district where the stalks in question had apparently grown. He took a photo of the present-day grove and then superimposed an image of the scorched bamboo on top of that photo (fig. 9, catalog no. 300).

Tomatsu's new bamboo work emerged from his participation in a project for rephotographing the nuclear artifacts at the Nagasaki Atomic Bomb Museum. The work, however, goes far beyond any conventional notion of simply rephotographing things. It exudes critical commentary in the vein of Tomatsu's continuing examination of time.

Only Tomatsu could have created a work like his composite photo of bamboo. His nearly half century of sharing in the life of Nagasaki has qualified him uniquely to pair the moment of 11:02 a.m., August 9, 1945, with the ongoing present. Only in Tomatsu's hands could we countenance such a bold statement, expressed forthrightly and matter-of-factly.

Tomatsu has also combined multiple images in his photo of a maple singed by the atomic blast in Nagasaki's Shiroyamamachi district (catalog no. 287). His preference, Tomatsu confides, would have been to take the specimen from the museum to the site of its origin. He would have liked to stand the long-dead trunk erect at the place where it grew and photograph the arboreal time, past and present. Permission to take the trunk out of the museum was not forthcoming, however, so Tomatsu placed the trunk in the setting digitally.

In viewing these works, we abandon at the outset any concern with whether they are digital composites or natural photographs. Any notions of technological artificiality dissolve amid the reality that these works convey and amid the questions that they pose. All too rarely does digital composition in photography become a setting for such profound commentary. We are to welcome any technology that allows for bringing disparate times together in the provocatively sincere manner of Tomatsu.

Combining images yields a similarly sophisticated and highly philosophical commentary in other works in the exhibition. A case in point is a photo of Senji Yamaguchi (catalog no. 131). He is standing before a photo of his horribly scarred neck taken by Tomatsu nearly 50 years earlier. Yamaguchi wears an expression, both tearful and joyful, that defies stereotype.

Another good example of transcendentally effective composition is Tomatsu's rendering of Sumie Hisamatsu, who died in the atomic bombing (fig. 10). He has photographed a hairpin of hers that was recovered from the ashes and has superimposed it on her hair in the memorial photo used at her funeral. Her visage appears tantalizingly close to speaking out to us in the here and now.

—
fig. 9
A photo of bamboo stalks imprinted by the atomic blast with leafy images
superimposed on a present-day photo of the site where the bamboo grew
(Nagasaki Atomic Bomb Museum, 1985 and 2008)

—
catalog no. 287
Maple Tree
This maple tree stood in Shiroyamamachi about 800 meters from ground zero.
It was about 79 years old at the time of the bombing.
(Nagasaki Atomic Bomb Museum and Hamaguchimachi, 2008)

—
catalog no. 131
Senji Yamaguchi
Yamaguchi, born in 1930, was working at the Mitsubishi Arms Factory at the time of the bombing and suffered burns over nearly his entire body. He survived, however, and became a vocal proponent of nuclear disarmament after attending the First World Atomic and Hydrogen Bomb Prohibition Meeting in 1955. Yamaguchi subsequently became a co-chairperson of Nihon Hidankyo, a confederation of organizations of victims of atomic and hydrogen bombs, and the chairman of the Nagasaki Atomic Bomb Survivors Council. (Nagasaki Atomic Bomb Museum, 1998)

fig. 10
A memorial photo of Sumie Hisamitsu photographed together with Hisamitsu's ornamental hairpin
(Nagasaki Atomic Bomb Museum, 1985 and 2008)

Tomatsu's montages of photos and physical objects are, like other techniques that he has refined, a means of linking points in time. Vortices of interference waves arise in the media of time and light between the eras invoked. Nagasaki time surges out from the diversity of rhythms and hues and presses upon us in all its complexity—impossibly dense in texture and curiously quiet in demeanor.

The Franco-Swiss filmmaker Jean-Luc Godard probed the limits of cinematic montage in the four-chapter video project *Histoire(s) du cinéma (1989–1998)*. Interestingly, Godard and Tomatsu were born in the same year, 1930. Godard discusses his approach to montage in an extended conversation with the celebrated cinephile Youssef Ishaghpour published in 2000 as *Archéologie du cinéma et mémoire du siècle* [The Archeology of Film and the Memory of a Century]:

> *Fundamental to everything is the continuous existence of two. I always start by showing two images, not one. That's what I call "image."*

A duality prevails, Godard thus reveals, in every image that he creates. The filmmaker would have us know that an image never subsists in a single context or historicity.

Visual images of the atomic bombing and of the Holocaust inherently transcend any single era and even any single characterization, be it "tragic" or whatever. The artist needs to draw the subject matter into the field of interference that arises between two images and cast it in that dualistic, plural context. Only then can the artist achieve a truly creative imaging and thereby impart life to the subject matter.

At issue here is something other than a facile assimilation or fusion of images as elements in a visual tableau—something other, too, than the annihilation of original meaning. Rather, this is about the divisive differences and the unifying commonalities that reside between two images, between two points in time, between two instances of light. It is about the way that those complexities pose questions and offer understanding that would be impossible with a single image.

Godard, incidentally, uses visual material from Nagasaki in his *Histoire(s) du cinéma*: the photo of the silhouettes of the soldier and ladder on the wooden wall of the army headquarters. He pairs that photo with a shot of the stiff corpse of a Jewish girl who has been strangled by the Germans and hung in the air. Each image is true to its original context, yet each also becomes a broader statement about the evils that people inflict on each other. The paired images, in their resonance and in their intertwining, urge us toward a deeper understanding.

Tomatsu reminds us with his photographs that images created as art present multiple possibilities. His unprecedented experiments in photography carry an ante of rare passion. For us to match that ante, we need to come to terms with the startling juxtaposition and mutual interference of the times depicted. The ante for us as viewers is a readiness to entrust our response to emergent understanding and to unbridled intuition.

Time: Permeation, Salvation

Tomatsu continues to walk about Nagasaki, and his strolls remain a wellspring of photography. This exhibition presents an extensive selection of recent results of those strolls—renderings of time and light in contemporary Nagasaki. Here are works that draw us into the overwhelmingly everyday permeation of the blast zone in the present tense.

These photographs exhibit, of course, a conscious craftsmanship, as in regard to juxtapositioning and other elements of composition. What is most striking, though, is the context. We see the present-day light of Nagasaki flickering here and there in deceptively ordinary snapshot-like photographs. Yet what we sense throughout is the apocalyptic flash of 11:02, persistent and continually mutating.

The overlapping images—the stratification of light, of time— encompass implications that predate the blast. Nagasaki had long exhibited a vigorous mix of cultural elements and a wildly refracted perspective on time. It and nearby Hirado were the only two Japanese ports that remained open through the nation's two-plus centuries of isolation, from 1616 to 1858. Nagasaki thus became a cultural crossroads; an entryway for innumerable foreign inputs; an avenue of churning, of alternating amalgamation and separation.

Tomatsu passes through Nagasaki's refracted admixture of time and offers salvation. Modernity and official revisionism have crushed our understanding of time into a monotonous, undifferentiated flow and have imposed an amnesic obliviousness to the possibilities engendered by the diversity of genuine time. At the sight of the archipelago of time addressed by Tomatsu, we garner hope. And we recall the reason described by Tomatsu in *11:02 Nagasaki* for focusing on the city and for returning there repeatedly:

> *Because I want to beat back my own amnesic tendencies,*
> *to view the persistence of the damage wrought by an atomic*
> *bomb, the ultimate weapon that emerged in the 20th century,*
> *a century known for its wars.*

"Persistence" is a word choice that would appear to reflect a driving sense of commitment. Tomatsu bears witness to the vital persistence of the time and light that permeate everyday life in Nagasaki. Lushly interspersed in the manner of scattered islets, the time and light transcend the evidence presented accusatorially by the damage.

Tomatsu's perseverance exerts a forcefulness sufficient to beat back our amnesic propensity. The photographer himself enters into the time strewn about as scattered islets, where he would live that time together with the other occupants.

An apocalyptic air wafts through the contrasting and vibrant hues of Tomatsu's innumerable snapshots taken while strolling about Nagasaki. And we hear the soft sound of waves. They are stroking the shore of Nirai, a mythical island realm across the sea. That island rises far beyond even the scattered islets of time on which Tomatsu has fixed his gaze. It is the realm of the spirits and the place to where all return in due course.

—

fig. 11
A shot from Tomatsu's
Machiaruki (Walking around
Town) series
(Kannaimachi, 1975)

—

All photos © Shomei Tomatsu
through the courtesy
of Nagasaki Prefectural Art
Museum

—

Translated by Waku Miller

Blast

Goro Takano

Did you forget your last night's dream? Again?

Don't worry, it is right here. Read it and remember.

In the dream, you're an obese Japanese novelist with a heavy case of senile dementia, who has no idea when a story you've been writing recently will be completed.

And, in the dream, your story (tentatively titled *Extravaganza)* is somehow about America. However, you don't remember what the story is all about anymore.

In fact, you don't remember your name and age. You don't even remember who I am. All you remember is that you're writing an extraordinary story.

Now you bump into the twenty-somethingth writer's block. You still don't know how to transcend it.

So you choose to take a rest. You sit on a living-room sofa and start to watch TV. A pile of fancy-looking chocolate-bar wrappers is on your table, right in front of you. And your chin and lower lip are left smeared with mud-like chocolate. Of course, as usual, you don't care at all.

Your child, a newborn baby, is sleeping next to you, soundly on a hippo-shaped cushion on the sofa.

Your sex-maniac spouse is not present. It is a benefit now for you neither to know where (s)he is nor to remember who (s)he is anymore. Otherwise, you might try to kill him or her.

If you could lose all your words, it might be another benefit. However, you still cannot. Because your dementia is not heavy enough? Because you're such a coward? Who knows?

Anyway, only you and the baby are in the scene. It may be morning, afternoon, or night. You try to forget about your manuscript for a while. You just imagine your obese body floating in the water, with your eyes, ears, nostrils, and nothing else above the surface.

Your room is on the top floor of a tall building, which seems to be located in the center of a nameless city. Through a large window, you can see the spring sunrise, the summertime thunderhead, or the winter moon.

A woman appears on the TV.

She says she is a Lecturer in Creative Writing. "Poor you, cannot start a new paragraph? Okay, I'll show you an intriguing exercise," she says. "Pick up five different words from all the paragraphs you've written so far, and make a new story out of all of them within a minute. Don't think. Rather, let your fingers think. Believe me, that will be the very next paragraph your story needs now!"

Following her advice, you pick up, intuitively, "sex," "heavy," "transcend," "extraordinary," and "hippo." And, while hearing your baby's gossamer-like breathing, your fingers begin to write the following lines on a piece of paper:

An extraordinary hippo transcends heavy sex
Heavy sex promotes a cute idea
A cute idea fires a tainted castle
A tainted castle invites a horny mouse
A horny mouse kills a handsome Japanese
A handsome Japanese visits a shabby nation
A shabby nation colonizes the entire world
The entire world ignores an individual soul
An individual soul discovers a handy hideout
A handy hideout welcomes a lonesome thief
A lonesome thief meets an American maiden
An American maiden dedicates a bogus prayer
A bogus prayer occupies vacant space
Vacant space encloses an extraordinary hippo

What a bunch of crap. What is this lecturer thinking about, you ask the TV monitor.

When you are about to dump the paper, the same woman turns to you again on the screen, with a frown on her face:

"Didn't this practice work at all? Alas, sorry about that. Then why don't you forget all you've written until now and start from scratch? Of course, you definitely need a good intro for a brand-new story, don't you? The next exercise will be so effective, believe me, that you can get it right now, just quick. All you have to do is to transform the following Grimms' tale in the way your fingers wish it to be. Not in the way your brain wishes, mind you. I'm pretty sure the end result will function perfectly as the ideal beginning of your new work!"

*There was once a poor woman who had two little
girls. The youngest was sent to the forest every day to gather
wood.*

*Once when she had gone a long way before finding any,
a beautiful little child appeared who helped her pick up the
wood and carried it home for her.*

*Then, in a twinkling, he vanished. The little girl told her
mother, but the mother wouldn't believe her.*

*Then one day she brought home a rosebud and told
her mother the beautiful child had given it to her and said he
would come again when the rosebud opened. The mother put
the rosebud in water.*

*One morning the little girl didn't get up out of bed. The
mother went and found the child dead, but looking very lovely.
The rosebud had opened that same morning.*

Staring at the TV screen, you find your fingers hovering in the air, as if
to scribble on an invisible piece of paper something you have never been able
to discover by yourself:

*Right after the Pacific war, in a small local city, there
was once a poor old Japanese woman who had two young
beautiful girls. The younger one was sent to a shady bar
downtown every night to entertain teenaged American GIs.
She always admired every American soldier, regardless of
his skin color. "Gibu mi chokoreito, GI" was a vogue phrase
among a majority of hungry street kids at that time. And all
Japanese men looked simply too skinny, too miserable, and
still too male-oriented to the girl. So she wanted to marry an
American GI someday. That was her only wish.*

*Once when she had worked until midnight before find-
ing any ideally good-looking GI in the bar, a beautiful young
American soldier appeared. He said to her, in the way even
she could understand, "No sex, I'm okay, only talk, TALK."*

*Then in a twinkle he vanished. The girl told her mama-
san boss, but she wouldn't believe her.*

*Then one day she brought to the boss a box full of
expensive-looking chocolates and told her the beautiful guy
had given it to her and said he would come again when she
ate up all of them. Secretly, the mama-san brought the box
back home and gave it to her illegitimate daughter whose
American father had already abandoned his Japanese family*

and headed back home. Naturally, the illegitimate daughter
ate them all up.

One morning the young girl didn't come to the bar.
The mama-san boss stopped by her shabby house, and the
girl's mother found her dead, but looking very lovely. That
same morning some playful GIs set the bar on fire under
the influence of alcohol, and it was closed down. And, that
night, another box full of expensive-looking chocolates was
delivered there.

What a fool's errand. Boy, this gets nowhere, you sigh.

"That's all for today. Thanks for watching, see you tomorrow," the lecturer says. You pull out a remote from under the hippo-shaped cushion and turn the TV to the next channel.

Suddenly, a man starts to preach on the screen.

For some reason, he appears faceless and bodiless. Only his hands are clearly illuminated by spotlights. Another camera shows a horde of people bowing to him in unison. He may be a kind of god, but you don't know what kind of religion he leads. And you remember, yes, remember, that he is what you have been waiting for.

You find yourself gazing at his stature in wonder. You stand up, and without hesitation, make a deep bow to the television.

During his sermon, the man on TV lifts up a naked newborn baby, composedly, from behind the pulpit. Sandwiching its torso between his large palms, he extends both of his arms horizontally, as straight as he can.

"Folks, imitate me," he shouts. "If you are watching this program on an upper floor of a hotel or an apartment or whatever, along with your baby like this one, go up to a window, open it right away, and stick him or her out of it, just like this. And, with your arms straight, hold your adorable baby safely in the air."

Holding your sleeping baby in your arms, you approach the large window like a marionette.

"If you can maintain this posture at least for an hour," the preacher shouts again, "it will prove clearly that your heart is full of true, pristine, parental love. If you should drop your baby, your carelessness will show clearly what kind of person you are at this moment. And I'm always here for a person like you."

You open the window. Timidly, you look down. On the street, the head of every occasional passerby looks merely like a grain of sand.

Tension mounts rapidly in your entire system.

Sandwiching the baby's torso between your palms, you face the outside landscape.

Raising your courage, you extend both of your arms horizontally, as straight as you can.

And you whisper to yourself: "I'll show you how much I love you."

Now, your newborn is sleeping soundly in midair, supported only by your two arms.

You're still keeping this posture. The preacher said "at least for an hour." So, only five minutes to go. You're sweating from every pore.

"I'm stupid, I know I am," you mumble to the sleeping baby. Two minutes to go.

Suddenly, a gale of wind blows hard. The newborn wakes up, and begins to cry fretfully.

"Stop it," you say impatiently. "Cannot you see what I'm doing? Do you want to fall down?"

The baby doesn't stop crying. Another gale of wind blows. One minute to go.

Just one more minute, and your love will clearly be proved. "Stop crying, you bastard," you shout.

And your baby starts to fall down.

During its freefall, it metamorphosizes into a nuke.

A few seconds later, an unimaginable blast erupts from the street, and you kneel down, as if to pray. The whole outside landscape vanishes, and only your building is miraculously left unscathed.

The TV shows the preacher leaving the pulpit with his black suitcase in his hand, amid the standing ovation of his followers. And, as the volume of the cheers begins to lower, a commentator's indifferent voice cuts in:

"Can you see where the baby he was holding is now? It is a lifelike doll, in fact, its name is Rosebud. It is now in his suitcase, perfectly disjointed."

You have never been so absent-minded before. Of course, you cannot remember where you are, who you are, what you were doing.

"I'll have you remember that," someone says behind your back, and you turn around mechanically.

"This is my very first time at Ground Zero," your publisher says with a grin. "How are you today? Do you still remember who I am? Did you eat up the whole box of fancy chocolates I brought to you last time? You did, didn't you? Not to worry, I'll bring you a new box of them next time."

You say nothing. All you can do is to just imagine your obese body floating in the water, with your eyes, ears, nostrils, and nothing else above the surface. Just like this cushion, you say silently to yourself.

"How's your *Extravaganza* going, by the way? Are you still having writer's block? Well, just as I expected," the publisher says, and takes something out of his black suitcase.

"Use this package again. How many did I give you so far? Twenty-something, maybe. Now you can put all the parts together by yourself, right?

Make this doll the last one, will you? Otherwise, you would be too much addicted and reach the point of no return. Got it?

"Plus, here is what you have long wanted. A list of available nationalities," the publisher adds, tossing a pile of documents onto the exact place on the sofa where your baby was sleeping. "It goes in alphabetical order. Today you're Japanese, so tomorrow you must be, let's see, Jordanian, I guess. Double-check the list by yourself, and get ready by the next time we meet, okay?"

This must be a dream, you say to yourself, holding the package in your arms. The publisher bursts into laughter. "How do you know this is a dream? Can you really figure out what a true dream is like? Do you remember, for instance, your last night's dream?"

You say nothing again.

"Don't worry, it is right here," the publisher says.

And you, the obese novelist with a heavy case of senile dementia, are led smoothly to the next blast.

The Diary of Noboru Tokuda
A Soldier in the Imperial Army

—

Noboru Tokuda

—

Date and place of birth: 15th of November 1910 in Kyoto, Japan
Drafted: 1943, as a sailor in the Navy Guard at naval bases on
Seram Island and Kai Island, Moluccas Islands, Republic of Indonesia
End of war: 1945
Internment camp: 1945–1947 in Singapore
Return to Japan: 1947 (when Mineo was five years old)
Death: 2007 (ninety-seven years old)

The U.S. Army skipped over his naval base in the Seram and Kai Islands.
Therefore, he had no experience of doing real battle with the U.S. Army but,
the supply of materials for everyday life, such as food, had been cut. Thus
the internees had to create a life based on self-sufficiency; that is to say,
through subsistence farming.

He recorded his daily life on the small island in the Banda Sea. He kept
a diary not in writing but by drawing pictures in a small sketchbook.
After returning to Japan, he described his experiences to his wife Sizuyo.
A clever writer skilled with the Japanese brush, she wrote out his explana-
tions on each page of the sketchbook.

The diary is 18 cm in length x 12 cm in width.

—

Mineo Tokuda,
son of Noboru and Sizuyo Tokuda.
Kyoto, 2011
Translated by Joel Klotz and Sakae Fujita

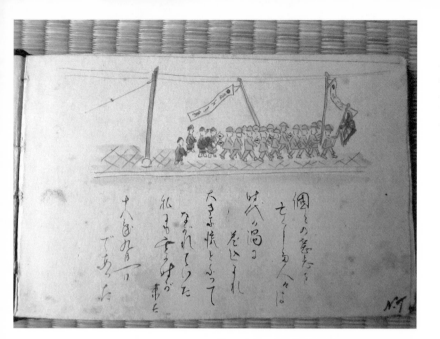

1

Those who lost their sense of individual purpose got caught up and carried away in the whirlpool of the times. My time came as well. It was September 1, 1943.

2

Tateyama Artillery Academy

Soldiers gathered one after another and were assigned to their barracks. They were drilled and trained, day and night. The system was very regimented.

—
3
Yokosuka Harbor November 15. That is the day I was born. Oddly enough, it was on this day that I left Japan. I felt full of emotion.

—
4
From the open seas of Izu, I could see Mt. Fuji beneath the late autumn sky. It was covered in snow all the way down to the seventh station. What a solemn, impressive sight. How many years will pass before I will be able to gaze upon Mt. Fuji again?

Finally, I had one last look at Japan. I could see a steam train going back and forth through Hakata. Farewell, Japan!

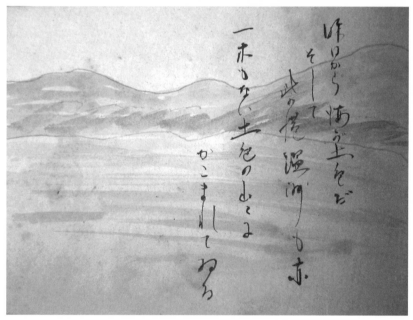

Since the previous day, the sea had taken on a brown, earthen color. This harbor in Wenzhou, China, was surrounded by earthy mountains without a single tree.

—

7

Yellow bananas and pine-
apples. The brilliant sun shone
on the streets of Gaoxiong,
Taiwan. I felt a deep sense that
I had arrived in a new land
to the south. Only Gaoxiong's
Shinto shrines looked like
something familiar from home.

—

8

To the left, I could see the
Philippine islands of
Corregidor and Batangas. I
imagined what the war's
early days must have been
like. Manila was also nearby.

Landing in Manila. Refreshing hues of green, yellow and red. We took a big step ashore.

マニラ上陸
緑と黄と赤
すがすがしく
上陸第一歩だ

Old town Manila was diverse and multicolored. For a moment I thought of Osaka, Japan. Trains, cars and people were interwoven with the colors red, green and yellow along the busy streets.

旧市街のマニラは全く
色彩の街だ

一寸大阪を思ふ

販路のある通りに
赤、緑、黄、の電車
自働車
人々が
織なして居る

ハルマヘラ
カブの街

Halmahera Harbor, Indonesia
The sun shone brightly here,
along the equator. The area
surrounding the harbor was
covered in groves of palm
trees. Behind that, it looked
like the jungle began. As I
looked at the scenery, I saw
nothing but green. There was
also a sad little wharf. To
the left of the wharf, I could
see the roof of a yellow
church building sticking out
above the palm trees.

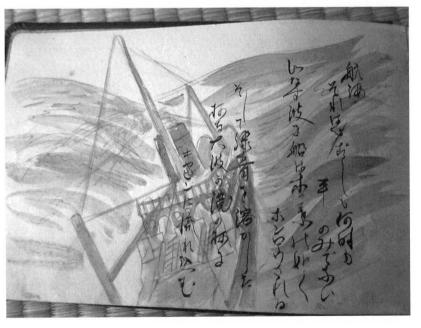

Voyage
The voyage was not always
flat. The ship tossed about
like a tree leaf in the moun-
tainous waves. The water
looked like the color of new
green leaves that had melted
together. The water formed
huge waves and then crashed
into the ship's cabin like a
waterfall.

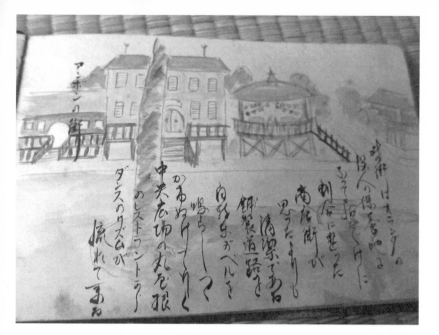

—
13

Ambon

This town was once a health resort for Dutch government officials. It was in relatively good order and cleaner than I expected. People dashed through the paved streets on bicycles, honking their horns as they went. Dance rhythms pulsed out from a restaurant with a domed roof in the central plaza.

—
14

We could see the ocean from the barracks on top of the hill outside of town. The color of the sea, the brightness of the sky, the shape of the clouds looked vivid and wonderful compared to those in Japan. We went fishing from a simple structure that had been made to float on the ocean's surface and which also served as a bathroom. Right away, five or six striped mullet flew out of the sea. Who would have thought that we would welcome the New Year in this sweltering hot place? As I wiped off the sweat and thought about Japan, I and the others celebrated with some mochi rice cakes. They tasted a little too fishy, and it took some effort to get used to them.

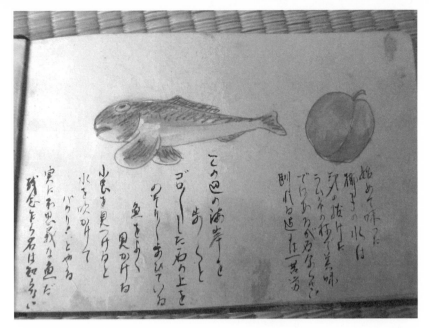

Walking along the coastline in this area, I caught sight of some fish slowly moving about on top of the scattered rocks. When they found some small insects, they splashed water on them and ate them up. What a truly strange fish. Unfortunately, I do not know its name.

The native people came close to our ship in their sampan boats and held up a bunch of thick bananas, shouting, "Trade, trade!" We lowered down empty bottles and leftover food from the ship using a rope.

We landed on shore, and soon a month passed. After getting comfortable here, we once again had to set out on a voyage to an unknown southern island.

船は珊瑚礁の島と島の間を警戒して
進むが無気の花島多いとふつた
それ程此島が多い
とも島も緑におほわれ
海岸にちゃんと椰子の木が
並んで獅子舞の
海面に
その影を
おとし
ている

アラフラ海
K諸ノ島

The K Archipelago of the Arafura Sea

The ship advanced onward through the islands of a coral reef as we kept a cautious lookout. Someone said that it looked like Matsushima, Japan. There were that many islands there. All the islands were covered in green, and the palm trees were lined up on the coastlines. Their shadows fell on the surface of the navy blue sea.

此の島に珍らしい
おその並木の道であ
唐節に帰化の建物以あり
多の住け人ど行華僑のもので
其の生活力の
勢さたけ
驚の外はない

18

On this island, there was a road lined with rare silk trees. There was also a Western-style building. Most of them belonged to Chinese merchants. I was very surprised by their impressive ability to make a living here.

飛行場の
周囲は草原
となり
タコの木や
パイナップルの木が
点在して一寸
植物園の初句
そうであった
野ぶたや野鶏
がたわむれつつを
見かけた

The area around the airfield was grassland dotted with octopus trees (Pandanus boninensis) and pineapple shrubs. It looked like a botanical garden. Sometimes we caught a glimpse of wild pigs and chickens frolicking about.

真白の
珊瑚礁の昼に映ゆ
目もくらむばかり
内地より持って行った温度計の
一番上の目盛も役に
たらない

不思議なるかな
飛行場を発着
飛行機の発着
中にありければ
飛行場の
点たるをも
知らない

At midday, the pure white coral reef near the airfield was blindingly dazzling. The gradations on the very top of a thermometer brought along from Japan were of no use (as the temperature exceeded the top reading).

Strange to say, I never saw any airplanes taking off from or landing at this airfield and do not know if any air corps personnel were there, either.

—
21

The rainy season began in March. I could not believe how much it rained every day. The inside of the barracks, which were in the middle of the jungle, became smelly from mold. Thin mushrooms started popping up in every nook and cranny.

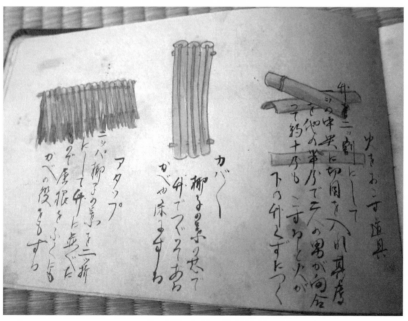

—
22

Tools for Starting a Fire
We cut bamboo in half and then cut a notch in the center of one of the halves. The other half of the bamboo was placed in this notch. Two men faced each other and rubbed the two bamboo sticks together for about ten minutes. The bamboo sawdust below eventually caught fire.

Coverings
The stems of the palm fronds were woven together with bamboo. We used them to make walls and floors.

Atap
These were made of nipa palm fronds that had been folded in two and lined up along with bamboo. We used them to thatch roofs, and they also served as walls.

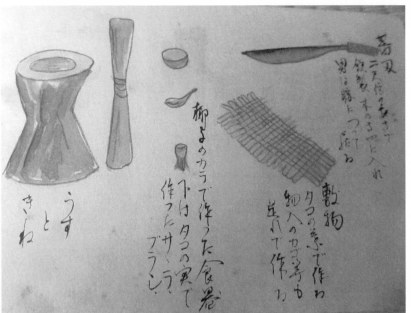

Barbarian's Swords
These swords were about two shaku in length (60 cm / two feet) and made of iron. Men carried them on their hips in wooden scabbards.

Rugs
We made them from octopus tree leaves. We also used them to make baskets for keeping things in.

We made eating utensils out of palm tree stalks. On the bottom is the whisk we made from shrub seeds as well as the mortar and mallet for making mochi rice cakes.

The women wore only a cloth around their waists. This cloth was called a sarong. The men wore a loincloth and a barbarian's sword on their waists. When they met us, they raised their right hand and greeted us, saying, "Tabetoan" ("good day, sir"). Bumping into one of them in the evening in the middle of the jungle was not a comfortable feeling.

—

25

Sampan Boats
*These boats were used only
by the natives as tools for
marine transportation. They
operated these boats and
went on trips as long as four
or five days.*

—

26

*Lizards as long as four shaku
(120cm/four feet) walked the
jungle. When we caught
and ate them, we found that
they tasted good. The three-
foot bats, however, smelled of
urine and tasted terrible.*

クビオカ

野生のものもあるが土人はこれを
作って食料としてゐる
切って土に挿して根を
作らせると八ヶ月程でビールの
瓶位の大きさのいもが五六ちあく。
其のまゝ煮ると甘藷ほど
甘味は違ふが口あたり
よくて大そう美味い
又すりおろして
餅の様にして煮ると
よく内地の餅を取った
あのタピオカ揚で
あり、土人はこれを餅の
粉にしてよく内地の粉を取って
揚る油で揚げて主食にしてゐる

タロいもは芋茎の頭の
様なものであるが少し違って
タロいもの葉が直立つて
ゐる。この芋うつかりして
食ふと何度でも
喉がイラくする

パンの木は実に大きな木で
二かゝえ三四人でも有る
其の皮も美麗であつた
実も大きく長さ七〇糎幅
五〇糎もあり
実は五百匁位もあつて
其れを横に切つて喰ふが
あります

27

Tapioca

There was some wild tapioca, which the natives used as food. When you take a cutting and put it in the ground so that it forms new roots, five or six potatoes would grow. Within eight months they each grew to about the size of a beer bottle. When we boiled them as-is and tried them, we found that they were not as sugary as Japanese sweet potatoes but that they tasted good. We also grated them down, rolled them into dumplings and boiled them. They came out similar to mochi rice cakes, and were delicious. From there, we extracted the starch and stored it away. This is the tapioca flour that often used to come to Japan long ago. The natives used this as a staple food in their diet, making mochi-like dumplings and deep-frying them in palm oil.

28

Cocoyams look like they are related to taro stems, although there is a slight difference: the leaves of the cocoyams stand upright. If you are not careful when eating them, they will irritate your throat to no end. Breadfruit trees are so giant that it would take two or three people to wrap their arms fully around it. The bark is beautiful, too. The leaves are large as well, measuring up to seventy centimeters (28 inches) in length and fifty centimeters (20 inches) wide. They actually weigh about 500 'monme' (1,875 grams), and you can fry and eat them.

炊事場は煙が出るのと火ふせで
兵舎から二百米も離れて居た
雨季には合羽を着て飯上げに来た
食事を取りに来ると
ザーツと来ると
飯もおかづも
雨潰になった

—
29

The kitchen was separated by about 200 meters from the barracks, because it often got smoky. In the rainy season, we put on raincoats and came to pick up our meals. If it started to pour, our rice and side dishes got peppered with raindrops.

珊瑚礁の此の島は
井戸を堀ってもだめで
島の二三ヶ所に水の湧く所があり
此處つで毎日トラックで
これ取りの作業員があり
此の湧き水も下流三四百米位で
地中にもぐり其の姿を消す
又不思議でのに一斗かんに
一ぱいの水でも青々として冷めい
朝の洗面にも一々湧かって用ひた
でもよくアミーバー患者が出た

—
30

Because this island was located on a coral reef, even if we dug a well, no water would come out. There were two or three places on the island where water bubbled up. Every day, workers struggled to draw water and transport it by truck. About 300 meters downstream, this spring water went underground and disappeared. Strange to say, even after filling up an eighteen-liter drum, the water still looked fresh and blue.

The village of Redfan faced the sea, and there were about ten huts that belonged to the natives.

When the sun hid behind the edge of the jungle and night fell, this part of the world became a paradise. The temperature suddenly dropped and the Southern Cross appeared in the heavens that glistened like smoky crystals. The sounds of insects and birds filled the air. In the trees, tens of thousands of fireflies came together and emitted a pale, flickering light. The nighttime was their paradise as well. In Japan, it gets coldest in February. In this place which lacked a clear sense of the four seasons, however, I could leave the window open, get under the mosquito net and go to bed gazing at the glittering stars of the Southern Hemisphere.

Cool mornings always made me think of resting dew and Japan's early fall. Here and there around the gunner's seat of an airplane covered in coral, I could catch a glimpse of bright red tomatoes that looked like Chinese lantern plants.

When we got up in the morning, we would scramble to be the first to go out and pick them. In the blink of an eye, our hats would become full of tomatoes. Their cool, sweet-and-sour taste had a certain indescribable quality.

We looked in the jungle for level ground and dirt and created a plot of land. The crops grew surprisingly well, and from around the tenth day, we struggled to eat all of the daikon radishes and other crops that had grown.

Wild pigs started to come around and damage the crops we had worked so hard to grow, so we set up a fence around the area. Sometimes we brought out guns to slaughter them. This became the best feast of all. It was not uncommon for one pig to weigh about thirty 'kan' (112kg/250lbs).

—
35

More than anything else, the palm tree was the king of the southern plants. I mentioned its fruit and leaves a bit earlier. I cut this flower at the stem at the time just before it was going to wilt. When I put it into a pot, the liquid from the branch somehow turned into alcohol, much to my amazement. The lower part of the leaf buds were like bamboo shoots, and became a tasty side dish. After boiling down the fruit to eliminate the water contained inside, we could extract the sugar. We used the palm trees in countless ways.

—
36

Geckos and scorpions were everywhere.

It was common for geckos to squeak and crawl around in places like the top portion of the mosquito net, which was illuminated by a dim layer of smoke.

The scorpions grabbed things with their front legs and then stung them with the hooks at the ends of their tails. If you were stung, you would have an aching fever for a whole day and night.

They ranged from about three to thirty centimeters in length and gathered together in damp places.

—
37
One day, we suffered a bombing attack and some of the jungle burned to the ground, but we were very fortunate that there was no great damage.

—
38
There was one time when we were driving a truck at night on a road near the airfield. Suddenly, we hit something. When we shined a light on it, we saw that it was a bomb, and I could feel my blood freeze.
We saw the rusty shapes of bombs lying around here and there that had been transported all the way from Japan.

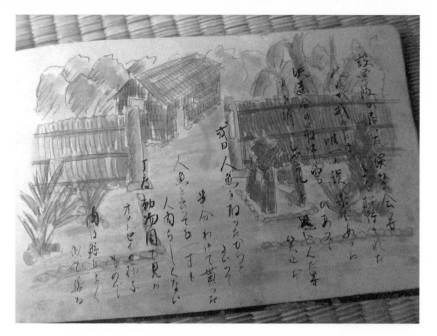

We were often invited to a show put on by the construction crew. This was our only source of entertainment. During the middle of a movie viewing party an air raid broke out. We turned out the lights and ran into the jungle to hide. This felt odd and almost laughable.

One day they brought back something that they had caught. They said that it was a mermaid, even though it did not seem like a human at all. It looked exactly like a seal that you might see at the zoo. They shared a portion with me, and it closely resembled whale meat.

—
40

Fishing became one of our regular events.

One day, we caught so many that we did not cook any rice and passed the fish around by the scoopful. We could not possibly eat it all. We caught a great deal of red and yellow fish with flashy designs, but unlike the other fish, this type did not taste good.

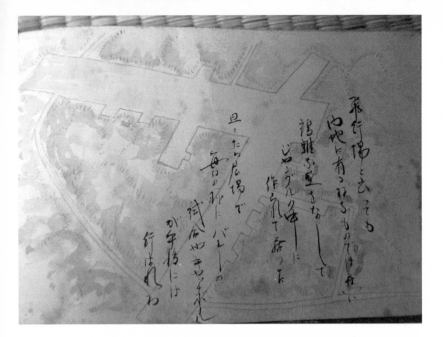

—
41

The airfield looked different from what you would find back in Japan.
It had been created in a complex shape in the middle of the jungle. Games of volleyball and catch were held on the level grounds almost every day in the afternoon.

—
42

After being blockaded on this island for six months, it came time for us to leave. Leading the kind of simple life that we did, I felt a bit of reluctance to part with the island.
And so the day came when we also had to part with the native people, who had gotten used to our presence.

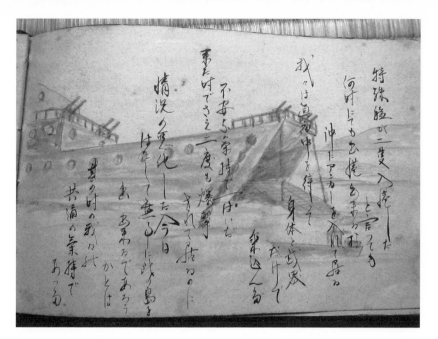

—
43

Two specialized warships entered the harbor. However, they dropped anchor a little ways out on the open sea so that we could depart at any time. We waited for the dead of night, and boarded the ship with just our selves and our weapons. I was filled with feelings of anxiety and suspense. When we had first come to the island, we had been bombed twice. Since then, the situation of the war had worsened. We all shared a common feeling, wondering if we would be able to safely leave the island.

—
44

The second day after we left Kai Island, we safely entered the bay at Ambon Island. I thought, "What a relief!" We all disembarked at the wharf on the far side of the city. I heard something later about one of the two ships that had transported us there. Soon after leaving the bay, it was attacked by a submarine and sank.

—
45

A kilometer from the place where we disembarked, we found an airfield. For the first time in a while, I smelled the scent of earth. The dirt whirled up and ascended into the air behind a moving truck.

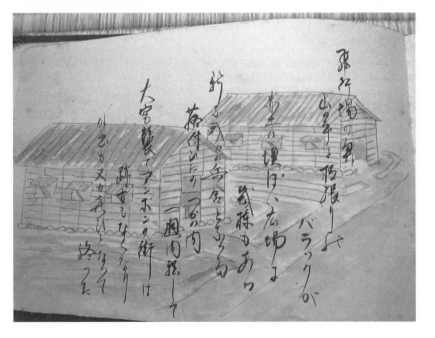

—
46

At the far end of the airfield, wooden barracks stood on a hill. There were also many large buildings in a dusty red clay plaza. These became our new barracks.
We only had a brief period of relative calm. About a week later, a huge air raid wiped away every trace of Ambon. Our short-lived elation at being able to go outside soon ended.

Before long, just our platoon was dispatched to a place closer to the ocean, and we moved into Atap barracks previously occupied by the infantry.

I felt a sense of liberation living among this smaller group of people. However, around this time the air raids intensified, coming day and night. I had trouble getting a good night's sleep.

Near the barracks there was a farm run by the Nanyo Kohatsu Corporation. They had created spacious plots of land and even had an orchard. Soon, we moved there because it had become vacant. Finding the farm right at that moment was an unexpected blessing, because we had gradually become hard pressed for food. When I think about how the infantry barracks were later reduced to worthless splinters by a bomb, I remember how chills ran down my spine.

49

The airfield was also destroyed more and more each day. The airplanes that could not fly were hidden here and there in the shadows of the areca palm trees. Every day, it was frightening to walk along the pathway to headquarters.

50

Headquarters was shifted farther and farther into the mountains. It was carved into the mountainside, and a tunnel was dug nearby. Each time the warning siren rang, we would enter or exit the tunnel. This became a part of our daily routine.

In addition to weapons, food and so forth, the tunnel's bomb shelter became a place that housed personnel. Towards the end, we even had to cook meals there.

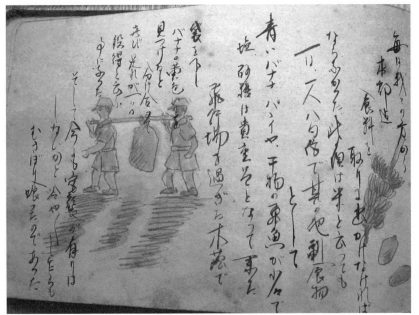

Every day, we had to leave the bomb shelter and go to headquarters to pick up food supplies.

Even though we had rice at this time, each person only received about eight shaku of rice per day (144 ml / 4.8 oz). Other supplementary foods included green bananas, papayas and dried flying fish. Small portions of salt and sugar became valued treasures. In the shade of some trees just past the airfield, we would stop and set the food bag down. If we found a yellow banana inside we would rejoice and share it. This became one of the perks of going to pick up the food. We eagerly devoured the food, all the while frightened that an air raid might break out at any minute.

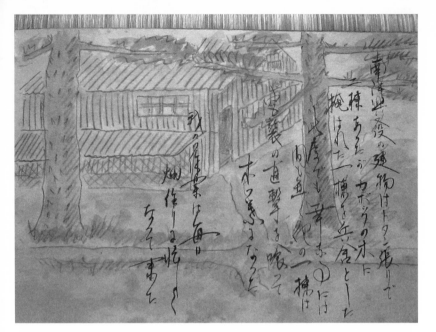

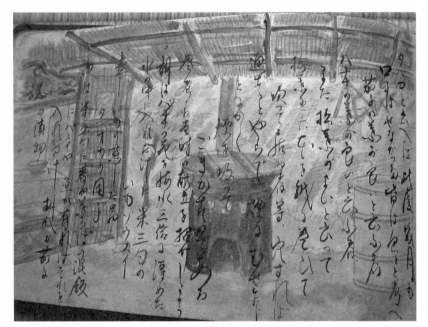

—
53
Two of the Nanyo Kohatsu
Corporation buildings were
made of galvanized sheet
metal. One building was covered by silk-cotton trees,
and this was used as a barracks. We were lucky in
this case as well. Before long,
the other building took a
direct hit in an air raid and
was reduced to smithereens.
Our farm work became
more hurried with each passing day.

—
54
We did not smoke any tobacco
for several months. Everyone
had their own thoughts: some
said that eggplant leaves
would work well, while others
said banana leaves, and still
others suggested pine needles. Some people took five or
six pine needles, rolled them
in paper and smoked them. In
our hard-pressed situation,
we tried to trick ourselves by
creating the illusion of smoking, as all the while we choked
on the pine needle smoke
fumes.
For reference, I will introduce
the menu from that time.
For breakfast, we had three
shaku (54 ml / 1.8 oz) of
potato rice gruel, which we
put into a broth of diluted sea
water that contained banana
flowers. For lunch, we had
steamed potatoes and tapioca dumplings. For dinner, we
have five shaku (90 ml / 3 oz)
of rice along with mixed
rice containing potato leaves.
We also had papayas, pickled
cucumbers or eggplant,
and if there was fish we ate it
with broth.

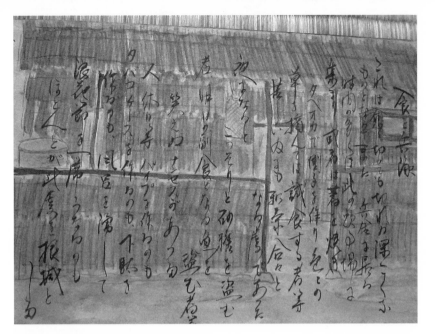

Soldiers and Food
*These two things became
more and more inseparable
and serious. During most
of the time spent in the barracks, soldiers gathered
in this kitchen. Some people
fried potatoes or made tapioca dumplings, while others
picked a variety of grasses
and tasted them. Amidst the
difficult war, the kitchen was
a peaceful and harmonious
place. At night, some people
nonsensically snuck into the
kitchen and stole sugar
or stole fish that was going to
be used to make a side dish
the following day. On our days
off, we also used this space
for activities such as making
pipes, tobacco cases
and wooden clogs, as well as
heating the bath and singing traditional Naniwabushi
songs.*

Papayas
*Papayas grow year-round,
and there are two types:
red and yellow. They taste
a little bit like persimmons,
but stink like manure. As
a side dish, the green ones
are like Japanese melons.
Strangely enough, when
the raw juice comes into contact with your hands, it
will begin to melt away your
skin. When boiled along
with meat, the shape of the
meat will begin to dissolve.*

Durians

The durian is often called the king of fruits. They taste exactly like cream that has been fried in oil. At the start, it might seem a little bit smelly and difficult to eat, but once you get used to it, the taste becomes unforgettable. The natives told us that when the durians get ripe, they build huts under the trees and eagerly wait for the fruits to fall. They seem to like durians so much that they would go to great lengths to get them, even if that meant having to leave one's wife in the hands of a pawn shop, as the old saying goes.

—
58
Mangosteens

In outward appearance, mangosteens look a little bit like persimmons. However, the thick skins are purplish red and the insides are pure white. This flavor is rare in Southeast Asia, and its light, sweet-and-sour taste is exquisite. They call the mangosteen the queen of fruits, and from my experience it lives up to this reputation.

Mangos

Mangos look like Japanese peaches that have been smeared with pine resin. They are not tasty to the extent that songs would be boisterously sung about them, but they do ripen in large numbers twice a year.

—
59

Soursops
The end section of the soursop fruit looks like a pineapple, but is softer and sweeter. It is also not as sour or fragrant.

Saos
The saos' shape looks like that of a potato, and it is sweet as sugar. It reminds me of a dried persimmon. I heard that it is considered the best raw fruit in the world.

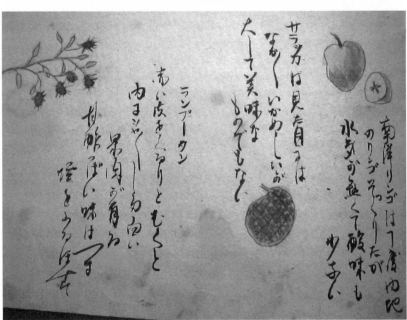

—
60

South Sea Apples
Apples of the South Sea are exactly like Japanese apples, except that they are not moist and not very sour.

Salaks
Salaks may have a harsh appearance, but they have no significant flavor.

Rambutans
When you peel away the rambutan's red skin, you can see the glossy white insides. The sweet-and-sour taste moistens the throat.

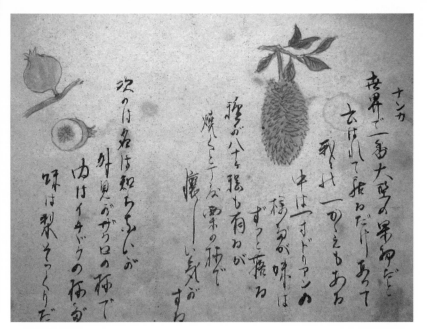

—
61

Nankas (squash)

As one might expect from what has been called the world's largest fruit, it was so big that we could wrap our arms around it. The inside looked a bit like a durian, but the taste did not compare. It has over eighty seeds, but when cooked, it took on the nostalgic taste of chestnuts.

I do not know the name of this next fruit, but it has an outward appearance similar to that of a pomegranate. The inside looks like a fig, and it tastes just like a pear.

—
62

The wild eggplant had extremely tough skin and a lot of seeds. They were small and practically inedible. The local eggplant were about the same size as Japanese eggplant, though, despite the fact that the skin was so tough and the seeds so numerous. They were white, yellow and green. There were also some wild litchi growing, but they tasted bitter and did not have much meat. On the plantations, they planted coffee and cocoa. Among other things, it was possible to eat the cocoa raw. However, it was not very tasty this way.

正月も過ぎる頃になると
一寸空襲も少なくなるか　でも
食料の方は無くなって来る
配給だけでは　とてもやり切れない
どうしても我々は理生の物を
あさらなければならない　又
トウガラシの木等年中赤いのが
なって居り　ハシゴ掛けなけ
ればとてもとれない　それ丈
とふ大きいが　又
朝顔の花、
南京の花、
いもの葉、芋
どれも一等のだし物
けいとうの花、
でも朝顔のシルが喉に
つかえる等して
一寸驚かされる

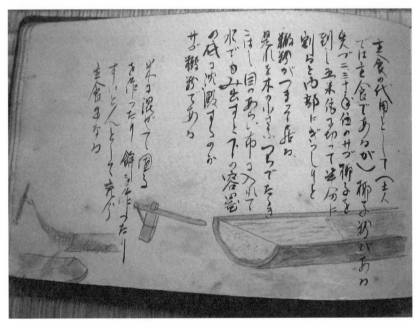

主食の代用として（主人
では主食であるが）椰子粉があり
失づ三十米他のサゴ椰子を
切し五米位に切って半分に
割ると内部にぎっしりと
澱粉がつまって居り、
是れを木の小さいつちでたたき
こはし、目のあらい布に入れて
水でもむ出すと下の容器
の底に沈澱するのが
サゴ澱粉である
米と混ぜて団子
を作ったり　餅にしたり
すいとんにして　主食とする

—

63

*After New Year's, the air
raids became a little bit less
frequent. The food situa-
tion, however, became more
severe. There was no way
we could get by just on our
rations. At all costs, we
had to search for food in the
wild. Some trees had chili
peppers that were growing
red year-round. The trees
were so large that we couldn't
possibly pick the peppers
unless we set up a ladder.
Cockscomb plants, morning
glory leaves, pumpkin leaves,
potato leaves and so forth
were all very good. The little
shoots of the morning glories,
though, would sometimes
get stuck in our throats and
surprise us.*

—

64

*As a substitute for rice, our
main staple food, we
had palm flour (this was the
staple food of the natives).
First, we cut down sago palms
twenty or thirty meters
in height and cut them into
pieces five meters long.
When we split these in half,
we found that the inside
was fully stuffed with starch.
We broke up the starch
with a small wooden mallet
and wrapped it in a rough-
meshed cloth. When we
poured water on the cloth and
squeezed it out, the sago
palm starch settled at the
bottom of the container
below. We mixed this with rice
and then made dumplings
and mochi rice cakes,
which became satisfactory
staple foods.*

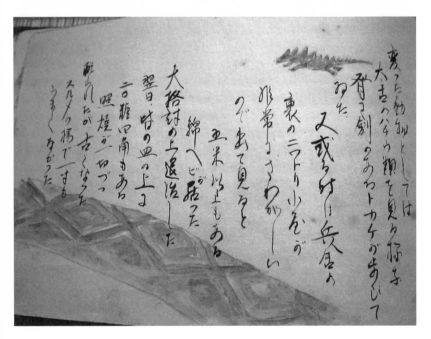

65

We could bear it if we had no sugar, but it was very tough when we ran out of salt. We ended up setting up a place near the coastline where we boiled seawater to get salt. We set a steel drum on its side, poured seawater into it and boiled it all day long. One steel drum used in this way for one day allowed us to collect about two sho of salt (3.6 liter/almost one gallon).

66

I also saw some strange animals. Lizards walked around that looked like reptiles from ancient times and had stingers on their backs. One time, there were some extremely loud noises coming from the chicken coop behind the barracks. When I went out to have a look, there was a five meter python there. I exterminated it after a huge scuffle. The next day, we passed around twenty centimeter pieces of snake teriyaki, one piece at a time. However, it tasted like dried squid that had gone bad and was not the least bit good.

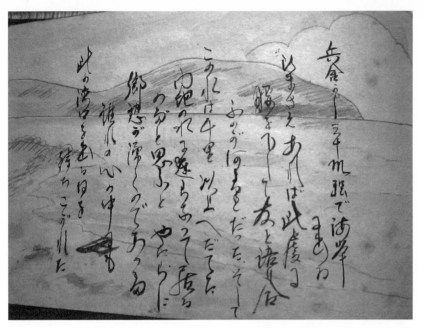

67

It was about thirty meters from the barracks to the coastline.

If I had spare time, my favorite thing to do was sit on the beach and talk with friends. I thought about how this water was connected to the waters of Japan, which was separated from us by over 2,000 ri (7,800 km / 4,800 mi), and felt a sense of nostalgia and homesickness. We all felt a longing inside our hearts for the day when we would leave this bay.

—

68

We went to the town in Ambon for the first time in a while. The conditions had changed compared to the previous year. The buildings stood throughout the town with their roof tiles crumbled away. We could tell how severe the bombings had been. What in the world had the townspeople done, and where had they gone? Only the area around the market looked the same as last year.

69

Because the enemy might come and land at any time, we set up an encampment on a mountain above the airfield. It was settled that this would be our place of temporary refuge in the case of an emergency. Every day we worked to carry food and ammunition up the mountain.

70

As the days passed, the air raids lightened. Our days became more leisurely, and this continued for some time. Eventually, we were able to venture out near head-quarters. A clean river flowed there that we had not been able to see for a long time. Some people spent a day fishing and enjoying the river. At that time, Truk and Midway had fallen in battle in the Central Pacific.

Last Time I Saw You

Kentaro Yamaki

My unit's mission was setting up a food supply base back then. I had thought it would be a much easier task at first but I was terribly wrong. Clearing and cultivating the tropical rainforest was hard as hell. My back muscles were aching severely from swinging the pickaxe all the time. My skin quickly turned dark with bug bites all over my body, and then there was dysentery to contend with. I had already seen some of the soldiers dying of malaria or dengue fever. Others had been forced to evacuate as they had come down with unknown diseases. I could be the next one any time. I got used to seeing dead bodies, but death itself never became something comprehensible. It would just come, and I feared it.

      During the day, the air on New Guinea Island was so damp that sweat was constantly dripping down my neck, chest and thighs. My whole body was drenched. In the steaming heat, every now and then an impulse emerged to rip off all of my skin. In the shack where we slept, candles turned into lumps of wax if they were left in the sunlight. The same happened to my brain day after day. The heat benumbed the ability to think of anything conceptual. Almost nothing else came into mind other than the swinging of the axe. Strange as it might sound, that actually kept me sane. The mere fact of having something to do each minute kept me sane. Through that seemingly endless repetition, I tell you, I had silently locked my mind to one image: the image of you back home. This, more than anything, helped me get through each day. When the night covered land and sea, my consciousness regained some sort of rationality. I would gaze into the night sky and tune into the noise of a million insects around me. It was the only time I could absorb myself and be absorbed in more thoughts of you.

That afternoon, the engine propeller had trouble starting, so the five of us, lead by Second Lieutenant Uesugi, set off for patrol half an hour later than scheduled. It was a regular sortie along the shoreline in a little boat. If we had caught a beautiful sunset during the ride, all of us would turn silent and be entranced. That evening, however, the clouds were hanging low and bursts of occasional rain stopped us from seeing anything magnificent. On the way back, we saw a fire spreading in the distance. It was our base. Periodic gunshots rent the air as we got closer. Our shacks had been set on fire. I looked to the sky above that was filled with billows of smoke. Were there souls to be seen drifting up in the air together with the black fumes?

"Sneak attack," said Saeki. "How elegant!"

By who? Americans? Australians? It didn't really matter as there was nothing we could possibly do. After looking at everybody in silence, Uesugi swung the boat towards the mouth of the bay.

"Forgive my lack of courtesy, sir, but we can't just leave our unit. It's a dishonor as a fighter," Matsui appealed.

"Don't say anything," Uesugi replied to him with an outstretched hand.

Strangely, I wasn't thinking about the death of my comrades nor of our impending destiny at that moment. I was pondering instead all the work we had done there across the shore. "All ends up in vain," I caught myself muttering as the rain started to hit us hard. A heavy storm was about to swallow the entire area. We tried our best to steer the boat to shore, but all of a sudden, it slammed into a rock. Almost immediately I was knocked off my feet, my head striking the prow. I felt an acute pain on the side of my head and the sound of the storm died down instantly. In my last moments of consciousness, I saw seawater seeping into the boat through my blurred eyesight. Then I fell into darkness.

Until I woke up, I never suspected it to be a dream: the grassland, the turquoise sky, my shoulder occasionally touching yours... I could hear you breathing quietly, right next to me. I could hear it so clearly. The sun was on one end of the horizon, the moon on the other. Without having any particular destination, we kept on strolling along. You slowed down at the top of a small hill, and I turned to look at you from a few steps ahead. While your dark long hair was flowing in the wind, you smiled at me. I just wanted to stand there, just be near you until the end of time. Against my wish, though, you started to disappear right into thin air, and so, too, did the whole of that vivid scene. Eventually, a crimson colored magma flooded it all. Off in the distance the familiar sound of a bird singing met my ears. I opened my eyes just slightly but shut them quickly as sunlight beamed in hard. Where was I? Was I all right? Had I really come back to that world? That flyblown place that smells like death? The world where comrades who I slept side by side with would be suddenly taken away because of big, purple spots found in their eyes? It seemed like it. It seemed like I hadn't escaped it. I felt tears welling up. I had thought finally I was with you. I had felt I could tell you something at last. I had wanted to tell you about my recurring regrets over not looking back to you when you called my name the last time at the train station. Do you remember? That place was packed, wasn't it? The crowd's collective consciousness, mesmerized by one grandiose national agenda, forcing me to get on that train car bound for Kobe port and from there who knows where, all without saying a word. I so wanted to see your face one more time. Only God knew if we would see each other again, and yet I didn't turn back just because... because...

"Oi, okiro!" Wake up! The tone of his voice brought every dimension of reality back to me. Instantly, I got up and looked into my superior's eyes. Uesugi acknowledged the light in mine, nodded, and tapped me on the shoulder. I looked around and found everybody alive. Saeki and Matsui were treating Takasago's swollen face. Where his right eye had been, was now just a bloody mess. The boat was lying wrecked at the end of the beach. As I stood up, I felt an immediate pain on the right side of my head. I fumbled in my pockets. I had a knife, a little water bottle and some matches in a tin box. The gun was gone. Only Uesugi and Saeki had remained armed with their rifles. Hammocks, drinking water and some other goods had been taken off the boat. We neither knew if the enemy was around nor if we were able to pick up contact with other troops. Our own unit must have been wiped out. It was just us and that merciless, glaring sun. Without a word being spoken, we put the goods on our shoulders and began to shuffle into the wilderness.

Last time I saw you I didn't tell any of this to you, did I? I guess time seemed to be too precious to bring up past memories that day. It was such a special day for me. Actually, I've only told a few people about my days in Papua New Guinea. Generally, I don't care to recall that period in my life at all. Still, it's funny how such subtle things can be a catalyst that suddenly brings back old memories with such distinctness. But now I have to tell you this. I must. Otherwise I would feel as if leaving something behind once again...

On the second evening something memorable occurred. We had found a clearing on a hillside with a good view over the terrain surrounding us. We were about to rest except for Saeki, who had to keep watch for the first round of that night. Out of the blue, Takasago slowly stood up as though he would depart to some far-off place. Abruptly, he turned around and started to speak.

"Have you heard that young kids are now summoned to fly planes for flights with no return? Is this what the war has come to?"

I didn't really know whom he was talking to as his single remaining eye was directed to the trees around us. His voice sounded unnatural. It was high-pitched and somewhat childish. He said that our nation could never have won that war in the first place. He kept on saying that it was the deadly stupid pride among us Japanese agitated by fabricated, state-backed Shinto mythology that made us believe in the possibility of a triumph over the Western opponents.

"It's the pathetic heroism, that's what it is! A sort of hopeless romanticism that thinks high spirits can conquer everything," he shouted.

Then he added that the only way to victory was to turn it into a racial war, to put up slogans like: Join the liberation war by the enslaved people of color against the white rulers of the colonies. He claimed that that way we could win international support from other nations and thus create multiple war fronts so that we wouldn't need to fight all the battles alone.

"How foolish of those lunatics. Forming an alliance with Germany destroyed that logic altogether. This whole war has become a nightmare without any—"

Suddenly, Takasago coughed roughly. The sound of it was disturbing as if his throat was full of phlegm. It was Saeki who had snuck behind Takasago and stabbed him with a knife I suspect had been dipped in a special poison.

"He deserves to be sent back to Mother Nature. I am sorry to watch that weakness which has taken over his soul," Saeki said briefly.

Takasago started to twitch.

"You traitors! You fanatics!' he screamed. "God! This life, so tiny. So powerless against all of this massive aggression. So easy to be convinced to throw it away for nothing. In the end, however, everything is supposed to become clear, isn't it? I should now know what this whole thing was about, shouldn't I?" Takasago seemed to even laugh a bit in his last seconds.

Uesugi didn't show any change of expression watching him dying. I thought maybe Takasago had eaten something strange that caused his mind to flip. Some of the plants and fungi that we came across while hunting for food had looked quite eccentric. Someone's death didn't stir my emotions so much anymore. Instead, I recognized a sense of satisfaction in me that someone had said out loud what many of us had come to think. I felt ashamed for that. I looked at Matsui. His face was directed to the ground with closed eyes. Shortly after, all four of us gathered big leaves and put them over Takasago's body and stood in a moment of silence. It was a clear, humid night. The stars were glittering like never before. Gazing at them took all thoughts away from my mind.

I was sitting in a tree above them, watching it all when the other three got killed abruptly a couple of days later. The watchman for that night was me, but I didn't notice any enemy activity until they opened fire. In the light from the little fire we had made, I saw Uesugi, while trying to protect the other two, being shot into pieces. His flesh flying off in every direction, he moaned for a short moment. Seconds later, Saeki and Matsui were lifeless lumps lying in the dirt. Then, there was a drawn-out silence. My ears were trying to detect every sound that was not from the myriad of sounds of the wild. I could sense that other ears and minds were doing exactly the same in the dark around me. My body was startled for a split second, when two English-speaking strangers appeared from the bush behind me without any noise that would have hinted at their existence. They walked out, saw the corpses and said briefly something about Japs, then walked off. I thought that they were going to inform their unit of their victorious skirmish. I slipped out of the tree quickly and quietly. I was determined to shoot myself with Saeki's gun before they found me, but when my feet touched the ground, oddly I felt different. After instinctively picking up the hammock and the rope, I snuck away in the opposite direction of the enemy. Only occasionally did the moonlight shine through the jungle, but my eyes could see the shapes in it surprisingly better than ever before. The outline of objects was piercingly clear, and with every step I took on the damp, loamy soil I felt a resonance stemming from one simple thought that told me to keep moving straight ahead. Its sole motivation: the farther I go the better.

A sort of exhilaration engulfed me. Out of nowhere, I felt a tingling force in me, which spurred me on. Hacking my way through the dense black bushes and the silvery shimmering foliage, it was exciting to feel the energy building and pumping through my veins. Cuts on my face and arms didn't prevent me from moving further and further onwards. The buzz of the bugs stimulated my mind to be fully awake. Fatigue was inconceivable. At some point I wished for the jungle to have no end, and the night no dawn.

Eventually, I stopped as the jungle ended unexpectedly. In front of my eyes I discovered a green patch beside a creek with waterholes dotted around. Behind that, the ocean was stretching out to the horizon. I collapsed on the grass and fell deep asleep. I woke up when the sun started to glare on me. I stripped bare out of my uniform and jumped into one of the waterholes, plunging into crystal clear water that glided along my limbs. It was amazingly cold. I drank from it to quench my thirst. For a long time, I hadn't experienced such a moment of pure joy and rejuvenation.

I decided to make that place my own and established a food supply from the plants and fruits of the surrounding area as best I could. I would always bathe in that pristine water after waking up and returning from the forest. I convinced myself that, should I notice someone, I would have my knife ready at hand to cut my throat immediately. Hesitation would not be an option. I ceased to think about anything else. I stopped using fire, forgot counting days and surrendered all memories. Time disappeared. Every day was another new day.

Then, one day, after who knows how much time had passed, two native women came along and found me by chance. Local officials soon followed, alarmed by the tales of a forgotten Private. "War is over," they said, and somehow I got transferred back to Japan. Oddly enough though, I don't quite recall much of it. I just remember the weight of the mixed feelings that I carried for the whole voyage from Port Moresby to Kobe: sadness about leaving the island, hopes to see you again and surprise for not spotting a single submarine.

Coming back to my hometown was a surreal experience. My parents thought I was dead and looked more bewildered than happy to see me again. My elder brother had been killed during the war. The town appeared so alien to me now. I looked for you. There was no trace. Your house had been burned down and people told me that you had moved to Hyogo together with your family. Like you, it seemed that the whole of society had moved on. Poverty was prominent on every street, and yet nobody would talk about the war time anymore. Everything was now gearing towards a new direction which was driven by the sheer motivation to survive and hold up whatever shelter one had. When I wanted to share with somebody what I experienced at the battlefront on those islands in the Pacific, I was often confronted by silent remonstration urging me to stop talking about it. Rumors of the aftermath of Hiroshima and the disabled veterans sitting near train stations seemed to be the only remnants of that lunatic age. I found that atmosphere hard to cope with but came to understand that people simply wanted to forget and bury the past in oblivion. So I tried as well. I couldn't. The days on that island were far too vivid to forget.

Over the course of time, I moved to Osaka and started to work at the fish market. The money that I received every day wasn't very much but the payoff was that I did not have to worry about hunger. When I strolled about town on my off days, I often thought of you. I wondered what would happen if I ran into you by chance. Would we hit it off? Would we still talk like the old days? It was never a thought of much substance, though, just a fleeting daydream. Caught in the biggest city of western Japan, I felt lonelier than I'd ever been in my life.

That day, I was on my way to visit my parents when the sight of you waiting on the platform of Sannomiya station brought me to a sudden stand. It took my breath away. I knew it was you. You hadn't changed a bit. After a short while you recognized my gaze and, for a moment, looked over to me in a vigilant manner. But when your eyes started to soften and your mouth began to smile faintly, I felt warmth in my heart that I can't put words to.

"Hisashiburi." First time in ages, you replied, with a soft voice when I walked over and called you by your name. For the first time in a long while, I felt this life to be worth living. I could not help pouring my heart out to you.

"I've got to go now, but please write me," you said quite abruptly after more than a handful of trains passed by. You looked me in the eyes, wrote your address on a piece of paper, and pressed it in my hand. Where you were heading off to, I didn't ask.

Then we met again, this time for a whole day and night. It was beautiful. Have you ever had moments when you sincerely wished that they would last forever, that the texture of that instance would gel and be part of you for the rest of your life? That's how I felt. Deep into the night then, you told me about your husband and your rather mundane marriage. It was hard for me to hear that, and I still don't know how to handle my emotions...

A small group of acquaintances, all soldiers during the war, asked me a while ago if I wanted to join them on Naoshima island, a small secluded island in the Seto Inland Sea, and actually, now I am here. It is soothing to be surrounded by nature again and have space to live self-sufficiently. The bamboo dwellings are comfortable to live in and the rice and vegetable fields give us food and labor to share.

I want you to know that it wasn't an easy decision and that I am sorry that it took a while to write back to you. I hope you do understand. I also hope that you find some common elements in what I went through and the story you confided in me that day. And you know what, the thing you were longing for, I feel it coming, Mai. I feel it nearing us. And so, if you feel intrigued to come here, a letter will be enough to make it happen. We will walk on the grassland to get to that hill, and your hair will be carried in the wind.

Gama
Ben Takara

Islands born from uplifted reef
have been melted down for a thousand years
by rainwater and carbon dioxide.
Now we have limestone caves everywhere
into the very deep of the earth.
In the midst of thick grass like pubic hair,
they open their spindle-shaped mouths.
In the abdomen of our islands
gamas exist all over.
Oh, *gama,* the sacred wombs of our islands.

I descend through a dark labyrinthine passage
with the light of a candle.
From above my head, big white breasts hang down.
I feel on my face sweet drops of water falling.
Rivers running around me, carrying mud at my feet.
Bottomless swamps hiding underneath.
Kuragaa seems to be running down
from the depth of the earth to the ocean.

Toward the darkness beyond the cave hall,
a space enough for several houses,
I call "ho ho-i!"
but no echoes return.

In the darkness, instead, I see numerous people
squirming, crying.
With his shoulder crushed by naval gunfire,
his eyes and ears lost, my father is groaning.
Somebody is nursing him.
Is it his comrade, or my mother?

A field hospital in the *gama* has been evacuated.
Now come U.S. hand grenades and gasoline bombs
thrown violently from the ground.
People running away, deep inside the *gama,*
Sighs of "comfort women" resounding.
How long has the war lasted?

In the end,
from the darkness underground
to the dazzling blue sky of midsummer,
captivated fathers and mothers creep up,
dragging their rotten bodies full of maggots.
In one of those mothers' wombs, my
small germ of life is just conceived.
My postwar life
born from the *gama*.

—

gama
cavern in Ryukyu dialect
Usually a natural limestone
cave common to many
Okinawan coastal villages,
often used as a shelter
during the American inva-
sion of Okinawa

—

kuragaa
underground river running
through the cave
Literally, *kura* = dark, and
gaa = river

Gama   Ben Takara

—

Tokyo: Shicho-sha, 2009.
Translated by
Ryuta Imafuku

A Matter of God *(Kamigutu)*

Ben Takara

Sari Sari Sari
with awe, I pray
my earnest wish
a lost child which is me
lost in heart, lost the way
not knowing my own fate
not knowing my own vocation
given from the heaven.
Lost the soul of *mabui*
taken out the spirit of *shii*
desperately depending on you, my god of
the sky axis.
Throwing myself on you
I finally come here
please, please
my god of truth
my god of high spirit
to this lost child which is me
please tell me my duty
show me a right way for the future
show me how to keep my heart
oh, my precious god.

Listen my child
feel my child
Go to your native village, to your
old house and pray, pray to the god of the river
where you got your first bath
offer your deep gratitude for the new hatch
obligation for leaving a nest
to the gods of fire, water of land
offer your deep gratitude for the new hatch.

Listen my child
feel my child
your duty is not to keep praying forever with *binshi*
think well
of your duty to write
given by me
decide if you take again my brush of virtue
decide if you keep writing with it
awake now
if you really take it
from now on
keep writing
keep diffusing the high spirits
of gods of three corners of heaven
listen my child
feel my child

oh, precious god ah, precious god
the rising sun burning
inside the light of candles
the will of gods floating
when my ears and heart
with awe, tremble
shaken

—

Sari Sari Sari
an Okinawan call to God
or somebody especially
important

—

mabui
soul in Ryukyu dialect

—

shii
energy or *vigor* in
Ryukyu dialect

—

binshi
a portable wooden box
of tools for prayer ritual
in Okinawa

A Matter of God   Ben Takara

—

Translated by
Ryuta Imafuku

The Deleted Line

Deni Y. Bechard

The morning commute had been surprisingly clement for early August. The secretaries arrived not dabbing their foreheads with handkerchiefs or wielding fans as Yukio sat at his desk, skimming American books for one that might catch his attention and be deemed, by the editorial committee and boss alike, worthy of translation. He removed his glasses and rubbed his eyes.

"You were in last night?" Masa asked from the next cubicle. He was a slouching young man whose pointy, overlapped eyeteeth gave him a vampiric look well-suited to the horror novels he acquired from abroad.

"*Hai,*" Yukio lied and nodded, phosphenes pulsing in his eyes. He'd made his voice terse to discourage any talk hinting at the office's collective fear of further layoffs. But the binging of the elevator distracted Masa.

A very old man in a *karate gi* stepped out. His hair was cropped close to his skull, silver and sparse, like the spines on a cactus, and he carried a history textbook.

—

karate gi

a karate training uniform

Heads floated to the tops of cubicles as the ancient fighter approached the receptionist's desk and bowed. In an Okinawan accent, he explained his desire to speak with whoever had edited the textbook that he held.

"We have many editors," she said.

"Certain lines were erased," the old man told her, as if the changes had been made with a gum eraser. "May I speak to who was responsible for that?"

She hesitated, her eyes blinking beneath her fringe of bangs.

"The Ministry of Education," she stammered. "They have textbook screeners."

"Yes, I understand," he said, still with great formality, though his voice held a hint of militarism. "But please, who is the person who erased the actual lines?"

Yukio scanned the office, and in the far back, behind his pane of glass, the boss was watching, head thrust forward, eyes like two jots of ink. He had the phone to his ear.

Masa whispered to Yukio, "The old *karateka* wants you. Watch out!"

—

karateka

a karate master

Takeo, a young guy and a hard worker, moving up through the editorial ranks like a vine, stood and pointed to Yukio.

"Yukio deleted it," he said.

The old man's head turned in a clean motion, like that of a flicked switch, and his eyes locked onto Yukio's, as in the films. Yukio ducked back into his cubicle, but just then the elevator binged again and security arrived.

The rumor that the boss didn't miss a detail was true. The second he'd seen the crazy martial artist he'd called security. The old man didn't resist, merely repeated his request. Receiving no answer, he bowed, and security led him away.

Despite the air conditioning, Yukio was sweating. Everyone came out from their cubicles, laughing and making jokes at his expense. As they discussed how terrifying the old man had been—come like that to punish Yukio—he saw in their eyes that they believed he would be the next one summoned into the boss's office and dismissed.

The boss shouted for them to get back to work. Then he called to Yukio.

"Have you found anything worthwhile at that conference?"

"Not yet, sir, but I have some leads."

"Good. I'm looking forward to a hot new title."

Three days before, at the start of the conference, he'd told Yukio to bring him a fresh perspective. "And we need a new book on Iraq, something fun and original."

After the boss strode back to his office, Yukio sat, sweat seeping from his armpits. He hadn't taken a day off in months. Insomnia was eroding his health. He no longer dreamed, and his rare sleep was as brief as when he nodded off at his desk, which was where it usually occurred. If not for the others seeing the old man, he would have believed the incident a hallucination, the delirium of stress and exhaustion.

The five-day conference was on the writing of history. Yukio attended each year to look for foreign books on subjects such as cod or salt or bathing rituals. He visited the stalls of English publishers and attended panels and readings.

But this year he'd gone seeking something impressive, a masterpiece that would cement his place in the publishing house. The first talk he'd attended was *Shock and Awe: Blogs from the Iraq War*. The author, Matt Lewis, dwarfed his audience. Well-built, with crystal blue bloodshot eyes, he wore his brown non-military hair swept back from his forehead, his stubble like a graphite smudge. During his reading, he appeared jittery, pausing to wipe his palms against his pants or to glance around the room, as if a bespectacled professor might be taking aim with one of the RPGs he'd described.

Afterwards, Yukio introduced himself.

"Hey," Matt said, "you speak English like an American." Then, after Yukio had thanked him, Matt corrected himself: "Well, actually, like a Canadian."

"I went to high school in Toronto," Yukio told him. But a little later, when he tried to navigate away, Matt stuck with him like a bear in a motorcycle sidecar. He followed, angling through doors or past crowds, keeping close, as if for protection, though his shoulder was the height of Yukio's head and about the same size.

Yukio attended a few more events with him but couldn't extricate himself to speak with other authors. They finished the evening in the bar, Matt buying them what he called "two starter shots," sweating and trembling until the tequila went down, chased by a beer. Then he calmed and drank more casually. His brow smoothed, and his accent, until then formal and generically American, became distinctly Southern.

With the two shots, the anxiety of Yukio's life bubbled dyspeptically to the surface. He forgot his urgency to acquire a new book, and instead explained how his wife had left a year ago to volunteer in impoverished countries, abandoning him to raise their reclusive thirteen-year-old daughter.

"I should have married a Korean or a Filipina," he said. "They wouldn't have run off. Our daughter doesn't even blame her. She blames me. For being boring."

He caught himself complaining and became self-conscious. Rather than shut up, he drunkenly promised Matt something foolish. He lifted his beer in a toast and said he would buy the Japanese rights to his book. Then, after Matt had ordered three more celebratory rounds, Yukio went home and collapsed on his bed fully clothed.

The next two days had gone by in the same fashion, Yukio spending a few hours at the office before migrating to the conference, where Matt attached himself. Sometimes, after a few drinks, Matt relaxed. But at others, he gazed about with bloodshot eyes as if the intensity of his mind might project out upon his surroundings and incinerate them.

"I went into the Army expecting something from the movies," he said, "and we made it like that. We strapped video cameras to our helmets and made war videos. We watched war flicks and listened to heavy metal to get pumped up. But, you know what? Mostly, I was bored and scared."

He paused, taking a long drink. "Now I'll tell you what's fucked up. I'm starting to remember it as if it was all one long movie that wasn't bad at all. I even feel pretty good about it sometimes."

And on he talked, his mother's death from cancer on his last tour, his loneliness returning stateside. His eyes were disturbingly blue, a walleyed nakedness to his gaze.

Each night Yukio returned home without new contacts or a masterpiece. He tumbled into his bed, but though intoxicated he couldn't sleep.

An hour after the incident with the old *karateka*, Yukio returned to the conference. Two days remained, but he worried that other publishers had snatched the best books.

The first speaker was a sallow young man with a PhD from Yale, his subject the history of redlining in the United States. He explained how banks and insurance companies once identified streets on which minorities lived, and refused to offer home loans or policies there. He read from his book *Ghettoize, Circumscribe and Hide: Redlining and the American Art of Making Minorities Disappear.* Such a book, Yukio told himself, would be of no interest to his boss. Not exciting or edgy enough.

After the reading, a Brazilian professor complimented the author's rigor but said that no one was going to take issue with his scholarship.

"It's self-evident," he declared. "More contentious work deserves attention."

A young female writer from Vancouver disagreed, then argued with the Brazilian about indigenous rights in the Amazon, and he pointed out that this was precisely the gray area that needed discussing—not the clearly egregious redlining that everyone could agree on—but the more complicated Indian rights issues.

"What's complicated about it?" she asked. "It's just as bad."

"No, it's complicated," the Brazilian said.

The young woman flushed and told the Brazilian that racial cleansing had no gray areas, and an elderly British professor awkwardly tried to make peace by synthesizing their arguments.

Then a big hand lifted in the middle of the room, and Matt spoke up.

"What about American soldiers?"

All heads swiveled in his direction.

"American soldiers are practically invisible in a lot of the U.S. There's a line between people who profit from war and those who fight. It's a question of class."

The young Yale PhD waggled his finger. "To compare the treatment of a well-paid professional army," he said as if grimacing, though he was simply trying to squeeze words through a maniacal smile, no doubt pleased to take the attention for himself—"to compare the world's most powerful military to underprivileged, segregated and abused minorities, that's shameful."

The room erupted with talk that soon fizzled when the moderator closed the session. The crowd mingled, picking at a table of sushi.

Matt had wilted, avoiding eye-contact, flinching each time someone raised his voice. His gaze was vacant, as if he might black out, or strangle someone unknowingly. Then he saw Yukio. He made a beeline, interrupting a conversation and banishing Yukio's hopes of meeting viable authors.

Once they were at the bar, he wanted to know how things were progressing with the book deal. Yukio tried to backpedal, saying that the editorial committee was still reading. In truth, he hadn't shown the book to his boss. *Shock and Awe* wasn't fresh.

Yukio changed the subject to that morning, describing the old man stiffly poised in his *karate gi* like an apparition from the dead. He worried that he was losing his mind, the old *karateka* a figment of his insomnia.

"That's strange," Matt said. "Why would he come looking for you?"

"Last year, the Ministry of Education screened textbooks and mandated some changes."

"Like what?"

"Just some lines regarding the Battle of Okinawa. The problem is that I made the deletions. It must have been a year ago. With the recession, everyone is trying to seem valuable. The girl who used to have the job was laid off."

He closed his eyes. The boss had been nudging female employees on to their conjugal quests, and Yukio had volunteered to pick up the slack. But he knew that he hadn't appeared invaluable at all, just desperate.

Yukio lay like a set of shrouded bones, a dull throbbing in his skull. The hangover wasn't so bad this morning.

He got up and shuffled into Ai's room. He hadn't seen her in four days. Normally, she returned from school to do her homework and draw, then had dinner and spent the night at his parents' house. Since Mika had abandoned them, this had been the pattern, to ease the demands of his work and, for her, the loneliness.

He sat at her drawing table. She was a strange child, praised by her teachers, though the clothes, nail polish and eyeliner she preferred were black. She appeared otherworldly, thin, hunched as if hollowed out. She read constantly and received excellent grades, but her passion was manga. It was not a pastime he approved of, but evenings, unable to sleep, he read the cartoons that she drew on paperboard.

When she'd begun, the images had been innocent enough, imitations of popular children's manga, but that had changed when Mika had left.

He'd been shocked seeing the new work. In the corner were the words, *Imagine that men came into the school...* They carried machetes along a hallway, faces gaunt with determination *...and that they cut up the children and set fire to the building.*

He'd blamed Mika for this, not just for leaving, but for the passions she'd imposed on Ai. Several years earlier, she'd found a job as the secretary of a humanitarian relief agency, and the destitution and brutality in the Congo and Darfur had become household talk. What else could have inspired such drawings?

The next panel showed men with near invisible eyes swinging blurred machetes. A girl ran out a burning doorway, her clothes catching fire. Beyond was a landscape of flaming houses. *It was like a city on the sun, and at the center of it all was a lake.* She cast herself into the water, her clothes disintegrating, barely covering her, scraps clinging to her breasts and loins in the way that so many manga artists portrayed their heroines.

She hung suspended in stillness, weeds swaying faintly.

The surface became a dancing glimmer, like a flame seen from within, and she realized that the water itself was burning.

The girl climbed not from water but from a heap of ash. She crossed her arms over her breasts, her body turned away as if to hide her nakedness with the paper on which she was drawn. The road was littered with bodies, and an old man called to her. Like a parent, he dressed her in the clothes of the dead.

His name was Hugo, and he explained that the world in which she'd lived had existed only within a book. He was its author and had been imprisoned for writing books in which nobody did as they were told and no one obeyed the rules. In prison, he had composed his greatest book. But as he was being released, his guards realized that he was sneaking it out beneath his shirt. They tore it from him and burned it, and as each word in it fell to ash, so too did its forests and cities. It was then that the girl, a character in his book, had to hurry from her burning school. She dove into the lake, for water, even water in a burning book, will briefly resist flames because of the memory of its freshness and the joy of swimming. For this reason, she had time to escape the lake, but just barely; when a book is burned, even the water described in it eventually turns to ash.

Yukio shuddered. Her teachers said she was different, but this frightened him. Did she know that he'd burned Mika's books and journals? He saw himself in the old man's face and name: Hugo. Day after day, the story followed the girl and the old man from massacre to massacre as they were stalked by War, a man half rotting flesh, half fire, trailing smoke and blood. Yukio had forbidden Ai to draw the images, but each morning she left new manga on her table.

Today's began with the question: *Why should I write what I have lived?* A TV screen showed images of bombed out towns. Each panel drew closer to the broken walls until it had entered the TV. *Why not experience what others have? My teacher says I should write what is close to my experiences. I try, but my mind drifts. It finds characters whose faces I have never seen, in the jungles, in a different light and a hotter sky, and I do not want to return.*

Child soldiers in Liberia wore wigs and wedding gowns to confuse enemy bullets, as if death could not recognize their dual identities. In the next panel, the Sioux danced in ghost shirts that could ward off bullets.

I will wear manga, she wrote. *Find me. Where am I?*

Corpses littered a plain. She had the vile imagination of a boy, something vaguely sexual about the dead, the detailed way she'd drawn their intertwined limbs, how they lay in each other's arms. Yukio searched, trying to identify her, but he could not.

In the next panel, the girl and Hugo were searching the plain, looking for someone, casting their gaze to the distance. Who were they seeking?

Feeling guilty for his absence, Yukio took a scrap of paper. She would love the story of the *karateka*, and he wrote it quickly. He added the words, *The Battle of Okinawa*.

He was almost to his office building when, through a break in sidewalk traffic, the old *karateka* came into sight. Haggard with rage, he glared at the pedestrians as he guarded the sliding doors. Yukio froze, and a woman stumbled into him from behind and uttered a startled apology. The *karateka* saw him and hurried forward.

Yukio spun and ran, his briefcase slapping his leg. At the corner, he glanced back. The *karateka* moved in an arthritic bowlegged shuffle, arms in rhythm with his feet. He wasn't going anywhere fast, and Yukio lost him in the crowd.

Eventually, he came to Yoyogi Park, its large paths and greens mostly empty but for homeless men. Sweat made dark patches on his chest and beneath his arms, and he sought shade in the gingko and cherry woods, holding his shirt away from his skin. The big crows were out in force, strutting about the lawns and cawing. Squatters gathered around a water fountain to bathe. One had twisted the nozzle and stood before the jet, holding his elastic beltline out as the water struck his dark belly and ran in streams down his legs. He had his head back, his face to the humid sky. If Yukio didn't find a good book in time for the editorial meeting in two days, he might be joining the poor fellow.

He sat on a bench, waiting for his shirt to dry. He hadn't been here with Ai in over a year, not since Mika had left. It was unthinkable. All that existed of her were postcards. He'd seen one from Kinshasa taped to Ai's manga, surrounded by scenes from that country. *What if mom dies there?* she'd written. *Will she regret her amazing life?*

Literature had drawn Yukio and Mika together, and they'd encouraged Ai to read, but whereas Yukio had seen tradition and education in his novels, Mika had loved their headstrong characters. It was as if she stopped before the books were finished. She did not register the tragic endings of those who gave in to desire; she merely felt their craving for destructive passions.

The night before she ran off, she'd been on the couch, reading about a man from a distant wintry island who longed to test himself in war. He crossed the world to do so and was so changed by it that he could never quite return home. She was wiping away tears, and he'd asked her what was wrong.

"It's sad," she'd told him. "There's no easy answer."

He'd thought her silly and dramatic, though now he understood that she'd not been speaking of the story, but of abandoning her own island home.

Matt was arguing in the middle of a group, as if staging a one-man Thermopylae.

He turned to Yukio. "I was just saying that people who haven't been to war never write about it well, but Iraq's going to give us a generation of writers who can."

"And what will we get, if it gives you great literature?" a British-Iraqi writer asked, a man who, in his lecture, had discussed his correspondences with family in Baghdad from his home in London. "What void will it fill?"

But the crowd fled because another lecture was starting.

"I need a drink," Matt panted, though with the satisfied air of a class prankster. In his book, he wrote about run-ins with Army authorities over blogging. Yukio didn't quite get Americans with their military authoritarianism and frontiersman rebelliousness.

Rather than discuss this, he found himself spilling his guts between rounds of shots. Matt's Southern accent was back like a case of strep.

"No kidding. The old guy chased you?"

"The history book had nothing to do with me."

Yukio explained how the year before, the Ministry of Education had screened hundreds of textbooks and ordered the removal of certain lines, such as, *The Japanese army gave hand grenades to residents, making them commit mass suicide and kill each other.* The line was rewritten as, *Mass suicides and killings took place among the residents using hand grenades given them by the Japanese army.* And others deleted, *by the Japanese army.* The Ministry of Education, he told Matt, had pointed out that no direct instructions or documents remained from army commanders, and it would be difficult to verify that forced suicide actually occurred.

"So why don't you just talk to him?" Matt asked.

"Who?"

"The old man. See what he wants."

"I was just doing as I was told. Why should I have to deal with some crazy guy?"

"Come on, man, you don't think I know about countries committing atrocities. I couldn't even begin to list what American textbooks probably leave out."

Yukio shrugged. He had no idea why he'd brought it up. It was easier not to discuss it at all. "I hate my job," he said as if to change the subject. Matt raised his eyebrows, maybe with concern for the publication of his book. He cleared his throat and rubbed at his jaw, pulling his fingers against his cheek. "Sounds rough," he said, but Yukio kept on, emptying his heart, one cramped ventricle at a time.

Suddenly, he noticed that Matt's eyes had become bloodshot again, making the blue seem all the more crystalline. Yukio was afraid of what he might have unleashed—as if Matt, like a comic superhero, was in the midst of transformation. He appeared deranged, caught in one of his mood swings.

"Yeah, I hate people, too," he said. "But it's better to know you're fucked than to be the sons of bitches here who think they're not. It's hard not to want to fight them even if I know it won't make a damned bit of difference."

He stood suddenly, a drunken air about him, as if something had to change and only by casting himself headlong could he make a difference.

"Come on," he said. "We're gonna be late."

The crowd was leaving the smaller conference rooms and moving with a tidal sway towards the lecture hall, where award-winning J. Ernest Rotmensen would speak.

"Have you read this guy?" Matt slurred. "He was nominated for the Booker."

Inside the lecture hall, the grizzled author sat with a boxer's hunch, rubbing his chin as if to remove the ashen streaks from his beard.

Once the crowd settled and he was introduced, he discussed his new novel loosely based on the Nazi occupation of the Netherlands that his parents endured.

Matt raised his hand.

Rotmensen paused mid-sentence and cleared his throat. "Yes?"

"I read your book," Matt told him hoarsely, "and... and of course it had some good stuff in it, but what you describe didn't really seem like war to me."

People shook their heads, and Yukio slid away.

Rotmensen scuffed at his beard. He narrowed his eyes, clearly calculating the risk of humiliation. "How so?"

"War is messy," Matt told him. "When you go into a fight, it's like being in a storm. You have impressions but just hang on. And it's not just that. Your book makes war seem bittersweet, as if we should all be nostalgic. I don't see the different between that and propaganda. Really, I don't. Your novel doesn't have the messiness of war. There are a bunch of pretty good people, and so that we can feel enough sadness, one of them dies. Otherwise, they all make it through. In war, people are just suddenly gone. They get shot or fucked in the head. And maybe in the end there's nothing to return home to. That should be a novel. Just some blips on the map that disappear, or... or, I don't know, the slow grinding away of who we are."

Rotmensen was nodding.

"Sounds as if you've thought this through. So I applaud you. But I hate to say that what you're describing doesn't sound like a story people would want to read. I'm not even sure it would be a novel."

Matt threw up his hands and told him, with all the earnestness of a college freshman, "So reinvent the form."

Rotmensen shrugged. "Be my guest," he said and continued as if Matt hadn't spoken.

During high school, Yukio had lived in Toronto, where his father had been stationed by his company. When it was time to return, his sister, Miho, two years younger than he, had balked. She'd hated Japan, hated her grandmother who constantly berated her for her bad Western manners. A few years later, she'd moved back to Toronto on her own. But Yukio had loved Tokyo, the quality of his written Japanese his only concern, so he'd devoted himself to literature. But maybe he'd overcompensated and not understood Japan's true cultural trajectory. At the publishing house, other editors joked that though he'd lived in Canada, he'd returned as if from the Kamakura Shogunate.

That night, he begged off drinks, complaining that he didn't feel well, and returned home only slightly tipsy. Matt's surprisingly poetic words were still in his head: *the slow grinding away of who we are.* Before sitting at Ai's drawing table, he turned on the TV to dispel the emptiness of the house. Often, this worked against him, for on the rare occasion that he dozed, he heard voices in his dreams and thought that he had fallen asleep in public, surrounded by strangers, and he jolted awake. Sometimes, when he fell asleep reading her manga, he dreamed his life in its sketches, everyone hollowed out and color-less, yet more urgent and expressive, more alive.

Now, seeing what Ai had drawn that day, he was certain that he'd become a figment of her manga. The new panels showed the arrival of the old *karateka*, his terse bow to the receptionist and his request. Yukio saw himself peeking from his cubicle, eyes like onyxes reflecting the overhead lights, fear evoked about his face in drops of sweat.

Just as the old *karateka* hurried towards Yukio, security arrived and caught his arms. *But I must speak with you!* the old man said as he was pulled into the elevator.

In the next panel, Yukio's manga self lowered his eyes to a text. It was the history book, and in it were words that Ai had surely found online. *One fourth of the island's population were killed in the eighty-two days of fighting that came to be known as* tetsu no ame, *the rain of steel—the battle with one of the highest casualties of any in World War II: over 100,000 Japanese soldiers dead.* Images filled the background of the panel, as if Yukio sat before the fighting. Planes strafed infantry. Grenades burst. As Yukio lowered his pen and began to cross out a line, groups of soldiers blurred, vanishing mid-stride.

Yukio considered the pages. She must have been pleased with his note, for she had done far more in a day than was usual. Panels showed pres-ent and past, Japanese soldiers telling the Okinawans that to be taken prisoner was a betrayal of their nation. The manga Yukio was about to erase a line as Hugo and the girl ran, seeking someone. Who was it they were looking for? In the present, the *karateka* rushed to stop Yukio. *To erase someone's death is to erase the life that preceded it—to kill a person twice!*

Yukio held the large sheets. She'd wanted to please him. She'd done this for him, but in her words, he found no forgiveness.

Voices from the TV woke him, and, ridiculously, after the night's vigil, he was going to be late. He had one day until the editorial meeting.

Outside his door, he stopped to get his bearings. A storm front was passing over the city, the world colorless, cartoon neighbors stepping past.

Maybe because Yukio was late, the old *karateka* was not waiting. At his desk, as he arranged manuscripts and papers with trembling hands, others asked about his absence and he lied that he had found an amazing book. His optimism would permeate the channels of gossip and reach the boss who, sit-ting at his large desk, would narrow his eyes—Yukio could see him behind the pane, doing just this, looking with Superman's x-ray vision into the insomniac wonders of Yukio's shriveling brain—and he would decide that Yukio, at the next day's meeting, would present a cutting-edge masterpiece or be dismissed.

All morning, Yukio lied—about the conference and the authors he'd talked up, and why not? Lying was like dreaming, and dreams had become the substance of his days. He even slept again, in his cubicle, and found himself as an old man standing before a burning book. *I am dreaming,* he thought. *Therefore, I must have been awake before.* From the book's ashes, a body rose, pale and naked, and he averted his eyes.

A murdered woman lay not far away, and he stripped her of her clothes and dressed Ai. She threw herself into his arms, trembling, her shirt wet with blood. It seemed familiar, and he looked down at the dead woman, at Mika's face.

He jolted awake and rubbed drool from his chin. He glanced around and gathered his belongings, ostensibly to return to the conference and have Matt talk his ear off. Casually, he told the receptionist about the next generation of American war writers who were now maturing. Masa and Takeo peeked over their cubicle walls.

In the street, he checked his cell phone. Matt had left a message: "Where are you, man? There's a cold one calling your name." A manga bottle cried out, *Yukio, come get me! Take me!*—like a woman who desired him, whose love might last if he were to sip it at just the right pace.

He started home, barely able to lift his feet, knowing that he could finally sleep. There would be no masterpiece. The boss might find Matt's *Shock and Awe* vaguely interesting. Then Yukio would lose his job. There was no point in returning to the conference. Now that he'd accepted failure, exhaustion flooded his limbs.

At the end of his narrow street, just beyond the neighbor's forest of potted herbs and succulents, someone was sitting. The old *karateka* rose as if in a dream, his skin and unwashed *gi* the color of smoke. He appeared so fatigued he could barely stand. Yukio began to turn so that he could run, but in the speech bubble above the *karateka's* balding head, words were wedged between ellipses—"Please... Wait... Speak to me!"

Yukio considered calling the police, but if the *karateka* was a delusion, they would think Yukio was insane. Or if this was all a dream, the police might massacre him. Besides, the old man had found his house. This would make sense only in a dream.

"I was waiting for you," the *karateka* said.

He swayed, as if he might swoon, but then blinked and steeled his expression.

"Why are you following me?" Yukio asked.

"Why? Why am I following you? You are the one who erased those lines."

"We no longer use erasers. We just hit a button. It's very impersonal."

"What does that change? It's like dropping a bomb then."

"No, we must move on and let go of the past."

"Let go of the past? Tell that to the dead."

Yukio hesitated. "But we must let go of the dead."

"That's like saying we must let go of our minds, of our spirits, and so then we let go of our heads, and if you want that, I can help you."

The old *karateka* lifted his right hand and made it as rigid as a blade.

"No, no," Yukio said. "We must stay sane."

"Sanity? You speak to me of sanity? I was a young man, but the dead outnumbered the living."

And then he calmed and knocked the wrinkles from his *gi* and told his story.

A week ago, in Okinawa, he'd gone for a walk. He followed a path that he hadn't taken in a while. Because of the American military base, he was accustomed to seeing soldiers, but as he came through a stand of trees, he saw American boats on the shore and troops dressed as they had been in the spring of 1945. Infantry ran along the beach, clutching sixty-year-old rifles, ducking sniper fire from Japanese soldiers in the bluffs.

The old man fell to his knees, gasping and clutching his chest. Someone yelled, "Cut!" and the soldiers stopped racing about. They jogged over and helped him up. They explained that they were making a film about World War II.

He hadn't felt the same after that day. He began dreaming the battle again. He woke, not sure what year it was. The shock had disturbed his mind, and worse, he was slated to go to Tokyo two days later, to be a judge at a karate tournament.

During his flight and his first night in the city, he felt groggy. He slept poorly, disturbed by that old haunting sense, which he hadn't felt in years, that his wife was next to him. In the morning, at the tournament hall, one of the students had been studying a history book while waiting. He put it down, and the old man picked it up at some point. Maybe because of his dreams or the war scene on the beach, he found himself looking for the Battle of Okinawa and found the line: *It is possible that mass suicides and killings took place among the residents.* He read it again and then out loud. The publishing house's address was in the textbook, and he left, accidentally taking the book. He'd been too addled to figure out how to get back to the tournament.

"But you came all the way to my house," Yukio said.

"I followed you and then got lost and waited in the street."

"For this long?"

The old man nodded, his cheeks hollow. "I wasn't sure which house was yours."

"I'm sorry," Yukio told him. "But there's nothing to do about this."

"One must take proper action," the old man said. "Hundreds of years ago, when weapons were outlawed on our islands, we practiced fighting with our hands and feet, or with farm tools, and, in this way, kept our art alive. Now, our government has turned its backs on the dead, but we must not. There is always a way to resist."

Yukio nodded, so tired he could barely stand.

"Your wife, what happened to her?" he asked. So many men shared this one constant—how they met their wives and lost them.

"I was married only months before the battle. She was pregnant, but she wasn't used to being with me yet. She was close to her family and visited them often. When the invasion began, our people hid in the island's caves. I was a medic, but I went to see my parents and sisters and my wife. The Japanese soldiers spread rumors about the Americans who would rape and massacre everyone. She was afraid and wanted to be with her mother. While I was treating the sick, she went to see her parents in another cave. Her brother blew up the family."

The old man stood, swaying slightly.

"And then what could I do? I could not grieve during that terrible battle. The dead were buried quickly. I was taken prisoner, put in a camp with the Japanese soldiers who had not blown themselves up after all. Then the bombs fell on Hiroshima and Nagasaki, and it seemed that no one would remember our terrible battle."

Again, Yukio felt as if inside his daughter's manga, the limits of his mind unclear, and he was terrified to imagine the landscapes through which she must wander.

The old man's knees buckled, and Yukio reached out and briefly held him.

"Let me help you," he told him.

But the old man pulled from his grasp.

"I must find my way back," he said. He turned and walked off along the street.

Yukio wrote through the night. Soon the sun would begin its tedious ascent. Light would infiltrate the rooms, and the possibility of sleep, and of a solution, would vanish.

He had finished the story of the old *karateka* for Ai, and he carried the pages, far more than he had expected, to her drawing table. He turned on the lamp and picked up her most recent manga. In a panel, the old *karateka* pleaded with Yukio not to erase the lines even as Japanese soldiers handed out grenades. The next showed the girl running as mortars fell and machine-gun fire raked the earth.

I have to tell her to stop. Not to do it. To wait for me!

Abruptly, he put down the page. It made sense. Why hadn't he seen it all along? All this time, through all these wars, she had been seeking her mother, trying to save her.

He closed his eyes and exhaled a long shaky breath like a sob.

It was time to leave for work. The day would start with the editorial meeting.

He showered and put on fresh clothes. At the door, he hesitated. On the off-chance that he wasn't going to be fired, he should hurry. Punctuality might help.

But he closed his eyes. He'd never been an original thinker, not like the women in his life, who lived by their ambition and wild ideas. What would Mika do—set off on an adventure—or Ai? He wished she had been home, even briefly, and that he might have asked what she thought. He shuddered just imagining doing so. And then he knew.

He went upstairs and into her room. Papers cluttered her drawing table and shelves, and he gathered them gently, holding them in his arms, thinking that this might be right.

The Emperor and the Mayor: A Conversation with Hitoshi Motoshima

Stephen Woodhams

It was a shock to discover that Lisa's contact in Nagasaki had reserved us a room in a hotel directly overlooking Ground Zero. There, by a small canal, is a black obelisk in a grassy theater of concentric circles. It stands alone marking the epicenter of the atomic blast on August 9, 1945. "This is the funeral of humankind" was the phrase that came to me, contemplating the place where 80,000 people died in an instant, leaving 80,000 more sickened and injured.

We were in Nagasaki to meet with Dr. Shunichi Yamashita, Director of the Atomic Bomb Disease Institute at the Nagasaki University School of Biomedical Sciences, where my wife's grandmother, a pediatrician, worked with children in the 1950s on a couple of goodwill missions to treat atomic bomb victims. Dr. Yamashita is a world expert on the effects of radiation on the thyroid, did his residency in Los Angeles at Cedars-Sinai, worked in Geneva for two years at the World Health Organization, and travels often to treat patients exposed to radiation in Kazakhstan and at Chernobyl.

After viewing the obelisk I didn't much feel like being in Nagasaki and wondered what we'd do for five days, staying so close to the center of the destruction. That evening we wandered along the Urakami River, mostly deserted in the twilight, and followed the construction of an overpass on the other side for almost a mile—soon there would be traffic whizzing along the bank. We took the funicular ride to the top of Mt. Inasa where there is a famous panoramic point. It was good to re-envision Nagasaki as a city of lights delicately strung out over its steep hills and to see its harbor and indelible sweeping bay dotted with islands leading to the East China Sea. It is a view that appeals to the sea-faring imagination. Many of the hills around Nagasaki are too sheer to build on, leaving a beautifully natural—intensely green—setting for its 500,000 or so inhabitants (40,000 of whom still suffer directly from the effects of the bomb).

That night, I didn't sleep well, sensing the black obelisk close at hand. At breakfast I noticed that we had a clear view of it through the foliage. But as we toured around the city and came to know more of its history before the bombing and saw how the inhabitants had rebuilt a vibrant town, the mood began to lift. We visited the Urakami Cathedral, totally destroyed near the epicenter, now restored. It happened to be Mother's Day Sunday and the church was full of women in white veils. After the service, celebrants carried a statue of the Virgin Mary through the streets. Nearby, the twisted outcropping of a belfry has been left where it fell in the grass, one of few such remains in Nagasaki outside of the museum.

We walked further up the road and saw the hutch where a heroic doctor, Dr. Takashi Nagai, lived and wrote many books about Nagasaki and the effects of radiation while slowly dying of radiation disease himself, in this case inflicted by altruistically screening potential TB patients with direct X-ray after the hospital ran out of film due to the war.

We also visited a fascinating museum park called Glover Gardens, where the European settlers, who introduced the West to Japan, lived and intermarried. For many decades, Nagasaki, by edict of the Shoguns, was the only point of contact with the West, particularly through trade with the Dutch and the Portuguese (this accounts for the high concentration of multi-generational Catholics in Nagasaki like Dr. Yamashita). Once a year, the foreigners, the only ones in all of Japan, were required to report in person to Edo-Tokyo, a trip that aroused great national interest as they journeyed there for weeks through a countryside lined with on-lookers. Then the Scots came to Nagasaki. They introduced the first mills, the first tarmac roads, and, along with the Dutch, the first dictionary of Western medicine, the first cars and even beer—Kirin to be specific. In return, these Europeans picked out the best vantage point on the bay for their houses; so the museum had expansive views, and as someone said, they must have had great parties. This spot is considered the setting of Puccini's *Madame Butterfly,* where she waits for her American captain. As we wandered around the gardens and the individual residences the sound of arias spun over the bay.

That afternoon, Lisa met with her host, Dr. Yamashita. Later that evening, he took us to a homespun dinner at a small restaurant where, from behind the counter, the owner couple marveled at our son's consumption of sashimi (but not mine) and slyly kept adding fish to his plate when he wasn't looking. Yamashita told us he had arranged, in addition to a tour of the medical school the following day, to introduce us to Hitoshi Motoshima, the former mayor, a vocal critic of Japan's policies in WWII and survivor of an assassination attempt in 1990 for saying so. This courtesy was extended by way of a significant contact, Dr. James Yamazaki, the former head of the Atomic Bomb Casualty Commission in Nagasaki, who knew both men and had hoped a meeting between us all would occur.

It is not an exaggeration to say that the story of Mayor Motoshima is key to understanding contemporary Japan and its postwar legacy.

In 1988, Mayor Motoshima was asked in a City Council meeting by a council member from the Communist Party for his reaction to the emperor's role in World War II. He answered, "Forty-three years have passed since the end of the war, and I think we have had enough chance to reflect on the nature of the war. From reading various accounts from abroad and having been a soldier myself, involved in military education, I do believe that the emperor bore responsibility for the war."

His response rocked the world.

The mayor is significantly one of the subjects of Norma Field's *In the Realm of A Dying Emperor,* in which she devotes a chapter to understanding the mayor as a political force in the context of her own family history in Nagasaki. When the book was written in 1989, Motoshima had spoken out while the emperor lay dying a very prolonged death, pumped full of fresh blood regularly by a nation unable to accept the demise of an immortal leader descended from the sun.

Of course, the emperor had already died as a full god after the surrender and been demoted with full support by the occupation forces to the status of demi-god. The reasoning gets complex, but basically, the United States was willing to fine-tune the theology. They wanted to keep a scaled-down version of the Imperial figure as a symbol of Japan, as a rallying point for reconstruction and general continuity, and as a kind of proxy for their own designs. Or as the new Japanese constitution put it: as "the symbol of the state and the unity of the people." After all, the emperor had been reinvented before during the relatively recent Meiji Restoration, given "supreme command of the Army and Navy" in the constitution of 1890, after centuries of shoguns and symbolic power.

Field writes that the mayor was the product of his Christianity and years of embracing American ideals, which included heavily censored free speech, the ultimate oxymoron. You could say that up until the mayor's comment, this side of the discussion had been silenced for fifty years. So when the mayor spoke, many people came forth to say he spoke for them.

The topic of Imperial complicity had been everywhere right after the war and in fact openly and fiercely debated among Americans and Japanese trying to determine what the role of the re-instated emperor should be. He was exonerated by the Americans in a worldwide climate that saw leaders brought to war crime trials as a matter of course, as an expected outcome. The few times when his name came up matter-of-factly during the trials it was expunged from the record by the occupation authorities.

When the emperor was used as a transition to democracy and absolved of any culpability, the topic went dormant, became off-limits. The father had resumed his role, though very differently, and the family could only talk behind his back. As the emperor lay dying a death that Field described as "a death long in coming to a death long in making," then the family, to extend the figure, became the nation gathered around, some hoping for a deathbed confession from their leader like a family gathered by the bedside of a dying patriarch. The emperor taking so long to die opened a window for doubt and old wounds and unresolved issues from the war. For the mayor, a simple "I am sorry or I am also responsible" would have done because, as he told Norma Field, "Everyone knew that the emperor knew that the people thought they had to die for the emperor." The mayor indicated that this was a collective guilt shared by all, and just as he had his responsibility to say what he thought, so did the emperor bear a responsibility for what the country had done in his name.

The problem lay in this quick transition to a make-shift democracy under the American occupation right after the war—called "democracy from above"—and described as a change so sudden that it left observers "to contemplate the profoundly confusing spectacle of adults who only yesterday had said they were going to die for the emperor now proclaiming themselves believers in democracy," according to Mr. Harada, the publisher of the collection of letters to Motoshima from thousands of citizens after his radical statement.

The American democratic ideals did, according to John Dower in his Pulitzer Prize-winning book, *Embracing Defeat,* lead to rapid liberalization of postwar Japan on some fronts, with positive results, namely the writing of the new constitution (an uneasy and unequal Japanese and American effort), the quick establishment of labor unions and organized work forces, and an active press and media. But while lip service was given to freedom of speech, censorship was so complete as to eliminate, in an Orwellian twist, any references to censorship itself, and signs of the occupation were commonly deleted from articles and photographs. The goal was for the United States to operate as a shadow government behind the Japanese authority with, as conventional wisdom would have it, the emperor in the role of unifier and binding national force.

General MacArthur took the place of the emperor in the true hierarchy of power in those years. In his time as Supreme Commander, MacArthur received letters of adulation and respectful greeting from approximately one percent of the population, effectively supplanting the emperor as the man of the hour, the supreme being. While the emperor was sent out to awkwardly greet the subjects he had barely acknowledged before, the general, in an ironic reversal, stayed in his palace, with limited contact with the public and the country, meeting chiefly business leaders and high ranking officials.

The emperor had an abrupt change of heart, to say the least, going on speaking tours to promote the recovery after his first address to the Japanese public. In a famous photo a woman searches for the grand figure of the emperor in a crowd, not recognizing the man in the suit next to her, doffing his hat.

Many expected him to step down, perhaps even commit suicide as a matter of honor—that he didn't left a festering wound for some. Norma Field's assessment of the letters addressed to the mayor after his statement reveal two responses to the war: those written by people who felt the present prosperity justified the horrors and sacrifices of war (which she calls a logical fallacy), this view playing into conservative, right-wing thinking, and those written by people whose experience was tainted by having never received an apology, a view that younger generations extend to include current social and political restrictions and problems.

The mayor has maintained in various remarks that the generation that came of age during the war will not be free of war as long as they live (this may apply to some of the older people we met). The mayor's actions stimulated the shifting generations, and age had a lot to do with how people responded, but respond they did. As Field puts it, "A dying emperor and a mayor threatened with death seriously stirred dusty memories and breathed urgency into text-book knowledge."

The emperor and the mayor were on a collision path, both in terms of the war legacy and as an outcome of U.S. policy: one as the figurehead now representing "democracy from above," and the other as a man who came of age during the war, brought up to value free speech and independent thinking.

Many of the letters written to Motoshima applauded his bravery and chided the public's silence all these years. An old man wrote, "your statement came as a shaft of light through a dark cloud." Another compared mislead-ing reports of the emperor's medical condition to misleading reports from the battlefield during the war, information being manipulated for the benefit of one person.

Though the mayor had long been thinking and studying these issues and slowly assessing his own culpability in the war, his statement came in response to a question that he felt obligated to answer truthfully.

According to Field, one writer described the moment using an analogy befitting a country that learned to play baseball from American soldiers: "Motoshima's mumbled utterance was the equivalent of a hit into right in what was shaping up as a miserable, no hit, no run defeat. The em-pathetic applause that greeted Player Motoshima when he unexpectedly found himself alone on base was the candid expression of postwar democracy, which didn't go down in a shutout."

All was not applause, though. The mayor was barred from many pro-fessional organizations, and among displays of public outrage throughout Japan, his home city of Nagasaki was bombarded with hundreds of vehicles broadcasting messages of criticism. It is also true that some of the people who supported the mayor did so on the principle of supporting free speech rather that the sensitive subject of critiquing the emperor.

Most significantly, at the time of publication of Norma Field's book, the mayor was living in fear under the protection of around-the-clock bodyguards because of the threats made on his life. Every room he entered was checked out first. He had to retreat from the public eye. This was a time of reflection and family unity—not so many beer-infused after work get-togethers typical of the Japanese work culture. But the emperor eventually died, the country moved on, the bodyguards were removed and shortly thereafter, a right-wing assassin fired a bullet through the mayor's right shoulder. This is the updated chapter from the Field book. The danger had not been exaggerated. The damage done with his initial statement or perhaps with his continuing to speak out on other issues like the "lost Koreans," a generation of people victimized by the war, left at the bottom of Japanese society. The mayor survived the attack, served another term, and continues to speak out to this day.

As the mayor told Norma Field, "Freedom of speech cannot be restricted to certain times and places. I don't think the conclusions I've reached after forty-two years of study are wrong... I have warm regard and esteem for the emperor as a symbol, but he still bears responsibility for the war."

It was a double-edged sword cutting through the generations: the older emperor a product of American policy, the younger mayor a product of American idealism.

The next morning, as promised, Dr. Yamashita organized a tour of the Atomic Bomb Disease Institute, which included an exhibit of the scorched and bloody shirt the hospital director had been wearing at the time of the attack. We reviewed the database on radiation victims, saw the original files created by the U.S. Army and even viewed jars with actual remains of atomic victims. I had a start when the professor showing us around the medical school opened the elevator door on a darkened hall full of human forms, which turned out to be very realistic mannequins slung over gurneys.

At last we were led to a conference room where sat Mayor Motoshima. It had not been a certainty he would be able to meet, but there he was, the featured attraction waiting in the conference room, an eighty-four-year old man with large, tinted glasses and a face accustomed to adopting a droll expression. Lisa lagged behind so our ten-year-old son and I entered first, and, according to our interpreters, Motoshima asked if Stuart were the woman he had come to meet (which of course would have made Stuart my wife). But since the mayor is known for his sly humor, it is possible that this was just that—a jest.

Mayor Motoshima laid out his views in the conference room flanked by the two doctors who were clearly enjoying his company, ready to respond to his humor and nuances. Tea was served. He began by discussing a survey conducted on atomic bomb victims and "interested parties throughout Japan," which revealed certain attitudes that both he and Dr. Yamashita said "were not good"—a sense of being owed something and bearing no responsibility for what had happened to them. Dr. Yamashita added his assessment of this imbalance: "Everyone claimed they were against nuclear weapons, but they accepted aid and support."

The mayor then said almost as a summation, Yamashita translating, "I think my continued assertion that Japan's reaction to the atomic bombing has been as a trauma victim is entirely correct."

I thought about this word, "trauma." Was the mayor suggesting that though Japan had suffered intensely during the war it still had to own up to what it had done before it could lament what had been done to it?

Yes, he had made this point emphatically in his public utterances, well-documented in Norma Field's book, but casting it as some kind of national therapeutic process was new to me. Seeing it as "therapy" seemed like a modern view, applied after the fact, this idea that the process would be painful just because it had been avoided for so long. It had been avoided because the lines between the victims and the aggressors were so blurred that not even the emperor had been held accountable. This approach also smacked of "tough love." Because in therapy the patient must take responsibility on some level (no matter what may have been done). The "bad deeds" were now ensconced in a healing context: one must speak the truth and not be afraid to do so. The free speech underpinnings were now joined to humanistic psychology, even to traditional religious principles in which judgments were made and confessions uttered before atonement could take place.

Dr. Yamashita translated the mayor's verdict: "This weapon is justified to punish the badness of Japan. It is correct."

"No, it was a horror," Lisa protested, though not wanting maybe to appear contrarian—after all, we were there to learn from them.

The mayor said, "I'd like to tell you a few stories. Before the war, Japan and also America had a holding on China, had interests there. Be that as it may, it is true that Japan started all of the wars, the Japanese-Sino War, the Japanese-Russo War, the First World War, the Greater East Asia War—(translator's note: now called the Pacific War)—Japan launched a sneak attack in Pearl Harbor, which caused huge damage and loss to America. It was as retaliation for this that America dropped the atomic bombs on Japan."

This sounded like the version I knew, and it was strange that the mayor felt the need to affirm these "facts" as though there were people—as there are—who might not agree with this version.

Then came some more back story: "Japan saw Americans and British as like animals at that time, and, how should I put it, all the Japanese people thoroughly wanted to have a war with America, England and Holland, and they thought we had to. Because the Japanese had a powerful army, a powerful army and a people who would not surrender, the Japanese would never have surrendered. There was no other way to make the Japanese admit defeat than to drop the atomic bomb."

As familiar, even as acceptable, as this sounded, there was still a different note being struck. Lisa picked up on my thought: Did the mayor himself believe Americans were animals, were bad, before the war?

"Before the war, yes," the mayor nodded, the assumption being that now of course, he had a different view and also that previously, his view had been limited.

He went on, "Well, there is a man called Martin Harwite. He was going to hold an "atomic bomb exhibition" in 1995 in America, but he couldn't do it, because he was strongly opposed by people in the USA. He's come to Japan before and written many books, which I've read quite fully. I think that what those kinds of leaders in America, non-military leaders, say is also correct."

Harwite was the director of the Smithsonian Institution's National Air and Space Museum who resigned over the controversy and dissension around the 1995 exhibit of the Enola Gay, the bomber that dropped the atomic bomb on Hiroshima. According to a *New York Times* article in May of that year, "This exhibit was to encourage visitors to re-examine their thinking about the use of atomic weapons to end World War II, in the context of the bombings' horror and of the arms race that followed."

The controversy of public uproar arose from this view of the effects of the bombing, which included documentation of the devastation and pictures of the radiation victims. At the time of his resignation, Harwite said, "What we were doing sounded logical."

Mayor Motoshima, too, seemed to be saying that we need to consider all aspects, as contradictory and disturbing as those views can seem.

While the ideal of peace was and is supported rhetorically, many politicians and leaders in the United States did not think we should have to face the details of the Enola Gay exhibit. It's worth noting, too, that no high-ranking U.S. official—let alone the president, as was urged recently—has ever attended an anniversary of the bomb in Japan. How to understand these anniversary events is of course politically and geographically determined; constituencies at home have much to do with the official national response. This positioning hearkens back to the map the mayor used to show visitors, including Norma Field, of the relative position of countries in the world, each thinking they're at the focal point.

Seemingly both countries have the same problem. Can peace be earned without resolving underlying histories, admitting involvement and a long chain of injurious cause and effects? No country likes to admit fault (especially if it sees itself as victor or vanquished). Politically, it is hard to boil down a plurality of views, or to reveal the naked intentions and state machinery, in such a public admission. It's also hard to judge the plaintiff and the defendant in a court where a nation plays both roles and the preponderance of evidence shifts in a political, nationalistic tide.

For many Americans, the atomic bombing was an open-and-shut case: they attacked us first. They brought it on themselves. On the other hand, in what is now a familiar scenario, the United States may have created its own enemies when decades earlier, Theodore Roosevelt encouraged Japan to adopt a colonial, controlling role in the East, as documented recently in James Bradley's *The Imperial Cruise.* One of the causes given for Japan's aggression was its frustration in accomplishing that end with a sense of betrayal at the reneging of tacit agreements.

The idea of the bombings, while a different idea altogether, seemed to get the mayor to where he was going. "Well, I will close my story now. Torpedoes…" Dr. Yamashita broke in to add "special weapon, self-sacrificing from a ship," presumably from Nagasaki.

"The thing is," the mayor said, "all the bombs used by the Japanese in the air raid on Pearl Harbor were made in Nagasaki. You've heard this before, right?"

The doctor added, "At Mitsubishi."

"And," the mayor said, "President Truman dropped atomic bombs over Japan to attain Japan's surrender."

The doctor stressed, "Based on what he made of the Japanese attitude."

Mayor Motoshima said, "I'd like to tell you this, and please remember this. In Japan, we were short of food, from before the war and even after the war. After the war food was scarce, no one, from small kids to adults, could even eat rice. In those times, when food was scarce in Japan, foods like wheat and powdered skim milk were brought from America. And especially as they were served to kids for school lunch, kids lost interest in rice and stopped eating it." The mayor was half-joking here and got a laugh from the doctors. "Therefore, wherever I went in Japan as a city mayor, I said, 'the dropping of the atomic-bombing was correct.'"

"After all," he added, "I think we Japanese should apologize to America. As you know, we accepted the 'Potsdam Declaration,' which was the terms of surrender, so we have to know that we should expiate our guilt, little by little."

"And there was a reporter who had been working in China for five years as a correspondent for a Hiroshima TV station. He visited me, and he agreed with my thinking on the issue of the atomic bombing. So I appeared in a TV program with him with the title: 'Hiroshima Reconsidered, Let's rethink Hiroshima,'" said the mayor.

After a pause, Lisa said, "But I've read some of the mayor's statements online. He also said that the atomic bomb wasn't justified to be dropped on civilians and that's also what we believe."

Mayor Motoshima responded, "Well, as soon as I hear about 'civilians,' I feel that the atomic bombing was really terrible for them, you know, so I believe that it *is* also okay to have that kind of thinking. Hmm, well, many ships had left Hiroshima Harbor for China, taking lots of military personnel. A great number of people, including adults and children, sent those armies off, waving Japanese flags, singing songs, and saying 'Kill the enemy, kill all the Chinese.' It was those people that became atomic bomb victims a few years later.

"Despite America's support, some people still say that America was wrong because the atomic bombing killed lots of people. However, I feel that I have to say that it was reasonable, and that we should think of it as correct. This is what everyone has to think about for themselves and decide which view is correct."

Motoshima continued, "The Emperor Hirohito was asked by a news reporter in a press conference (editor's note: on October 31st, 1975): 'What do you think about the atomic bombing?' He answered, 'I'm feel extremely sorry for the people, but I think that it was reasonable.' So, I put his words into my own. 'Oh sorry,' he said, 'It was unavoidable.' So I said, "It was reasonable," making a phrase of his."

Lisa asked, "Really, Hirohito said that?"

The mayor responded, "Yes, I suppose everyone in Japan read this in the newspapers. The emperor said, 'The atomic bombing was unavoidable,' so I said 'It was reasonable.'"

The doctors laughed here, presumably at this play on words, and the way the mayor seemed to be agreeing with the emperor he had criticized to make his own point.

"Why did everyone get so mad at Mayor Motoshima?" Lisa wanted to know.

"Well, those people who attacked me have their own way of thinking. They say that Japan was correct in the war; therefore, we can't agree on the point of whether the war was right or not."

The doctor amplified, "For some Japanese—even if beaten we believe we are right and these attitudes continue."

Lisa said, "They still wanted to fight?"

I added, "It seems natural that they would be mad about the war."

The mayor, picking up a thread, "We, Japan, started the war, and we Japanese killed many people. Only around a tenth of the total number of war victims were Japanese."

I said, referring to the Japanese balloon attacks in Oregon, "In America only six non-combatants were killed."

The mayor gave me a wry smile. "You are not wrong," he said, but continued as though this fact was an anomaly or part of an unrelated train of thought. "The place where the largest number of Japanese died was the Philippines. The number was 500,000."

Lisa grimaced—which was a fitting reaction, given the point that followed.

The mayor said, "In China, about the same number of Japanese died. When people express disappointment about the atomic bombing, I have to say, 'Yes, I agree with you.' However, during the war, 3.1 million Japanese died. I'll tell you the details of largest loss of Japanese lives. In March of 1945, 100,000 people died in the Great Tokyo Air Raids. And in April of the same year, because of the landing of America troops in Okinawa, 200,000 people died. Well, in Hiroshima in the same year, the number of people who died due to the atomic bombing, between August 6th and the end of that year, 1945, was around 200,000."

The mayor stated, "On August 9th, when the atomic bomb was dropped in Nagasaki, about 70,000 people died, though 140,000 people died in Hiroshima from the atomic bombing. However, according to the research of the man at Hitotsubashi University, 1.4 million Japanese, mainly soldiers, died of starvation or malnutrition."

The doctor said, "Very sad thing," adding an emotional nuance to the mayor's recounting, which gathered steam:

"Let's talk about China. Japan says that around 20 million Chinese people were killed by the Japanese in China during WWII. 20 million Chinese, okay? However, the Chinese president told the Russian president that the number was 30 million, not 20 million.

I asked, "Is this something taught in schools here? Is this accepted by the public?"

The mayor said, "No. People still just keep their skeptical eyes on the wrongness of the atomic bombing. However, I guess it'll change soon. I really do think so. I mean, the point is whether these people have responsibility for the war or not. That's the issue. For example, there is a famous atomic bomb survivor, whose name is Senji Yamaguchi. He says, 'I have no responsibility for the atomic bombs. America is wrong.' He is my close friend, but with views like that I think he lacks education."

As the interview wound down, Mayor Motoshima said, "Well, before you start writing about atomic bombs, I think you'd better visit lots of the places involved." Then, "I have to go soon. I have to go and meet a woman who works in the kindergarten, she asked me to take a photo with her."

Some polite censoring went on around the mayor's final comment, which made both doctors laugh. "What did he say?" Lisa exclaimed, sensing something slipping through the cracks.

"He says…" The doctor paused, his face caught between a frown and a smile. "That he likes women very much." What the mayor actually said was that he liked my wife very much.

"And you," he said to my wife in the official transcript, "you're a most excellent woman. I'd like to work together."

People are surprised that we got to meet with him—indeed, the mayor himself seemed a little mystified. He told us "not to come see him again," but by that he meant that he was getting past the time for interviews.

What Mayor Motoshima said in this orchestration of his thinking—
a series of points and references laid next to each, with haunting statistics
allowed to reverberate and with dramatic statements made for shock value—
was perhaps to awaken the dead, to attract attention like a billboard with a
challenging claim, to issues he feels have been buried for so long that there is
no other way to attract attention to them. Many of these statements made me
realize that I needed more context to understand the mayor's remarks, both
on their own terms and as a product of the postwar contact zone.

I did not understand how a peace mayor could accept an attack that
destroyed his city and many of its people, leaving devastating radiation effects.
I realized that we were seeing versions of the mayor perhaps strung out over
a lifetime, boggling the mind, leaving us at times to gasp in protest at his light
treatment of the United States and harsh evaluation of Japan.

The mayor is known for his hands-on research, and in fact, it was from
study and reading that originally he formed his views on the emperor's culpability and Japan's aggression in Asia, and so as he speaks, he pieces together
a montage of statistics, moral equivalencies, quid pro quo post mortems.

His equation today is a simple juxtaposition of numbers: why are
people so fixated on the atomic attacks that killed hundreds of thousands
when the Japanese themselves lost and killed millions in Asia during the
war and the years leading up to it? Such destruction can seem apocryphal
almost—out of sight and out mind—which is why the mayor feels compelled
to speak. It is not forgotten in China, though, and it is documented in books like
Chang's *The Rape of Nanking,* among other sources.

But—a hundred thousand, a million—who can come to terms with
any of these numbers?

We received a document from the mayor at our hotel later, because
Lisa had asked him for a piece for her magazine. Only the title had been
translated so far—*Don't Arrogate, Hiroshima!*

Hiroshima, also an attractive city, is more of a tourist base. People
wander everywhere, maps in hand, whereas in Nagasaki, outside of the schoolchildren on field trips, only a few visitors trailed through. And after much
debate, Hiroshima left a symbolic, ruined building standing downtown.

One thing I thought would be secure was the notion that nuclear
war was inherently wrong and never to be waged again, even that the atomic
bomb should never have been dropped in the first place—that nothing could
justify its use, and in fact, that Japan itself was preparing to surrender prior to
the attacks. There is a whole well-known discussion of why the bomb was used:
as a necessary ultimatum against a nation that would never admit defeat,
as the devastating blow to a country bent on establishing supremacy, as
the opening salvo of the cold war, even as the product of an investment and an
on-going science experiment. Science and militarism went hand in hand, and
there is the staggering, almost absurd notion that the bomb led to the rise of
modern day Japan.

But scientists and politicians did embrace the power of technology that the bomb represented as a way of rebuilding the decimated country and developing Japan's influence and prestige—in the vein of that which would destroy you, makes you stronger. In this sense, it was an ironic "Sputnik moment." The blast shows us once and for all that we have fallen behind.

This connects to the question: how did Japan rise so successfully and quickly from the ashes of WWII? Conventional wisdom suggests that not having to support a large military machine helped the financial recovery. But the answer as revealed in Dower's *Embracing Defeat* is intricate and perhaps best summed up in the emperor's haiku written after the U.S. turned over control in 1952. The emperor wrote:

> *The winter wind has gone*
> *And long-awaited spring has arrived*
> *with double-petaled cherry blossoms*

Or, as he put it when the occupation ended: "I understand that since the conclusion of the war people have expressed various opinions, but looking at this from a broad perspective, I do not think there has been any change between prewar and postwar."

As if the country that Japan would become after the war existed already.

This blurring of a before and after perspective supports the analysis that in a fundamental way, Japan picked up where it left off before the war, on a continuum of industrialization and westernization that began in the Meiji Restoration (a time that, in an appropriate parallel, also saw the end of the Shogun culture, a country run by warlords and the power of the sword).

This is something the emperor was glad to reflect on and even promote. And there are reasons for this amnesia: the same conglomerates that thrived building weapons for the Japanese military machine were allowed by the American authorities to continue their corporate hold on the economy, in part because they were in place and ready to roll in the reconstruction period. The development of Honda is one example. The through-line—or turn around, if you like—was so complete that it included re-conditioned war criminals, many of whom were now in positions of power in government and industry, within a year or two of the war trials. The postwar's success was built on the prewar structure bolstered by U.S. support of earlier institutions.

Other counter-intuitive effects of the American occupation came into play, which might surprise Westerners who find Japanese traditions and conventions so different and "other" in this Asian-American contact zone. As Dower puts it when discussing what he calls the "hybrid nature of the post surrender model... it turned out one did not have to be the bearer of a Confucian cultural heritage to promote autocracy, hierarchy, harmony, consensus and self-censorship."

In other words, in postwar Japan, Western influence and dictates helped create and shape something traditionally thought of as being Japanese.

Our last night in Nagasaki, we met a peace activist, just back from a nuclear conference at the UN. She serves as an interpreter for the *hibakusha*—"explosion-affected people"—on educational tours, often to the United States. Dinner was at a Chinese restaurant by the cool new Nagasaki Prefectural Art Museum on what is now a spacious, attractive waterfront, opening out to a view that includes a new wispy suspension bridge built by Mitsubishi, as a show-piece and, we were told, so that factory workers could commute to and from the other side, where there isn't much except those lovely, jungley hills. The berths in the marina below the modest stretch of cafés contained exactly four pleasure boats—a puzzling sight—because according to the peace activist, "Japanese aren't rich—we can't afford yachts." But it may also be that Japan is leery of its rough coastal waters.

Could eating at a nice café on the waterfront lead to the forgetting of what happened here, of moving beyond it, as the children eating ice cream in the peace park may have done? Nagasaki and Hiroshima live on as markers for events just within reach of current memory.

The Nagasaki University School of Medicine, which we'd toured, is significant both because it was near the epicenter and almost completely destroyed—with scores of students in the medical school incinerated at their desks—and because from the start, as doctors and researchers, its mem-bers began tracking the effects of the bomb. Some of the surviving students and doctors fled with the ailing director to a nearby shrine on a hill, above the smoke and conflagration, and began to write down their observations and draft carefully reasoned letters about the inhumanity of such an attack, even hours after the bomb detonated.

We climbed up that hill to the spot marked by flags, and on the way passed a small temple run by a very friendly woman, who seemed determined to invite us in for tea and ply us with fruit (which we thought might be for the altar above). We managed to get by and continued climbing, eating the enormous apple but saving the orange for the shrine.

This was a hard-fought spot, like many in hilly Japan, reached by twisting, vertigo-inducing steps that finally ended at a hollowed-out cave. Here people stick money into the side of the mountain, traditionally to honor the local spirits, or leave offerings by a set of tiny shrines, each carved figure wearing a miniscule red bib. I tried to imagine the refugees from the hospital and school huddled in this small place with no exit while the radioactive fire whistled up from the maelstrom below, and marveled at their presence of mind.

Mindful of my balance, I turned my head and gazed out over the hills of Nagasaki, in bloom now with springtime pollen. The early afternoon wind was yellow with it. The fish banner flapped, then sank overhead before catching a gust like a sail on a boat coming about, and snapped in my face.

On the way back, the woman was waiting for us with a plastic bag full of convenience store bread, some roots she'd dug from her garden, a pouch of peanuts like you'd get at a baseball game and other things. Tea was fated. We drank it in a little nook in the temple, where there was also a small kitchen and in the corner, a fax machine. We did not have a common language—none of our Japanese words worked—but that did not stop her from talking and laughing and smiling, which of course we reciprocated for what seemed like a long time. This may sound like a beautiful thing, and it was. By the end, she had us kneeling on the mat in front of the altar, burning incense and chanting a Buddhist prayer after her. This made more sense than some of our pantomime conversation.

Our offering, as we left, into the box with the slats, also seemed to make sense to her. She clasped her hands, raised them towards us, and bowed, sincerely. We exchanged addresses and signaled our intention to write.

On the way down the hill we ran into Dr. Yamashita, in a white lab coat, walking between the university and the hospital. He called out, "Elizabeth," as I imagined a doctor might have called out to Lisa's grandmother, fifty years before. We told him about our encounter at the shrine.

"What could you talk about?" he asked, genuinely puzzled, assuming a language barrier.

"It was hard," I said.

"Exactly!"

"But we're going to be pen pals."

The last morning in the dining room at the hotel, after scanning the menu with its now familiar choice of eggs, three styles, bacon or ham, Japanese soup and salad, I said obliviously in the jaundiced voice of a traveler, "Same old breakfast. History repeats."

Lisa, glancing out the window over the obelisk, didn't miss a beat. "I hope not."

—

Transcript of interview
translated by
Kyoko Nommensen

Don't Arrogate, Hiroshima!
Reflections on the Registration of the Hiroshima Peace Memorial as a World Heritage Site
Hitoshi Motoshima

In 1996, the World Heritage Committee determined that Japan's nomination, the Hiroshima Peace Memorial, would be registered as a World Heritage Site. This should have been the result of an agreement among representatives of twenty-one countries, including America, China, Japan, Mexico and the Philippines. The Hiroshima Peace Memorial expresses the ghastliness and inhumanity of atomic weapons, a feeling shared by all countries. It was nominated by Japan as a peace monument for the entire human race, eternally appealing for the elimination of nuclear weapons. However, throughout this process, America and China refused to recognize the decision.

People in Hiroshima think of the Hiroshima Peace Memorial as a symbol for the elimination of nuclear weapons from the world, and of the wish for permanent world peace. On the other hand, to many Americans and Chinese, it is a ruin of war, destroyed in retaliation for the Japanese invasions. I think Japan should have given more thought to the nomination of the Hiroshima Peace Memorial as a World Heritage Site.

Between Japan, China and the United States, it seems we have yet to reach a mutual understanding of the Pacific War. If the citizens of Hiroshima had remorse for the war, the Hiroshima Peace Memorial would not have been nominated or registered as a World Heritage Site.

Togo Shigehiko, Tokyo correspondent for the *Washington Post*, remarked:

> *As is always the way with the atomic bombings in Japan,*
> *more than anything, they are treated like tragic truths of the*
> *world, drifting freely in memories insulated from history, from*

cause and effect, from responsibility, and from politics and public influence. As an effect of the atomic bombings, people tend to focus on this tragedy itself, which shows the attitude of the Japanese society in its entirety toward World War II. Because of this attitude, it is unfortunately the case that Japan is less able than Germany to earnestly consider questions of responsibility for the war.

A lot has been said about the tragedy of the atomic bombings. However, not much is said about why the atomic bombs were dropped.

Early in the Meiji period, the Conscription Ordinance was issued and military forces were established which determined the subsequent development of the town of Hiroshima. (Translator's note—The military conscription ordinance of 1872 established an army and a navy requiring all males who reached the age of twenty, irrespective of class, to register for military service, and to be ready for all emergencies. In the conscript army, the ordinary citizen was raised to the level of the samurai and was imbued with the Japanese warrior's code.)

When expansion to the continent became the national policy, the government made Hiroshima a critical site because of its capabilities and geographical location. Therefore, important military facilities for the production of ammunition and weaponry, machines, ships, uniforms and food, as well as military hospitals, schools and bases, came to occupy a major part of the city. The harbor of Hiroshima, Ujina, also took on an important role as a military transportation base, such as in the transportation of soldiers to China.

In the war with China and throughout the Pacific War, when military personnel were sent from Hiroshima's port of Ujina to the Chinese mainland and South East Asia, the enthusiastic shouts of *"Banzai! Banzai!"* from the people of Hiroshima shook the ground. It was precisely these elderly people, mothers, young ladies, junior high-school students, and children who wildly waved Japanese flags and enthusiastically shouted for joy upon any news of military success that later became "victims."

In order to defend the homeland, military command was geographically divided between the first headquarters in Tokyo and the second headquarters in Hiroshima, and thus Hiroshima became the axis of the battle. By June of 1945, Hiroshima itself had evolved into a gigantic military facility. It is natural that the most important military center sustained the most powerful bombing attack. The destruction of Hiroshima is best understood with the Buddhist proverb, "As you sow, so you shall reap." Though, of course, it is truly awful that many innocent people also suffered in the retribution.

Further, to the notion that Hiroshima is the site of the greatest war suffering in the last one hundred years of war history, and therefore should be a peace capital, or a holy site for humanism, I must obstinately object. Thinking of the bomb shelters in Chongqing and the bullet marks still visible on the gates of Nanking, I say that China has suffered the most in war in the past one hundred years, at least by extent and amount of misery. Despite this, however, in all of China there is not a single Peace Memorial Park. And there is not a single international event in China where people remember and mourn the victims of war. Nor in China are there donation boxes in front of eternal lights.

Give me back my father, give me back my mother
Give me back my grandparents
Give me back my children
Give me back myself, give me back the people in my life.

The poet Sankichi Toge survived only eight years after the war. His theme was the inhumanity of atomic bombs. I wonder to whom he is saying, "Give me back my father, and give me back my mother." On reading this poem, I am reminded of the "Three Alls Strategy" the Japanese military unleashed in northern China:

1. Kill all.
2. Burn all.
3. Loot all.

In northern China, the Japanese invading army created a desolate wasteland, killing everyone, shooting and burning innocent people.
Give me back my father, give me back my mother.
I wonder, Sankichi Toge, if this wasn't what was said by the orphaned children of northern China?
The thing Japan has to do now is apologize to Asia and the countries involved in the Pacific War, commencing with China. We have to beg their forgiveness. We have to do this for Japan's past as well as for its future.
However, to do this, the Japanese must apologize for their attack on Pearl Harbor and also forgive the atomic bombings of Hiroshima and Nagasaki. It is not good to hold on to anger and ill-feeling. What is necessary is to develop the ability to forgive.
Hiroshima and Nagasaki should stand at the forefront of "World Reconciliation."
The twenty-first century must be the "Century of Reconciliation."

—

Translated by
Carl Nommensen

Park City
Masataka Matsuda

This play is an attempt to (im)print the images of both present day Hiroshima and historic Hiroshima through the camera obscura called theater.

How can we possible connect the actual Hiroshima today with the unprecedented tragedy the city suffered in 1945? It seemed impossible to reproduce this connection through a narrative that relies on conventional theatrical techniques. And yet, confronted by the impossibility, we explored the possibilities without falling into nihilism.

Our first inspiration came from the photography of Keiko Sasaoka. Using a slide projector, she projects her photographs of Hiroshima on the wall of the theater. This device becomes the core of the play's presentation. It creates a boundary, a window to the exterior inside the interior of the theater, inviting the reality of Hiroshima into the internal space.

In the character of Shima, I've created a character willfully obsessed with the tie between his name and Hiroshima, as if the connection were fateful. The Shima character recklessly attempts to tackle the unbearable burden Hiroshima has carried since that historic day. The audience observes his delusional experience onstage.

There are three streams of time in the play: the time of the stage performance revolving around the slide projector; the time passing with Sasaoka's photography projected on stage; the time passing on the monitors attached to the audience members' seats, screening the urban landscapes of Hiroshima. Exposed to these multiple layers of time, the audience members may experience visions of the invisible Park City inside themselves.

Masataka Matsuda
Kyoto 2011

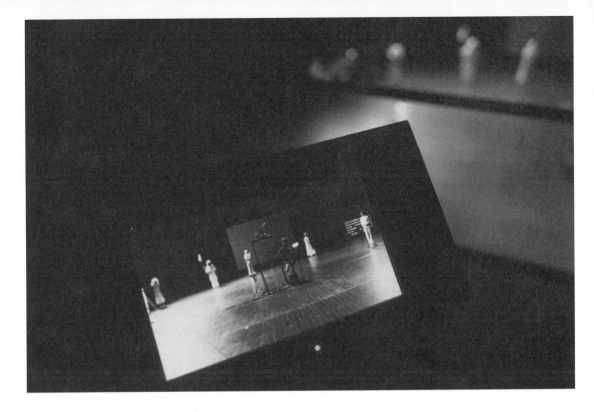

—

Cast of Characters

TOUR GUIDE
SHIMA
NOTETAKER
OBSERVER OF FALLEN OBJECTS
NARRATOR ABOUT / TO AKIKO
PSEUDOGUIDES 1–2
LOVERS 1–4
WOMEN 1–4
TOURISTS 1–6
BALLOON-HOLDER
MAILMAN

—

Translation by
Kyoko Yoshida

—

Photography by
Keiko Sasaoka

PART I

SASAOKA *enters and turns on the slide projector.*

MAILMAN *enters carrying a heavy bag of mail.*
He begins to sort through it.

TOUR GUIDE*, leading her group, enters stage right.*
TOUR GUIDE *rings the bell.*

TOUR GUIDE: Ladies and... welcome to... today. Attention... life jackets are stored in the blue boxes in the back of the boat. The lavatories are located in the back left. Smoking is prohibited. Please use the designated areas in the back... in the back... the capacity... six... so please take turns when you go up. During the tour, looking ahead, this is your right, and that is your left.

MONITORS: the view of Hiroshima seen from the sightseeing boat.

TOUR GUIDE *moves to the center, followed by the others.*

TOUR GUIDE: The A-Bomb Dome was originally called the Produce Exhibition Hall, and at the time of bombing, it was known as the Industrial Promotion Hall. Exhibitions of Hiroshima's specialties and art exhibits were held here. The first atomic bomb was dropped at 8:15 am, August 6, 1945. This led to a total of about 200,000 deaths. Victims, in dire need of water, threw themselves into the rivers of Hiroshima, including this Motoyasu River.

MAILMAN *looks up and moves.*

SHIMA: A bicycle passes by.

All scatter.

MONITORS: camera 7 (telephoto).

SHIMA: A group of high school students was offering a silent prayer in front of the one-thousand crane monument. We shall never forget. Never. Never. Never. The scene reminds me of Ms. Sasaoka's words: in this city, there are two streams of time passing. But what is the Other Time? The Time of the Dead? No, such time exists nowhere. It cannot exist.

MONITORS: *a bird's-eye view of Hiroshima.*

TOUR GUIDE: Suppose the Peace Memorial Museum is the base and the A-Bomb Dome over there is the vertex, forming a large isosceles triangle. This city is a delta with several rivers running through it, so the triangle signifies the city of Hiroshima. And right in the heart of the triangle stands this cenotaph, which means that this city, the people living here today, will never forget the dead sacrificed here.

All gather around TOUR GUIDE.

SHIMA: We assume this tone of voice to address the dead and we listen for the voice of the dead. Here, at least, we are absorbed in such attitudes, such gestures, such activities. We're rather enthusiastic. Here, we can concentrate. We become pretty solemn. Here, at this theme park for meeting the dead.

TOUR GUIDE *moves to stage left, followed by the others.*

TOUR GUIDE: Now we are passing under Aioi Bridge. Because of its rare T shape, it was picked as the target for the A-bomb. The bomb exploded 1930 feet above a hospital behind the A-Bomb Dome—it was called Shima Surgical Clinic.

SHIMA: Shima. That's my name!

TOUR GUIDE: Now passing under Sorazaya Bridge.

TOUR GUIDE *and the rest exit through the front.*

The Time of Photography 1: group photos (4 minutes).

NOTETAKER: A quote from Robert Musil: "The profession of most monuments is to call forth a remembrance, or rivet the attention and give the feelings a pious direction, and in this, their major profession, monuments always fail. They scare away precisely what they should be attracting. One cannot say that we don't notice them; one would have to say they un-notice us, they withdraw themselves from our senses. This is a thoroughly positive quality they have, tending toward real forcefulness!

Why are monuments erected to great men? It seems to be a neat bit of malice. Since one can no longer harm them in life, one pushes them into the sea of oblivion with a commemorative stone around their necks."[1]

I think of the A-Bomb Dome. The Dome was not built as a monument. It is nothing but a ruin left behind.

The end of the Time of Photography 1.

MONITORS: camera 7 (telephoto).

TOUR GUIDE *and the rest enter stage right.*

TOUR GUIDE *(PA):* The Peace Memorial Ceremony has been held every year on August 6 since 1947. In 1955, at the height of the antinuclear movement, it became a national event.

OBSERVER OF FALLEN OBJECTS *(monologue):* A shower of blood, fat and muscle tissue fell with a rattling noise near Lebanon, Tennessee, in August, 1841. A rain of fish in Singapore in February, 1861.[2]

All scatter. Some are taking photographs here and there.
OBSERVER *continues her monologue.* PSEUDOGUIDES *walk about.*

TOUR GUIDE *(PA):* At 8:15, at the toll of the bell, we'll observe a moment of silence, praying for peace and paying our respects to the A-Bomb victims. Please stand up.

SHIMA: Park City is full of monuments. It's a concentration of monuments.

TOUR GUIDE: This way. Not that way.

MONITORS: camera 7 (telephoto) shows NOTETAKER in close-up.

PSEUDOGUIDES 1 & 2 *materialize in front of* OBSERVER.

PSEUDOGUIDE 1: Where from? I'm asking you where're you from? Want a guide? A guide for the Peace Park? Whatcha up to? Research? You could use a guide.

NOTETAKER *(to himself):* I see. Indeed.

—
1
Robert Musil, "Monuments." Translated by Burton Pike. *Selected Writings.* Continuum, 1986.

—
2
Weird, Weird Rain. (http://paranormal.about.com/library/weekly/aa082602a.htm)

OBSERVER'S *monologue grows louder.* PSEUDOGUIDE 1 *keeps talking.*
Some take photographs here and there.
After a while, PSEUDOGUIDES *leave.*

OBSERVER: Minneapolis, Minnesota was pelted with frogs and toads in July,
1901. The total 'frogfall' reached as thick as three inches deep.
    In Bournemouth, England, in 1948, a shower of herring, most likely
unsmoked.
    In Chilatchee, Alabama in 1956, catfish, bass and bream fell together
with the rain—all of them alive.
    In North Sydney, Australia, in 1966, a large fish fell from the sky. It fell
to the flooded ground and swam away.
    In Nafplion, Greece, in May, 1981, a rain of frogs. The species was
native to North Africa.

A parachute falls.
NOTETAKER *takes notes of the parachute.*

NOTETAKER: After the two bombings of Hiroshima and Nagasaki, copies of a
letter were parachuted over Japanese cities. The letter said: "Unless
Japan surrenders at once, this rain of atomic bombs will increase manyfold in fury."[3]... Whose fury is this? The divine fury? Aren't the two bombs
already beyond imagination? The two were too few for *them*—oh, I'm
already calling those who dropped the bombs *them*—so few that they
wrote about this rain of atomic bombs. What culpability were we accused
of with such fury?

OBSERVER: In July, 2001, a red rain fell on Kerala, India. At first a meteor was
thought to be responsible for the strange-colored rain, but an analysis
showed that the water was filled with fungal spores. Still, where all of
those red spores came from remains unknown.

SHIMA *is looking at* NOTETAKER.

NOTETAKER: *Summer Flowers* by Tamiki Hara. To read Tamiki Hara's stories
in Hiroshima—"When Mr. Maki was riding on crowded streetcars, too,
someone on the other side of the car would frequently nod to him. When
in an unguarded moment he nodded back, the person would say something like "My heavens! Mr. Yamada, isn't it?" –a case of mistaken identity.
When he told this story to others, he learned that he was not the only one
to have strangers greet him. Indeed, in Hiroshima even now someone was
always trying to find someone."[4]

—
3
A letter from Luis Alvarez
to Ryoichi Sagane, August 9,
1945.

—
4
Tamiki Hara,
Summer Flowers. Translated
by Richard H. Minear.
Princeton UP, 1990.

I am startled at the words 'even now.' How come I feel this 'now' is the *now,* the present moment I am reading, rather than the *now then* when it was written? I could be mistaken for someone missing. I could resemble someone absent.

PSEUDOGUIDES *reappear and walk about.*

MONITORS: Sasaoka Camera shows PSEUDOGUIDES and SASAOKA.

SHIMA *stands by* NOTETAKER, *who continues his monologue to* SHIMA.
All bend their heads to the front, followed by gestures of being mistaken for another person.

ALL: Sorry...

TOUR GUIDE: Now on your right, these tall buildings are the Motomachi High-Rise Apartments. There're about 5,000 households, both prefectural and municipal. This building was designed in an L shape, so that the sun comes into every apartment once a day. It was built thirty years ago.

All gather around TOUR GUIDE *and the group soon exits through the front.*

THE END OF PART I

PART II

MONITORS: testimonies of the Motomachi Apartment residents (6 minutes).

FEMALE RESIDENT 1: Here, you take the elevator to the even-numbered floors and then take the staircase to the odd-numbered floors...
There were shanties... right after the bomb. This was built to clear the shantytown. So of course, there were more Korean people.

MALE RESIDENT 1: In those days, you'd park your car right by the building, and people would dump whatever, and your car'd get dents and scratches. You'd never know what'd fall from above. That's not the case anymore.

FEMALE RESIDENT 2: Me? I wasn't here then. I'm from the countryside. My brother and his wife lived here. I came to look for them, I mean, after the A-bomb. Searched through the city. Back then I was twenty-three. Anyway, you don't see any homeless here. There used to be some in the park in front, but they got kicked out. They'd built their tents... But the superintendents had to... because it's a public park.

MATSUDA: Were there shanties over there in those days?

FEMALE RESIDENT 2: Uh-huh. In those days. They all moved in here, I guess. Here you can see the sea from high up. *(sings)* You know the ferryboat song? *(sings)* A Korean song. Somebody taught me. I don't know what it means.

MATSUDA: Who taught you the song?

FEMALE RESIDENT 2: Huh?

TOUR GUIDE *and* NOTETAKER *remain onstage.* WOMEN 1-4 *join them.*

MONITORS: the fabricated testimonies.

Title: The Fabricated Testimonies

WOMAN 1: Ever since I became ill... I was in bed all the time... Boy, that was a bit too much, to stay still like that... I'm no athletic type, so it's nothing like... well, now I just walk around, like, leisurely, around this area. For twenty, thirty minutes. Once in a while for a change of scenery, I'd go to a different spot... like the riverbank, y'know, I'd go down there, but then, these tiny gnats are flying there, tons of them in a thick cloud... those bugs, they are too small to see, and you don't make' em out till you plunge into the middle of that cloud, and they are already inside your mouth and all... That's why I don't walk down to the riverbank that often. That's just me... Sure, it feels nice down there, that's true... particularly from this time of the year on... Like your body becomes lighter... I've been eating less these days, so... And you notice things your eyes don't see on normal days, y'know. Like, hey, I didn't know this or that was around here... things like that would catch you by surprise, y'know.

WOMAN 2: Indeed with a building this tall, some people would jump off once in a while. Uh-huh, kids would see it, like on their way home from school. So we patrol outside during those hours, shooing the kids away, so they don't see it... I mean, we don't tell them to go away, but we pay attention so that kids won't catch the sight. No, that's not good for them. But kids have a sense of what's going on, and they get curious—we're concerned about that. In the past, there was no lock on the door to the rooftop. The view was great, especially days with fireworks, and anybody could go up there, freely. Now the door is locked to keep people out. Because we thought people were jumping off the rooftop. But there are other ways, like climbing over the staircase landing, so just blocking the rooftop wouldn't do it. Really, we're concerned. People talk about it, too, if you know what I mean.

WOMAN 3: So she spilled some cooking oil on the floor but didn't notice at first 'cause she was on the phone or something. She saw she had spilled quite a bit and panicked 'cause what if it catches on fire? She was wiping the floor in a panic and slipped. Knocked really hard on the floor—on something like a floor mat? I mean, the stuff is quite shaggy and kind of plushy—there, she fell and knocked her head... Yeah, she was lucky it wasn't a hard floor. Even so, it made this heavy thud. I was at the front door, just about to open the door, so I could hear it well, and I was like, Wow, what's that? My heart skipped a beat. And she was sort of missing her memory—just for that moment. Like she passed out or something. Actually, when I called her name, she couldn't reply right off the bat, so probably that's what happened. I said, Do you want me to call an ambulance? And she was like, Yes, please. So I did right away.

WOMAN 4: Let me read the essay my little sister wrote: Today at school, we had a special class and made some soap. Someone from the factory came and taught us about soap. He said, soap is more friendly to the environment than laundry detergent because detergent is made from petroleum and therefore pollutes rivers, but soap is safe to be released in rivers. He said, soap is safe even for fish to eat. We learned that considering the matter of the environment, it is better to switch to soap. After that, we made some soap, recycling the waste oil from the school lunch center. We had to stir the mixture for such a long time that my arms got tired and sore. Naoki gave up stirring in the middle, so I had to stir all the way through. It was a lot of work. But soap was made, and it was good enough to wash hands with, so I was impressed. If we use soap instead of detergent at home from now on, our planet will become cleaner. I will tell my mother about it.

Meanwhile, the actors on stage form a line in the front and begin gestures of taking their hats off or redoing their shoes.

MONITORS: blackout.
LOVER 2 *enters with a megaphone.*
SHIMA *enters.*
LOVERS 1 & 2 *wave at each other.*
LOVER 1 *rows the boat.*

SHIMA: Hello.

NOTETAKER: Hello.

SHIMA: I am Shima. I was asked to join the theater for this play.

NOTETAKER: Hiroshima?

SHIMA: No, I'm Shima. Shima as in 'island.'

NOTETAKER: I see. Shima is your name.

SHIMA: Yes. The A-bomb exploded above Shima Surgical Clinic. My family is from Akita, but I'm also from a family of doctors. As it happens, my grandfather was an army surgeon and was dispatched to Hiroshima to help with the rescue right after the bombing.

NOTETAKER: I see.

SHIMA: I've become convinced of the strong tie between myself and this Hiroshima whatever the coincidence is. For it wasn't my intention to name myself Shima, and I've been Shima as long as I can remember. What a destiny.

NOTETAKER: Because of your name Shima?

SHIMA: Hiroshima has lost its hero at its ground zero and become Shima. Therefore, I am the ground zero myself.

NOTETAKER: You mean you're the ground zero?

SHIMA: Or rather, my name is.

NOTETAKER: Are the two different?

SHIMA: Slightly. I'm re-baptized Shima because I've encountered Hiroshima. In Hiroshima, I'll live as a different Shima.

NOTETAKER: Shima.

SHIMA: Yes.

NOTETAKER: Shima.

SHIMA: Yes.

NOTETAKER: Shima.

SHIMA: Yes. Ah, I am Hero-Shima. Hero-Shima. Hero-Shima.

PSEUDOGUIDES *torture* SHIMA.

MONITORS: *camera 4 shows the torture in close-up.*

NOTETAKER: This is a midsummer's nightmare. And I'm a bystander. Shima-san!

SHIMA: I am Hero-Shima.

NOTETAKER: And I am a bystander.

TOUR GUIDE *dances.*
OBSERVER *enters mumbling to herself and finds a washtub.*
LOVERS 1 & 2 *on the boat enter.*

LOVER 1: I love you.

LOVER 2: Do you really?

The two speak through the megaphone.

OBSERVER: Wow, a washtub fell? A washtub fell, eh? It came falling from up
   there and banged into your head?

MAILMAN *passes by on a bicycle.* NOTETAKER *takes notes of the sight.*
SHIMA *roars into the washtub.*

TOUR GUIDE: Things don't fall on their own out of nowhere.

OBSERVER: It fell from above.

TOUR GUIDE: What's above? The ceiling of the house?

OBSERVER: From above. Far from the heavens.

TOUR GUIDE: It didn't fall, the bomb was dropped.

OBSERVER: It came falling.

TOUR GUIDE: Who dropped it?

OBSERVER: That's not the point.

TOUR GUIDE: Somebody has to drop it to bomb a city. Stop talking that way, like
   it's rainfall or something, muddying the responsibilities. Look up. The sky
   won't drop anything.

NOTETAKER: The man is shouting something on all fours.

OBSERVER: Tadpoles…

TOUR GUIDE: Tadpoles too were dropped by someone. Don't look at the sky.

OBSERVER: On June 9, 2009, a rain of frogs fell over Park City.

NOTETAKER: Just like no one hears so many children wailing all at once in a
   faraway city, I'm afraid no one will hear this man's cry.

The Time of Photography 2: The Motomachi Apartments.

SHIMA *looks around.*
At the end of the music, WOMAN 2 *enters from the front.*

MONITORS: camera 6 (infrared) shows WOMAN 2 in close-up.

WOMAN 2: After the rain, we spent the night together, and I leave your place and walk to the station. I sense you everywhere, filling me up. At every single leaf of the green trees on the avenue, I sense your fingers. Even at some nameless flowers, I sense your nape and my body reacts with pleasure. So you're not here but I'm with you still. From the tips of my nails, to the tips of my toes, you fill me up. A streetcar arrives and an old lady gets off leaving her umbrella behind. Ma'am, your umbrella! I pass it to her and sit down feeling relieved, and... no, you're not with me anymore, and outside the window the sky is turning bright, and the city passes by. Everything passes by endlessly without you. I can't catch up. It hurts. My heart aches right here. Ai, ai, ai. I can't breathe. I miss you. I miss you. I miss you. Ai. Ai. Ai, miss you, ai, miss you, ai, miss you, ai, miss you, ai, ai, ai, miss you...

LOVER 1 *rows the boat alone to stage left.*
LOVERS 3 & 4 *enter with plastic bottles.*

LOVER 3: What about here... or here? Oh, does it hurt? I'm sorry... Now what about here... or here? *(chuckles)* Ticklish? No, it's not ticklish, it's something else... It's all right, all right... It'll change, you'll feel otherwise... *(chuckles)* See? Hurts no more, right? There, there you go... Lemme try here... Don't you be afraid, baby. What about here... or here... or here? There... don't you feel something?... That's because this is your first time. You'll love it. You'll never forget. Whatcha gonna do, huh? Whatcha gonna do? What about here... or here? Now what about this again? *(chuckles)*

LOVERS 1 & 2 *sit on the chairs.*
MAILMAN'S *bicycle passes by.*
NOTETAKER *lights up* LOVERS 3 & 4 *with a floodlight.*

MONITORS: camera 9 shows LOVERS 3 & 4 in close-up.

The end of Time of Photography 2

A conversation between LOVERS 3 & 4, *drinking water.*

LOVER 3: My father used to say he prefers tea to water.

LOVER 4: I've always been determined to drink from the same faucet as the man I love.

LOVER 3 *exits from stage left with the* PET *bottles.*
LOVER 4 *(now* NARRATOR) *approaches the camera.*

NARRATOR ABOUT/TO AKIKO: At the end of the movie *Sasayaki: Moonlight Whispers,* there was a song by Spitz that goes, "Goodbye. Your voice will keep me going." The song reminded me of Akiko and made me sad. On the night of December 29, 2000, we were at the karaoke bar together. All the temp colleagues at the time except Kaneda—Iwasaki, Kishibe, Morioka, Mizutani, and me—and Akiko. Now we're all married, some even with kids, but Akiko's time has stopped. Two nights before the end of the twentieth century, we were having the time of our life, Spitz's songs were Akiko's favorite, and she sang and sang. Since that night, I haven't seen Akiko. Someone told me she fell ill. Goodbye, Akiko. Your voice will keep me going. How far will I reach just as I am?[5]

TOUR GUIDE: Today, six rivers run through the city of Hiroshima. From east to west, they are Enkoh River, Kyobashi River, Motoyasu River, Honkawa River, Tenma River and Ohta Canal. And the bridges over the rivers of Hiroshima—there are nearly 2700 bridges all over the city. Hiroshima is also a city of rivers, a city of bridges.

NOTETAKER *walks about, shining a flashlight around.*
OBSERVER *is sending signals by semaphore.*

TOUR GUIDE: This way. Not that way.

A man slowly enters holding a balloon.

OBSERVER *(spotting the balloon):* Ah! Agh!

OBSERVER *follows the balloon*
BALLOON-HOLDER *comes close to the slide projector and bends his body in an L shape.*
NOTETAKER *takes notes of the balloon. His flashlight throws light on the balloon.*
SHIMA *puts on a jacket and walks about.*

The Time of Photography 3: the Peace Memorial Museum

NARRATOR *exits through the front. The bicycle passes by.*
LOVER 1 *enters.*

MONITORS: NOTETAKER operates camera 2 (long shot).
Standing is LOVER 1, on whom NOTETAKER focuses his camera.
MONITORS: the image of LOVER 1's past.

5
The translator consulted the website *Spitz: Sign of Love* by Aoi Hayashi

LOVER 1 *(from the monitors):* I am here and yet I am here. You see, I am here and I am there too. Your naked eye can see I am here, but I am also there. Now, let me show you my past.

LOVER 1: There was a French philosopher who was extremely afraid of night. Night is the time for sleep, when the world of dream takes over. For the philosopher who valued clarity more than anything, it was nighttime that deprived the world of clarity. He would tremble feebly, climbing into bed. He even yearned for insomnia. Yet he couldn't resist drowsiness and his eyes would close. According to his ex-partner, a streak of tears would run down his cheek as he fell asleep. *(LOVER 1 opens a paperback and reads a passage.) Otherwise than Being* by Emmanuel Lévinas: "The oneself proper to consciousness is then not again a consciousness, but a term in hypostasis."[6]

NARRATOR *enters front, pushing a pushcart.*
LOVER 1 *stands in front of the mailboxes with the oar and the megaphone in his hands.*
NOTETAKER *focuses his camera on NARRATOR.*

The end of the Time of Photography 3

MONITORS: camera 2 shows Narrator in close-up.

NARRATOR: Akiko's keepsakes—Akiko's wristwatch, Akiko's scarf, Akiko's hat, Akiko's lipstick, Akiko's microphone. Akiko is 5' 3 tall. Akiko's shoe size is 7 1/2. Akiko has round shoulders. Akiko's nose slopes up a little. Akiko has smooth eyelids. Akiko has dimples. Akiko's ears are rather small. Akiko has two moles—one under her lips and the other under her eye. *(sings)* "Goodbye. Your voice will keep me going. How far will I reach just as I am?"

BALLOON-HOLDER *walks in front of the audience seats and toward the back of stage right.*
BALLOON-HOLDER *stops.* OBSERVER, *lying down on the floor, maintains surveillance of the balloon.*
NARRATOR *sings.*

MONITORS: the sightseeing boat on the river.

WOMAN 4 *enters and joins a die-in (after NARRATOR'S "will keep me going.")*
NARRATOR *dresses herself up as Akiko. She and WOMAN 2 join the die-in.*

—
6
Emmanuel Lévinas,
Otherwise Than Being: Or Beyond Essence. Translated by Alphonso Lingis. Duquesne UP, 1998.

NOTETAKER: About 20 feet above the ground, a round white balloon is floating. Underneath is a man walking, a thin thread in his hand, which connects to the balloon, and therefore, the balloon won't float any higher than it is now. When the man stops, the balloon stops too. When the man moves, the balloon also moves. The man and the balloon maintain an exact distance by the thread.

NARRATOR *and* WOMEN 2 & 4 *are chanting something.*
BALLOON-HOLDER *slowly walks onstage, stops, and resumes walking.*

TOUR GUIDE: This way. Not that way.

TOUR GUIDE'S *voice grows louder.*
OBSERVER *maintains surveillance of the balloon.*
SHIMA *enters.*
MAILMAN *slowly circles the stage on the bicycle and stops at the mailboxes at the second round.*

MAILMAN: Of course, accuracy comes first. You can't possibly misdeliver a letter. You understand that much, don't you. No further explanation needed. The point is—now listen carefully—the point is to deliver efficiently. Caution is not a bad thing, but however cautious, if you don't return by lunchtime, that is no good, unless you're making the last delivery for humankind. So your job is not just delivery. At the post office, letters come flooding in from all over the world. Incessantly! You have to sort them too. In the process, you may find a letter that was never meant to be sent to this city. That is, the letter was sent to the next but it shows up in this city. You can't possibly cross the territory just to deliver it, can you? Sort them accurately and deliver them systematically. Your shift lasts till evening, so you keep sorting till the bell rings. When the bell rings, the person from the next shift will show up. The person standing right behind you will be the one. He will keep on sorting from evening till dawn. Not just the ones to deliver. There are letters leaving this city, too. Anyway, today you'll follow him—he's more experienced. So watch and learn your delivery area, get the map into your head. You can't possibly get lost during your delivery. Ever!

MAILMAN *delivers mails into the mailboxes.*

TOUR GUIDE: This way. Not that way.

Three parachutes fall.
MAILMAN *gets off the bicycle and looks up at the sky.*

MAILMAN: The blue sky. The seamless blue sky.

MAILMAN *continues on his bicycle.*

SHIMA: A bicycle passes by.

NOTETAKER: After the two A-bombs in Hiroshima and Nagasaki, copies of a letter parachuted over Japanese cities. The letter said:"Unless Japan surrenders at once, this rain of atomic bombs will increase manyfold in fury." ... Whose fury is this fury? The divine fury? Aren't the two bombs already beyond imagination? The two were too few for *them*—and I readily call those who dropped the bombs *them*—so few that *they* wrote about this rain of atomic bombs. What culpability were we accused of for such fury?—that's what I jotted down a while ago, here.

MONITORS: black out.

BALLOON HOLDER *moves to the right wing of the stage.*
Standing at the edge of the stage, PSEUDOGUIDE 1 *expels those in the die-in* (WOMEN 1-4).

PSEUDOGUIDE 1 *(through the megaphone)*: This place is off-limits. I say OFF LIMITS. You're not supposed to play dead here.

PSEUDOGUIDE 1 *exits through the front, pushing the pushcart.*
WOMAN 4 *continues her die-in.*

THE END OF PART II

PART III

NOTETAKER *reads Tamiki Hara.*

NOTETAKER: "When I went out and bought flowers, it was with the intention of visiting my wife's grave. In my pocket was a bundle of incense sticks I had taken from the *butsudan*. August 15 would be the first *bon* since my wife's death; but I doubted that this hometown of mine would survive that long unscathed. It happened that the day was a no-electricity day; early that morning I saw no other men walking along carrying flowers. I do not know the proper name of the flowers; but with their small yellow petals, they had a nice country flavor about them, very summer-flower-like."

Shima addresses Notetaker.

SHIMA: Hello.

NOTETAKER: Hello.

SHIMA: I am Shima.

NOTETAKER: Yes, Shima. I remember.

SHIMA: Well.

NOTETAKER: What's the matter?

SHIMA: Well. I've been calling myself Hero-Shima, but I've made a grave mistake. I... I...

NOTETAKER: What's the matter?

SHIMA: I said that my grandfather helped with the rescue in Hiroshima. But it was a mistake. He was sent to Nagasaki.

NOTETAKER: Oh, is that so.

—

butsudan
a small Buddhist altar
kept inside the home

—

bon
a Japanese Buddhist
festival for remembering
one's ancestors,
held in midsummer

Park City   Masataka Matsuda

SHIMA: What a despicable mistake I have made!

NOTETAKER: Stay calm, please.

SHIMA: How could I? I was deluded by the suffering called Hiroshima and ended up fabricating my grandfather's past.

NOTETAKER: No, you don't mean it.

SHIMA: Yes! Hiroshima's magnetism beguiles me so much that my compass lost its bearings. I pretended to undertake Hiroshima, but all I wanted was to become the hero of Hiroshima.

NOTETAKER: I see, but does Hiroshima call for a hero to begin with?

SHIMA: I... I have misappropriated Hiroshima...

NOTETAKER: I can't hear you.

SHIMA: I am not Hero-Shima. This Shima is just I.

NOTETAKER: Huh?

SHIMA: Call me Shima.

NOTETAKER: Shima.

SHIMA: Yes, I am not Hero-Shima. This Shima is just I. Call me Hiroshima.

NOTETAKER: Hiroshima.

SHIMA: No, I am not Hero-Shima. This Shima is just I. Now call me Shima.

NOTETAKER: Shima.

SHIMA: Yes! I am not Hero-Shima. This Shima is just I. Now call me Hiroshima.

NOTETAKER: Hiroshima.

SHIMA: Hiro-Shima! Here's Shima!

NOTETAKER: Which one are you?

SHIMA: I don't know, I don't know.

NOTETAKER: What in the world are you?

SHIMA: Aaaargh! In the French language, the letter H is silent!

NOTETAKER: Then, are you 'Iro-Shima'?

SHIMA: Aaaaaaaaaaaaargh!

Shima passes out.

NOTETAKER: My name is Ogura, in ideograms the same letters as the city of
    Kokura in Kyushu Island. I think of Kokura. Between Hiroshima and
    Nagasaki, there was Kokura. Between 8:15 am, August 6 and 11:02 am,
    August 9, there was Kokura. On August 9 at 2:49 am, a B-29 nicknamed
    Bockscar, loaded with an atomic bomb, left the base in Tinian Island.
    The primary target was Kokura. But it was covered with thick clouds. The
    bomber, having circled above the city three times to visually confirm the
    target in vain, turned toward its second target Nagasaki before its fuel
    ran out. Nagasaki was also covered with clouds, but not so thick, and
    the bomb was dropped through a narrow gap in the clouds. Without the
    clouds, it would have been dropped on Kokura. *(A parachute falls.)* With-
    out the clouds, it would have been dropped on Kokura. It was dropped
    on Kokura without clouds. It was dropped on Kokura.

WOMEN 1-4 *enter.*

WOMAN 1: Death notices have been arriving.

WOMAN 3: At our place, too.

WOMAN 4: We don't want them at home.

WOMAN 1: Must be a wrong address.

WOMAN 3: I have nothing to do with it.

WOMAN 4: I have nothing to do with it.

WOMAN 1: I have nothing to do with it.

WOMAN 3: I have nothing to do with it.

WOMAN 4: I have nothing to do with it.

WOMAN 2: Then whom shall it reach?

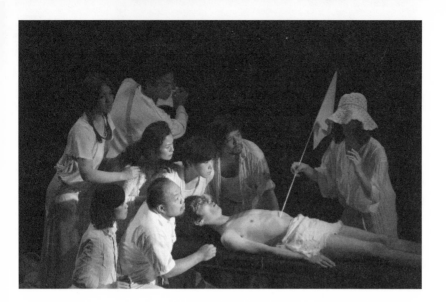

WOMAN 1: Can't it be sent to you?

PSEUDOGUIDES *bring in a stretcher, mount* SHIMA *on it, and undress him.*
PSEUDOGUIDE 1 *is whistling.*
PSEUDOGUIDE 2 *puts the washtub under the stretcher.*

WOMAN 3: I have nothing to do with it.

WOMAN 4: I have nothing to do with it.

WOMAN 1: I've read what's inside.

WOMAN 2: Then whom shall it reach?

WOMAN 3: I knew it was wrong, but I took revenge for the misdelivery.

WOMAN 4: A kind of entitlement of the misdelivered though a bit creepy to read
    about some dead person I have nothing to do with.

WOMAN 2: Then whom shall it reach?

WOMAN 1: How was it?

WOMAN 3: No big deal?

WOMAN 4: I returned it to the mailman to have the address double-checked.

WOMEN 1, 2 & 4 *leave the group.*
WOMAN 3 *sings.*

WOMAN 3: "I love you, I love you, I love you desperately/ Please say you love me/
No matter what you say, I'm here to stay with you/ I want to be with you
till the end/ I want to be with you till the end/ Let me cry, let me cry, let
me cry my heart out"[7]

NOTETAKER *takes notes.*
TOURISTS *gather around the stretcher and chat.*
TOUR GUIDE *rings the bell.*
All take off their hats (except TOUR GUIDE*).*

MONITORS: The Autopsy on SHIMA after 'The Anatomy Lesson of Doctor
Nicholas Tulp.'

NOTETAKER *moves the video camera.*
TOUR GUIDE *moves the flagpole and the others' eyes follow it. She pauses on*
and off.

The following lines come from the monitors:

TOUR GUIDE: This is the A-Bomb Dome.

TOURIST 1: When was the A-Bomb Dome built?

TOUR GUIDE: In 1915, due to the economic boom of the first world war, it was
built as the Produce Exhibition Hall.

TOURIST 1: When was the A-Bomb Dome built?

TOUR GUIDE: In 1933, it was renamed the Industrial Promotion Hall to accom-
modate such exhibitions as the Japan-Manchurian Trade Show to
promote continental expansion.

TOURIST 2: No, neither the Produce Exhibition Hall, nor the Industrial Promotion Hall, but I mean the A-Bomb Dome.

TOUR GUIDE: Yes, well, so the A-Bomb Dome used to be...

TOURIST 3: The A-Bomb Dome was never built. Rather, it emerged that summer
day completely out of the blue due to the bomb.

TOUR GUIDE: You may put it that way.

—
7
With You till the End,
a song by Sawako Nishida;
lyrics by Kaoru Mizuki;
music by Hideyuki Fujiwara.

TOURIST 4: As a manifestation of the ruin that was never built?

TOUR GUIDE: You may put it that way.

TOURIST 4: When did the ruin become the A-Bomb Dome?

TOUR GUIDE: Before anyone knew, the place was designated.

TOURIST 5: It came falling.

TOUR GUIDE: No, it was dropped.

TOURIST 6: Who is this person?

TOUR GUIDE: This person used to be called Shima.

NOTETAKER: Hiroshima?

TOUR GUIDE: No, just Shima. Shima as in "island".

SHIMA: Ah, as if I were Iro-Shima.

SHIMA'S *voice, "Ah, as if I were Iro-Shima," spreads in refrain.*
All bring their heads close to listen to his voice.
TOUR GUIDE *rings the bell.*
TOURIST 2 *carries away* SHIMA *on the stretcher to stage left.*

The Time of Photography 4: downtown Hiroshima

TOUR GUIDE: This way. Not that way.

MAILMAN'S *bicycle goes round.*
SHIMA *enters wearing nothing but a piece of loincloth.*
NOTETAKER *takes notes.*

NOTETAKER: A man is walking as if scraping the ground with his toes. He is
almost fully naked, his groin barely covered with a piece of cloth.

The end of the Time of Photography 4

MONITORS: the image of SHIMA wandering about the city.

MAILMAN'S *bicycle comes round.*
The bicycle hits SHIMA. *Letters scatter.*
NOTETAKER *takes notes.*

NOTETAKER: The man dashes out in front of a mailman and falls. The mailman jerks his bicycle so hard that envelopes scatter on the ground. He picks them up one by one. The man is saying something to the mailman. Without replying, the mailman rides off.

SHIMA *addresses* MAILMAN, *who does not pay attention to him.*

SHIMA: What is this letter? Is this a death notice? Are you delivering death notices? All you do is deliver without saying anything? So you are delivering the death notices of those gone missing in this city? Then do you have my death notice with you? Where do I find my death notice?

NOTETAKER *takes notes.*

NOTETAKER: The man's voice grows louder. He approaches the mailman. The mailman remains mute, concentrating on his work.

SHIMA *and* MAILMAN *face each other.*

SHIMA: What is this letter? Is this a death notice? Are you delivering death notices? All you do is to deliver without saying anything? So you are delivering the death notices of those gone missing in this city? Then do you have my death notice with you? Where do I find my death notice?

MAILMAN: You either issue a death notice or dispatch a death notice. These are the only two ways to become engaged with a death notice: to issue a death notice or to dispatch a death notice.

MAILMAN *mounts the bicycle.*
MAILMAN'S *sounds of operation reverberate on stage.*
NOTETAKER *removes his clip-on microphone and puts it up, urging* SHIMA *to speak.*
SHIMA *turns to the front while speaking.*

MONITORS: first blackout, then the image of SHIMA standing in front of the cenotaph.

SHIMA *(through* NOTETAKER'S *microphone)*: I was walking through the city. I wasn't sure whether a dog had died or was about to die, but there were three people huddled under the eave of a house, looking down at the dog that had turned into an old rag. One said, The time of dogs is short. No, it's fast, said another. Perhaps so, compared to man, but nonetheless it is the same, said the other. I was passing by as if nothing had happened, indeed nothing had happened—that wasn't my dog, or I wasn't the dog. Indeed, I'd walked through the town like this many times. No matter how much one reflects on the dead—whether dog or man—rather than contemplating the different kinds of time, the graver error, the more serious problem to me, is to go past the site altogether. Someone said, Something irretrievable will happen in due time. Or perhaps it was my premonition. An incident so outrageous like a divine retribution against all of humankind. As reparation for the deaths of the unknown many, you too will be given death—whether death will just visit me or the entire city is unfathomable. Yet, at the moment of catastrophe, even if the entire city vanishes away, I feel as if I will not die with all other people. I die the only death I die. I die. According to my private economics, the price of my death is the indifference of all things living.

PSEUDOGUIDES *enter. Ghosts gather around the mailboxes.*

PSEUDOGUIDE 1 *(through the megaphone)*: Where from? You need a guide? Been to the Peace Memorial Park?

TOUR GUIDE: This way.

PSEUDOGUIDE 1 *(through the megaphone)*: What's up?

TOUR GUIDE: This way. Not that way.

NOTETAKER *takes notes.*

NOTETAKER: A guide is pulling the man's leg. A watch stands by, keeping a lookout.

PSEUDOGUIDE 1: Want a nice guide?

MONITORS: the Motomachi Apartments seen from the river.

NOTETAKER *takes notes.*
SHIMA *tries to escape* PSEUDOGUIDE 1*'s solicitation. The two fall.*
PSEUDOGUIDE 2 *keeps a lookout.*
OBSERVER *starts semaphoring.*

TOUR GUIDE: Now the small island ahead on your left is Nakasu, so-called "Bird Paradise." Do you see birds on the tops of the trees? The gray ones are herons, the white ones egrets, the black ones cormorants. There are more than a hundred birds here. Hiroshima was born out of such deltas. About four centuries ago, Lord Terumoto Mori built Hiroshima Castle on the largest delta among many and developed the area as his capital—this is the origin of Hiroshima.

SHIMA *walks from the front to the washtub and passes out.*

The Time of Photography 5.

MONITORS: blackout.

MAILMAN *goes round on the bicycle.*
TOUR GUIDE *rings the bell.*
PSEUDOGUIDES *enter stage front.* PSEUDOGUIDE 1 *has a megaphone.*
LOVER 2 *moves a chair and seats herself. In her hands, she holds an envelope like something precious.*
TOURIST 3 *enters stage front holding a camera and takes photographs.*
LOVER 4 *enters stage left, holding a handkerchief and a* PET *bottle. She wipes off her sweat, drinks some water.*

TOUR GUIDE: Now we'll turn around here and cruise back to the pier. Please
        enjoy the rest of your trip. This concludes our guided tour.

NOTETAKER: A woman with binoculars is waving her arms to send signals. Like
        she wants to negotiate with someone up in the sky. Her expression is
        serious, her gaze straight, she repeats the same gesture.

NOTETAKER *takes notes.*

NOTETAKER: The man falls, with a big reverberation... Staring into the washtub
        full of water, he gradually gets worn out, and finally only his right hand
        remains in the tub. The washtub is made of metal, full of rust, and the
        nails of his remaining right hand are thereby covered with rust.

The end of the Time of Photography 5.

The actors come to a pause.
Only the bicycle keeps going slowly.
When the slide projector's noise comes to an end, TOUR GUIDE *lets down her flag.*
SASAOKA *exits.*

THE END

The Atomic Bomb Survivors: A Jungian Contribution

Janice Nakao

The field of psychological trauma has been a long-standing interest of mine, dating back to my postgraduate days in the 1980s. In 1980, the American Psychiatric Association officially deepened and expanded the clinical descriptions and understanding under the new diagnosis, "Post Traumatic Stress Disorder" (PTSD), which had previously been termed shell shock, combat stress, delayed stress syndrome, and traumatic neurosis. The new classification included responses not only to combat but to natural and other catastrophes, such as rape and child abuse.

In a hospital setting in Chicago, I was a member of a five-person Crisis Intervention Team, providing front-line crisis intervention and treatment in the context of a community mental health system. We treated a multitude of traumatic events including sexual abuse, domestic violence, rape, criminal violence, assault, and human rights abuses. As our work became known, we found ourselves called into shelters for the homeless, into firehouses, police stations, schools, and government offices. We heard stories from many brave individuals willing to bare their souls: firemen grieving the death of a fellow firefighter, a guilt-ridden policeman who "fired" in self-defense, an adolescent girl raped by a band of schoolmates, traumatized co-workers held hostage in a lover's quarrel, and battered women seeking shelter from abusive spouses.

As I recall these experiences, I am reminded of Jung's advice to the neophyte psychologist to abandon the "scholar's gown and wander with the human heart through the world."

The thread of my early days in trauma work has become interwoven through my professional identity, accompanying me as I began analytic training in 1998. I entered analytic training carrying numerous trauma stories, unsure of how my past professional life would find its way into my analytic work. As I immersed myself in the training process, my past and present professional

After the Atomic Bomb
Janice Nakao

interests began to weave a pattern of experiences related to traumatic syndrome combined with an analytic perspective.

Reflections during my training analysis brought images from the collective unconscious, cultivating a greater awareness of my cultural heritage as a Japanese-American. In certain dream states I was presented with "pictures" from the East: images of Asian art works, portraits of unknown figures, and finally images of first-generation relatives and their voyages from the East to the West during the early 1900s. Attention to my process engaged me in these unfolding images. The most compelling and significant images were of the atomic bomb explosions over Hiroshima and Nagasaki. Both sets of my grandparents had close connections to these cities, though all four grandparents had migrated to the United States before World War II.

I began to feel compelled to explore the psychological path of the atomic bomb survivors and became aware that one of the most important historic events in the twentieth century had never been addressed in my family. I wondered how something so critical to my family history could go unspoken. Was my family so identified with being American that this event was seen as unimportant? Sadly, many of the family members with whom I might have explored this question were no longer living, so I pursued this line of inquiry mostly on my own.

Uncannily, I came to the decision to write about this on the evening of September 10, 2001. The synchronicity of the two events—my decision to explore the consequences of the atomic bomb, and the destruction of the World Trade Center and part of the Pentagon on September 11, 2001—further galvanized my desire to go forward. I began to explore the psychological meaning of these two world events: the introduction of nuclear warfare, which

changed the political landscape of the twentieth century, and the first terrorist acts on American soil, which have profoundly altered our country's sense
of security, freedom and identity in the world.

Following the terrorist attacks, I felt unsettled, fearful and curious
after seeing a video tape of Osama Bin Ladin pointing the finger at the United
States for the atomic bombing in Hiroshima. I recalled a statement Jung made
in *Answer to Job:*

> *Man can no longer wiggle out of it on the plea of his littleness
> and nothingness, for the Dark God has slipped the atom
> bomb and chemical weapon in his hands and given him the
> power to empty out the apocalyptic vials of wrath on his
> fellow creatures.*

After the horrific events of September 11th, I was no longer able
to "wiggle" out of facing one of the most tragic events in the history of mankind and to witness an event which killed a significant number of people in
my family lineage.

My intent in writing about this has been to seek and to discover meaning as a descendent of those who were obliterated by the atomic bomb, and
finally to mourn the loss of significant family members. I am a third-generation
Japanese-American, and my maternal and paternal grandparents had roots
in both Hiroshima and Nagasaki. Psychiatrist Dori Laub has said, "One has to
know one's own buried truth in order to be able to live one's life." My buried truth
has been the denial of my family to bear witness to this atrocity. Recovering
this truth has become a calling, and the steps in my own individuation have
led me to the witnessing of the Hiroshima survivor's experience.

I now understand that my long-standing interest in trauma had been
in many ways an unconscious preparation for this endeavor.

The atomic bombings in Hiroshima and Nagasaki marshaled the
world into the nuclear age. The sound of the explosions, which devastated
these cities in 1945, still reverberates today. Survivors of this atrocity suffered greatly from the psychological shock of the bombing, and the exposure
to the effects of radiation poisoning continues to haunt survivors and later
generations.

The American psychiatrist Robert Jay Lifton is well known within
the psychoanalytic and psychiatric fields for his contributions to the understanding of traumatic syndrome, and it is his work which has resonated most
profoundly with my calling. (All quotes in this article, unless otherwise noted,
are Lifton's, from *Death in Life* and *The Broken Connection.*) As a psycho-
historian, Lifton emphasizes the necessity of bringing the individual into a
conscious relationship with humankind's collective existence. In his study of
atomic bomb survivors, he focuses upon survivor responses to the atrocity,

while weaving the historical backdrop of World War II into his understanding. In doing so, the issues of death and death-related images come to the forefront:

> *Focusing on survival rather than trauma puts death back into the traumatic experience, because survival suggests there has been a death, and the survivor therefore has had a death encounter, and the death encounter is central to his or her experience.*

—

The survivor's death encounter has important implications for our understanding of traumatic syndrome, as Lifton writes, "... death potentially transforms anything and everything."

The potential transformation of the death encounter into a healing path for survivors demands the development of a symbolic process. This symbolic process is often impeded by what is known as psychic numbing as a defense against unbearable pain. Subjectively, the survivor's feeling states may present as deadened, but also take the form of intense feelings of guilt and rage, as well as shame and anger.

During the 1960s, prior to his study of atomic bomb survivors, Lifton had studied Japanese youths, exploring a psycho-historical process characterizing the interplay between individual psychology and historical change. In this study, he began to see the influence of the atomic bombings on Japanese culture. The youths he studied were undergraduates with no memory of the war. Lifton was struck by the power of the peace symbol and its influence on the culture, as well as the anti-war sentiment of the mass demonstrations during the 1960s:

> *The atomic bombings were experienced, even by Japanese born after they took place, as both an annihilatory culmination of a disastrous period of homegrown fascism and militarism and a sudden infliction of a new and equally unfortunate historical destiny—a destiny which could, moreover, be repeated, and which was open to everyone. What I am saying is that nuclear weapons left a powerful imprint upon the Japanese which continues to be transmitted historically and psychologically through the generations.*

In 1960, Lifton began his study of atomic bomb survivors, known as *hibakusha,* by interviewing forty-two Japanese men and women chosen for their "general articulateness and particular prominence in atomic bomb problems." This group of survivors had been in close proximity to the hypocenter where the bomb was dropped and included those within the city of Hiroshima, those who came to the city within fourteen days and entered an area extending about two thousand meters from the hypo-center, those who came into physical contact with bomb victims through providing aid or disposal of bodies, and those who were in-utero at the time and whose mothers fit into one of these first three groups.

The interviews focused upon: recollection of the original experience and its meaning seventeen years later; residual concerns and fears of all kinds; the survivor's inner formulation of the experience; and struggles with *hibakusha* identity.

As Lifton embarked upon his study and confronted the survivors' experiences, taking in the details of the horrific atrocities they encountered, he noted the "vividness of recall, which seemed to reflect both the indelible imprint of the event and its endlessly reverberating psychological repercussions."

At the end of the first week of interviewing survivors, he found himself "profoundly shocked and emotionally spent." This experience demonstrated to him in an immediately personal sense the phenomenon of "psychic closing off," which was emblematic of the survivor experience.

As a defense mechanism, similar to dissociation and splitting, psychic closing off (or psychic numbing, a more intense variation), occurred almost immediately upon the survivor's confrontation with the devastating effects of the atomic bomb. It meant, simply, the inability to feel. Although the survivors continued to have a sense of what was going on around them, they unconsciously turned off their feelings. This dissociative process turned out to be a critical discovery emerging from his research into survivor psychology.

A City of Nightmares

The panorama of death following the atomic bombing of Hiroshima bears repeating for future generations, as scenes of unimaginable horror met the eyes of survivors everywhere. Needless to say, the bombing had a profound psychological effect upon the survivors. In his study, Lifton states:

> The most striking psychological feature of this immediate experience was the sense of a sudden and absolute shift from normal existence to an overwhelming encounter with death.

Many survivors interviewed recalled initial feelings related to death and dying, such as 'This is the end for me'; 'My first feeling was, 'I think will die.' People also expressed feelings that, 'The whole world was dying,' or in the words of a minister who escaped injury, who expressed an apocalyptic Christian image evoked as he walked through the city:

> The feeling I had was that everyone was dead. The whole city was destroyed... I thought all of my family must be dead, it doesn't matter if I die... I thought this was the end of Hiroshima, of Japan, of humankind... This was God's judgment on mankind...

A thirteen-year-old shopkeeper's assistant was trapped under his house:

I kept screaming "Mother!" very loudly, and then I saw my mother staggering toward me... I think she pulled the debris away from my body, and then there was a hole I could crawl through... But my mother was very weak and began to collapse and fall on her side... If I had been a little older or stronger I could have rescued her... Even now I hear my mother's voice calling me to help her...

Lifton also notes this maternal image was "reminiscent of reports about Japanese soldiers in WWII: trained to go to their deaths with the phase "Long Live the Emperor" on their lips, they instead called out, "Mother!" Lifton believes these cases "suggest an effort to reassert the ultimate human relationship in the face of death's severance... "

The survivors' lives were catapulted into a new dimension in which "... life and death were out of phase with one another, no longer properly distinguishable—which lent an aura of weirdness and unreality to the entire city."

In his classic *Hiroshima Diary,* Dr. Hachiya wrote:

Those who were able walked silently towards the suburbs in the distant hills, their spirits broken, their initiative gone... They were so broken and confused that they moved and behaved like automatons. Their reactions astonished outsiders who reported with amazement the spectacle of long files of people holding stolidly to narrow, rough path when close by was a smooth road in the same direction. The outsiders could not grasp the fact that they were witnessing the "exodus of people who walked in the realm of dreams..."

Many people would succumb to death in the hours, days, and months following the atomic bombing. The effects of toxic radiation from the atomic bomb were felt almost immediately or within the first twenty-four hours.

It consisted of nausea, vomiting, and loss of appetite; diarrhea with large amounts of blood in the stools; fever and weakness; purple spots on various parts of the body from bleeding into the skin (purpura); inflammation and ulceration of the mouth, throat, gums (oropharyngeal lesions and gingivitis); bleeding from the mouth, gums, throat, rectum, and urinary tract (hemorrhagic manifestations); loss of hair from the scalp and other parts of the body (eplation); extremely low white-blood cell counts when they were

*taken (leukopenia); and in many cases a progressive course
until death.*

Thus, the thousands left behind were to endure severe anxiety, some for over a lifetime, as they faced a *second death encounter* "characterized by the fear of epidemic contamination to the point of bodily deterioration... a sense of individual powerlessness in the face of an invisible, all-enveloping, and highly mysterious poison." Survivors who appeared well in the aftermath of the bombing would face illness, sometimes many years later.

The Psychology of the Survivor

In his research study of Hiroshima survivors, Robert Lifton identifies five psychological themes of traumatic syndrome: death imprint, death guilt, psychic numbing, conflicts around nurturing and contagion, and struggles with meaning or formulation.

The magnitude of the atomic bombing over the city of Hiroshima engraved an indelible death imprint upon the psyche of the survivors. People wandered aimlessly through the ruins of Hiroshima in horror as they witnessed scenes of destruction: corpses frozen by death while in the action of flight; people burned who looked like boiled octopuses and smelled like sardines; a man in shock holding his eyeball; mothers clinging to their dead children; fires burning as if the city had become the inferno of hell; survivors crowded in ruined buildings, injured and lying in urine, feces, and vomit; flies and maggots everywhere. Scenes like this became fixed as indelible imprints of death upon the psyche of the survivor.

The total destruction of the city became other-worldly to a young sociologist exposed at 2,500 meters:

> *Everything I saw made a deep impression—a park nearby
> covered with dead bodies waiting to be cremated... very badly
> injured people evacuated in my direction... The most impres-
> sive thing I saw was some girls, very young girls, not only with
> their clothes torn off but with their skin peeled off as well...
> My immediate thought was that this was like the hell I had
> always read about... I had never seen anything which resem-
> bled it before... And I imagined that all of these people I was
> seeing were in the hell I had read about.*

A psychologist, who at the time of the bombing was a university stu-dent, told Lifton that he had found himself underneath a collapsed house, pinned under its heavy beams and abandoned by two friends who had unsuc-cessfully attempted to pull him out:

I began to see my mother's image before me... I regretted that
I was going to die. I thought I was young, and had been suc-
cessful in a very difficult (academic) competition... I wanted
to study more in the life ahead of me... And I was dying with-
out seeing my parents.

From these first-person accounts, we can envision how the images contained within the death imprint were composites of the survivor's past and present, reflecting backward in time and to the survivor's current experience of that past and the anticipation and continuing experience of the death imprint. These images contained unbearable feelings of terror, horror, and fear, shattering the survivor's connection to the larger human matrix. In his work in Hiroshima, Lifton found that the "magnitude" of the disaster itself made it difficult for people to find "adequate transcendent religious explanation— Buddhist, Shinto, or Christian—for what they and others experienced." The one sustaining mode of immortality found among the survivor was symbolized by nature, which was found to be the most viable.

The courage to confront, metabolize, and finally integrate these indelible images of death was often impeded by the survivor's inability to bear overwhelming feelings of guilt. Many asked themselves unconsciously, "Why did I survive while letting others die?" Lifton wrote that the *guilt over survival priority* centered around the survivor's "lifelong identification with death, with dying" and "with an anonymous group of 'the dead:'"

For the survivor can never, inwardly, simply conclude that
it was logical and right for him, and not others, to survive.
Rather, I would hold, he is bound by an unconscious percep-
tion of organic social balance which makes him feel that his
survival was made possible by others' deaths. If they had
not died, he would have had to; and if he had not survived,
someone else would have.

As a result of being traumatized through witnessing these horrific scenes of death, survivors often 'froze' in a total state of helplessness. They were unable to respond appropriately, whether physically or psychically, to situations they faced, undergoing a symbolic death, "in order to avoid a more permanent physical or psychic death."
The survivors had in many ways merged with the dead, living their lives 'as if' they were dead. An internal dialogue became their identity; "*I almost died; I should have died; I did die; or at least I am not really alive; or if I am alive it is impure for me to be so; and anything I do which affirms life is also impure and an insult to the dead, who alone are pure.*"
The survivors found themselves caught in a cycle of guilt and self-blame, which centered around what he or she might have done or what they

failed to do for other people. One experience told in a poem was the story of a mother whose thirteen-year-old son asked her one morning for a tomato. She told him he could have one, but later. He never returned to her, and she never found his remains. She later constructed an altar to honor her son, on which she put a tomato. This ritual served as a means of appeasing her guilt after refusing her son's last request of her.

A testimony by a history professor reflecting upon his walk through the city after the bombing poignantly images the sense of guilt he experienced through the eyes of the dead:

> I went to look for my family. Somehow I became a pitiless person, because if I had pity, I would not have been able to walk through the city, to walk over those dead bodies. The more impressive thing was the expression in people's eyes... looking for someone to come and help them. They looked at me and knew that I was stronger than they... I was looking for my family and looking carefully at everyone I met to see if he or she was a family member, but the eyes, the emptiness, the helpless expression, were something I will never forget... There were hundreds of people who had seen me... And I often had to go to the same place more than once. I wished that the same family would not still be there... They looked at me with great expectation...

This man felt accused by the pleading eyes who he felt were accusing him of letting them die, while he "selfishly" went on living.

Another common memory of the survivor, which depicted this cycle of guilt and self-blame, occurred when the injured or dying were refused water by the survivor. This act of refusal was influenced by the rumor that the poisoned water would be harmful to the injured. In contrast was the deeply imbedded cultural belief that water could restore life. Consequently, this "scene of refusal" was the frozen moment in time in which the survivor became immobilized, unable to perform a "last act" for the injured and the dying.

In her book, *The City of Corpses*, Yoko Ota recalls soldiers with severe burns, calling out for water as she and her family sat along the riverbank. "Water! Water! Water, please!" the soldiers cried. In order to stop these pleas, people said to them, "With burns you shouldn't drink, or you'll die. We can't give you water." The denial of these requests for water plagued the consciences of the survivors. Lifton spoke to many who were troubled by their feelings around refusing to bring water to the dying. They expressed the common sentiment that, "Since they were to die anyway, I should have given them the water they wanted so badly."

The dead as seen through the eyes of the survivors render "us accountable for our relationship to others' physical and psychological existence." This role of the dead is not unique to the Hiroshima survivor, but common to all of us.

Lifton writes: "For we all enter into similar commitments to the dead, whether consciously or unconsciously, whether to specific people who lived in the past or to the anonymous dead…" For the Hiroshima survivors, this meant coming to terms with their own "inadequate" responses under the extraordinary circumstances, and in essence, forgiving themselves for what they might have done for the dead.

Psychic closing off and psychic numbing

At the time of this enormous, tragic, man-made disaster, survivors were unable to remain open to any experience for any length of time. The scenes of destruction were too much for any human being and so, within minutes of the blast, the survivors would shut themselves off from experiencing the tragedy around them. Lifton calls this "psychic closing off," and it often led to a more intense state of psychic numbing, which stands at the heart of the traumatic syndrome: "If I feel nothing, then death is not taking place." The emotional state of psychic numbing is similar to what others' have called the disaster syndrome, the "stunned" and "dazed" behavior of victims of so-called ordinary disasters.

"Psychic closing off" served as a "highly adaptive function," enabling people to respond to situations that ordinarily might have been to much to face. Perhaps feeling enough, but not too much, enabled the survivors to "dislodge" themselves from "debris or from the fire" rather than being totally immobilized in states of utter helplessness. In doing so, the survivor was able to "limit his investment in that encounter" and "undergo a reversible form of symbolic death in order to avoid a permanent physical or psychic death."

A physicist interviewed by Lifton experienced a "state of emptiness" after walking for a week among corpses, searching for the bodies of relatives:

> As I walked along, the horrible things I saw became more and more extreme and more and more intolerable. And at a certain point I must have become more or less saturated, so that I became no longer sensitive, in fact insensitive, to what I saw around me. I think human emotions reach a point beyond which they cannot extend—something like a photographic process. If under certain conditions you expose a photographic plate to light it becomes black, but if you continue to expose it, then it reaches a point where it turns white... Only later can one recognize having reached this maximum state...

Numbing takes the survivor into a state of emptiness.

Another theme which dominated the survivors' personal relationships and their general attitude was a suspicion of counterfeit nurturance. On one hand, if the survivor felt as if the need for nurturance was denied, the survivor felt abandoned, while on the other hand, if this need was responded to, it was viewed as "inauthentic" because it confirmed the survivor the status of a "victim," who felt a sense of humiliation and shame for possessing a death taint. When help was offered to the survivor, it evoked feelings of "special need," reminding people of their "weaknesses" and creating "severe conflicts over autonomy." The offering of help to the survivor was often met with feelings of resentment, hostility, and suspicion of counterfeit nurturance.

For the *hibakusha,* the ultimate "counterfeit element" was life itself and ongoing identification with the dead. Incorporated into their beings were all of the horror, terror, and gore related to death. An atomic bomb orphan whose family died in the bombing supported himself by being a shopkeeper's assistant. He performed a ritual of going twice daily to the family altar, which contained memorial tablets of his mother, father, and brother:

> Even though they are dead now, every day in the morning and in the evening I still give a kind of report to my father, mother, and younger brother... as if talking to my parents... I tell them, with a feeling of gratitude that I have been able to spend another day safely...

Imprisoned in "death" by his identification with his dead family, this young man was left feeling disconnected, cut off, and disenfranchised from his connection to humanity. His daily ritual helped him to reestablish his connection to those he loved. The restoration of trust in order to rebuild this broken "lifeline" became a Herculean task for him and many of the Hiroshima survivors. The shopkeeper's assistant, expecting to see no one living in Hiroshima, is touched by what he sees four months after the bombing:

> When I came to Hiroshima in December, there were shacks standing here and there... I heard that there would be no people living in Hiroshima in the future, but within a few months I found these shacks standing... with people living in them, and this made me feel I too had to do something to keep myself going... I began to think that as long as I was alive, I had to go on living...

When the shopkeeper's assistant returned to the ruins of Hiroshima and found live people there, a reconnection to the human order was discovered.

The restoration of trust in the human order involves transcending states of death guilt, shame, and death anxiety in their most profound states. The suffering of painful and unrelenting feelings of guilt was tied to the survivors' witnessing of "unbearable" deaths. Lifton writes that this witnessing could be utilized as a way of "transmuting pain and guilt into responsibility" and became a fundamental ingredient to the reintegration process:

> The only way one can feel right or justified in reconstituting oneself and going on living with some vitality is to carry out one's responsibility to the dead. And it's carrying through that responsibility via one's witness, that survivor mission, that enables one to be an integrated human being once more.

One particular survivor stands out in this regard, a physician named Dr. Hachiya, severely injured by the blast of the atomic bombing. He had 150 scars, which permanently disfigured both his face and his body. His heroism is evident from a memoir he wrote called, *Hiroshima Diary,* which chronicles his experiences from August 6, 1945 until the end of September, when his diary ends. Two days after the blast, while he was convalescing in the hospital he administered, he began keeping a record of events. By reading his daily thoughts and activities, we begin to understand the devastation of the nuclear horror as well as how he moves himself toward transcending of this horror by recognizing and appreciating the rhythm and movement of a simple life. Nature is cherished in its splendor. Friendships and family relations embraced. His medical and scientific work becomes redemptive. The former enemy is also thought of not in terms of past horrors but in personal terms of friendly acquaintance, and later, professional collaboration.

Analytical Psychology: Treatment of the Trauma Survivor

In this final section, I will attempt to explore how Jungian analysis could provide for a survivor a pathway out of the atomic complex through its gradual reintegration, leading finally to the restoration of a vital ego-self relationship. By proposing how one might employ several principles of Jungian treatment, I hope to illustrate how the methods of analytical psychology can help to heal the trauma survivor. As a vehicle for this, I have chosen a Hiroshima survivor as a "case example." Through the survivor's words, we learn of her struggle to rebuild her life in the aftermath of the bombing.

—

Mother and Child
Janice Nakao

Yoko Ota

Yoko Ota was forty-two years old at the time of the bombing and became one of Japan's best known writers of A-bomb literature. Following exposure to the bomb, she wrote five books in the form of memoirs: *Women of the Sea, Land of the Cherry Blossoms, City of Corpses, Human Rags (Ningin Ranru),* and *The Town and People of the Evening Calm (Yunagi no Machi to Hito).* She won literary prizes for her books and was constantly called upon to speak about the A-bomb issues in the mass media.

Ms. Ota was living in Tokyo as a writer until the fire bombings in Tokyo made it impossible to live in the city. She made her way back to Hiroshima to reside with her mother and sister five months before the atomic bomb attack. In her years after the bombing, Ms. Ota found it impossible to leave the experience of the atomic bomb and to write on other subjects:

> The reverberation continues to this day... I tried to write other works. I tried to write works unrelated to the atomic bomb, different works. But the image of my hometown Hiroshima branded onto my mind drove away the vision of other works... I had witnessed with my eyes and heart and listened to people talk about the reality of the destruction of Hiroshima and the annihilation of people. And that reality produced a vision of a concrete piece of writing that... crippled my zest for writing other works.

Ms. Ota struggled until her death in 1963 to reconcile herself with the atomic experience. Often expressing feeling of anger and rage about the constraints placed upon her by her identity as a *hibakusha,* Ms. Ota's lack of resolution found its way into bodily complaints. Lifton writes that she "suffered from chronic debilitation which was sometimes diagnosed as nervous weakness and at other times was associated with such specific physical conditions as gall bladder and heart disease."

Treatment of Ms. Ota

Ms. Ota had a difficult and troublesome family life prior to the atomic bomb. When she was seven years old, her mother placed her for adoption following the dissolution of her second marriage. Two years later, at the age of nine, she returned to live with her mother after her mother remarried for the third time. Whatever the circumstances were that necessitated this decision to place her for adoption, Ms. Ota's losses impacted her emotional-psychological development. This pattern of abandonment centered around a parent/child motif and was enacted in a repetition compulsion by Ms. Ota, who later abandoned her son by placing him for adoption after the dissolution of the first of her three marriages.

Formation of the Atomic Complex

Ms. Ota describes her experience after the bomb:

> I was sound asleep inside the mosquito net... I dreamed I was enveloped by a blue flash, like lightning at the bottom of the sea. Immediately thereafter came a terrible sound, loud enough to shake the earth. With an indescribable sound, almost like a roll of thunder, like a huge boulder tumbling down a mountain, the roof of the house came crashing down... I was standing there in a complete fog, struck absolutely dumb, I felt no pain; I was not frightened; I was somehow calm... How could everything in our vicinity have been transformed in one instant?... In my daze, I had a different idea: that it might have no connection to the war, that it might be something that occurs at the end of the world, when the globe disintegrates.

When we envision a Jungian analysis with a trauma survivor or an atomic survivor like Ms. Ota, we enter into a liminal space. The psychic impact of the event catapulted Ms. Ota into another world, to the "end of the world."

The analyst acts as witness to the survivor's encounter with death and together they weave a narrative of the experience. By acting as a witness to the analysand's story, the analyst stands with the analysand at the moment of annihilation, when the atomic survivors self veered toward extinction and the terror of non–being. In this death encounter, the ego meets death, severing the pathway to the survivor's connection to the human matrix. The survivor in the retelling of the story unconsciously asks the analyst: "Will you feed me or attack me, will you hold me or attack me?" As she listens, the analyst begins to construct a narrative of the experience, a witnessing through spoken words of the analysand's 'horror' of the experience. With someone like Ms. Ota, the analyst would be mindful of her history of parental loss, paying attention for overt or unconscious clues as to how these issues would reverberate in their dialogue and manifest in the transference and counter-transference field.

Ms. Ota left Hiroshima for a small village outside the city a month or so after the bombing. In Richard Minear's book *Hiroshima: Three Witnesses,* Ota describes being awakened in a frightened state:

> Just as I was returning to "normal"... I began to be subject to an indescribable terror. At night, if the sound of the rain suddenly turned harsh, I would be overcome by the feeling that the bluish flash had come again, that the roof I was sleeping under might collapse without a sound and I would jump up and examine the ceiling. My acute sensibility came back to life, yet I still thought I would die, albeit somewhat later than the sleeping.

Paradoxically, Ms. Ota is confronted by the effects of the atomic complex (terror) after thinking that her life had returned to "normal." The idea of returning to normal after a disaster of this magnitude prompts a compensatory response from the unconscious for having adopted a faulty attitude. In essence, the unconscious speaks, saying to her, "No you aren't, you must look at your terror and master it!" Her encounter with death might have been explored, metabolized, in a dialogue with the analyst as witness.

In her book *City of Corpses,* Ms. Ota describes her struggles to produce works about topics other than the A-bomb experience. This struggle is symptomatic of the ego's identification with the atomic complex and the survivor guilt, which severed or blocked the capacity to access the life-giving symbols of the unconscious. The analyst helps to "mediate" the integration of the opposites enabling the analysand to "arrive at a new attitude."

More important were her subsequent literary struggles to be more than an A-bomb writer, which is a "corollary of the identity struggle of the *hibakusha* in general." She writes that it was impossible to make use of the fictional mode as she was violating "a survivor's sense of sacred historical truth."

> As a subject for fiction it is very difficult... I don't want to write fictitious things—I just want to write the truth—to describe it as it was without exaggeration... Fiction is usually a mixture of truth and lies. But I don't want to write lies about the A-bomb the way some others have...

What Ms. Ota views as a violation of historical truth is a literalization of the atomic experience and symptomatic of an impaired capacity to transcend the original experience. This signifies an impaired transcendent function.

Identification with the Atomic Complex

Ms. Ota's identification with the atomic complex prevented her from imaginatively re-creating her work and finding a way to reintegrate the complex more therapeutically. The atomic complex blocked the symbolic process by "allowing" her only one form of writing. Attention to her symptom, viewed symbolically, might have helped to redress the psychic imbalance:

> Most people seem to look upon me as an interesting person, and it is often said that I am one of the best women writers—but when talk of the A-bomb comes up, I find myself in a very bad mood... I think I am still very angry at the A-bomb... Maybe I need more time—more distance—before I can write further about the A-bomb. I would like to write about things that have nothing to do with the A-bomb. Because when I write about the A-bomb, I feel physically ill and I have to rest.

The analyst grapples to hold, bind, and contain intense annihilation anxiety as the survivor abreacts to the events. The story will need to be told over and over again, until it winds itself down. The analyst must imagine from her own counter-transference experience, offering to the analysand ways of seeing, hearing, feeling, and thinking about the experience.

In *City of Corpses*, Ms. Ota describes with great sensitivity scenes involving children who were either injured or had died. She was particularly affected by a father who lost his daughter:

> A man was sitting on a rock at a place where until the morning of the sixth there had been a bend in the road. Next to him there was an air raid trench. A mat had been spread in the trench, and the body of a girl of twelve or thirteen had been laid down facing the other way. A white cloth covered her. Beside her pillow had been placed a small red bowl holding a ball of white rice. An incense stick with a pointed red flame was sending up smoke. New clogs had been put on her feet and fastened with thin thongs. I asked the man sitting on the rock, "Is she dead?" He nodded and said, "Uh-huh." Tears welled up in the young father's eyes; tears overflowed in my eyes, too. The father had clothed her in a pretty traveling outfit, and she reminded me of Otsuru, the character in the play who made a pilgrimage to Awa. The parental love expressed in the tender treatment of his daughter's dead body reverberated in my heart like the echo of a gentle poem, I who had lived these three days amid devastation. I walked on sobbing loudly, through dead bodies so numerous there was no place to set my feet.

In this moving scene between a father and his deceased daughter, we see the dark side of the Self. As she experienced this universal image of parent and child, I wondered how this poignant situation involving children might have reawakened her childhood, in particular, her feelings of abandonment and loss, love, and dependency. By repeatedly identifying, naming, and interpreting the analysand's experience of the death encounter and its related themes (abandonment), toxic states of terror, fear, and threats of abandonment would be neutralized through the dialogue and a reconnection to humanity re-established.

—
Four J's
Janice Nakao

For someone like Ms. Ota who was imprisoned by the atomic complex, the expressive arts might help to engage the unconscious and assist in its reintegration. The unconscious is creative, thoughtful, and provides meaning by assisting consciousness as it rebalances itself. A dialogue of this nature might begin by asking her if she has a compelling image which moves in her. Asking her to describe the image with sensitive exploration to the details of the image: shape, color, texture, and the feeling tone evoked can animate the image. Resistance to this process is common because of the analysand's fears of becoming overwhelmed by the effect generated. Careful attention to the counter-transference guides the analyst in monitoring the unconscious processes unleashed, where numinous effect comes in like a storm to the analytic hour.

Active Imagination

The image of father and daughter might be explored in the context of an imaginal dialogue established between Ms. Ota and the father. Although this method can be done in the classical solitary way, for reasons of empathic containment, its witnessing by the analyst would provide the needed containment for the potentially powerful affect that can be unleashed through this method. Ms. Ota would be encouraged to formulate questions, which she would want to ask the father. This powerful method proposed by Jung takes the image and "dreams the dream onward." In active imagination, the analysand uses the ego to dialogue with an image.

Sand Tray

Another compelling image for Ms. Ota was the Hiroshima Castle which was obliterated by the atomic bombing. Its destruction symbolized for her a process of disintegration—physical, social, and historical—all fused into a single image. She describes the destruction:

> I reached a bridge and saw that the Hiroshima Castle had
> been completely leveled to the ground, and my heart shook
> like a great wave... This destruction of the castle gave me a
> thought. Even if a new city should be built on this land, this

castle would never be built and added to that city. The city of Hiroshima, entirely on flat land, was made three-dimensional by the existence of the white castle, and because of this it could retain its classical flavor. Hiroshima had a history of its own. And when I thought about these things, the grief of stepping over the corpse of history pressed upon my heart...

Using the Hiroshima Castle as an image, I would ask her to go with me on an imaginal journey back to this scene, with the anticipation of having her recreate the image in a sand tray. The use of the sand tray might be an effective tool for constructing images of Hiroshima, expressing metaphorically Ms. Ota's psychic state. This journey into the imaginal might begin in a dialogue between us:

JAN: The Hiroshima Castle is a very compelling image and an important one in your work. I would like you to close your eyes and focus your mind's eye on this scene. As it comes into your awareness, please describe it to me.

MS. OTA: I see the castle in its glory. "... no matter which part of town you were in, Hiroshima Castle and its crumbling foundation of stone also seemed very near, rising up in bold relief against the mountains. With its quiet tones of white, black, and grey, the tall old castle provided the flat city one sort of variation."

JAN: What you are seeing in your mind's eye is the castle as it stood in the past, before the bombing, or what?

MS. OTA: Oh God, it's different than how it looked in real life. It looks the same but it's different.

JAN: How so?

MS. OTA: I guess you could say that it has been rebuilt... even though it hasn't been rebuilt. It still lies in its ruined state.

JAN: But within your psyche the image has been rebuilt. The psyche is trying to rebuild your "ruined state."

In this imaginary dialogue between myself and Ms. Ota, I was trying to capture how the unconscious might respond to Ms. Ota's effort to create a dialogue with the unconscious. The image of a rebuilt castle would be a compensatory image helping to rebalance Ms. Ota's feelings of loss and grief. At some point, I might encourage the use of the sand tray as a means of depicting scenes of Ms. Ota's experiences. The visual recreation of the subjective experiences of death and destruction would assist in the re-integration process.

Atomic Complex: a Lifelong Struggle

Ms. Ota was unable to integrate the atomic complex leaving her in a depressed state. Caught in an identification with the dead, the aura of fear continued to surround her. She said to Lifton in an interview, fifteen months before her death in 1963, after having a tooth pulled, "Since I experienced the atomic bomb, there is always a danger that the bleeding will not stop and that leukemia might develop." She evidently lived in constant fear of the medical aftereffects of the atomic bomb, which is psychologically and historically understandable. She died of coronary illness, which may have been the outcome of a psychosomatic process. Early sensitivities concerning love and dependency were likely exacerbated by her A-bomb experience and undermined her struggles to overcome her conflicts.

Despite all of this, her contributions to the world through her literary writings provided a rich source of information and understanding of the A-bomb experience. In light of her struggles, we can appreciate her passion and fortitude to formulate for all of us the atomic experience.

My trip to Hiroshima for the August 6 commemoration of the bombing was, for me, a significant journey of witness. During my week-long observance, I witnessed a collective healing process and learned through it how the Japanese culture joins together to memorialize a tragic world event. In 1946, as the one year anniversary of the atomic bombing approached, a wooden structure called the "Soul-Reposing Tower" was constructed near Ground Zero. On August 6, the city gathered around the tower to honor the atomic dead through silent prayer. Survivors lit incense and flowers were presented in memory of the dead. These ceremonies and other rituals performed during this memorial became what Lifton called the "annual moment in time around which the entire *hibakusha* identity… " revolved.

Jung believed that man expressed his most fundamental psychological conditions in ritual, and that if the necessary rituals were not provided, man would devise his own as a means of stabilizing the personality in transition. He wrote that rituals do not affect the transformation, but provide the necessary containment for it.

On that first anniversary, at 8:15 a.m. sirens were sounded throughout the city and a one minute silent tribute was paid to the victims. (This ritual continues to this day.) The Mayor of Hiroshima took the platform and read aloud to the world the first Peace Declaration:

> This horrible weapon brought about a "Revolution of Thought"
> which has convinced us of the necessity and the value of
> eternal peace. That is to say, because of this atomic bomb,

the people of the world have become aware that a global war in which atomic energy would be used and would lead to the end of our civilization and the extinction of mankind. This revolution in thinking ought to be the basis for an absolute peace, and imply the birth of new life and a new world.

—
Michio Miyagi
Janice Nakao

In 1949, the Japanese Diet (with occupation approval) passed a law designating Hiroshima as an "International City of Peace." The city as a symbol of peace became an important psychic motif for *hibakusha*. A park was built near the center of the city close to Ground Zero. Within the park are monuments including the official Atomic Bomb Monument or Cenotaph (completed in 1953), the Peace Memorial Hall (1953), the Peace Memorial Museum or Atomic Bomb Memorial Exhibition Hall (1955), and the Children's Atomic Bomb Monument (1958), as well as other monuments dedicated to the dead.

I approached the Cenotaph in the sweltering blaze of the Hiroshima sun and stepped inside to view the names of the dead. As I searched for my family name—Nakao—a peacefulness washed over me, as if I had finally come home to an aspect of my history which had been hidden but was now being recovered.

One of the most significant symbols at the park in the form of a ruin is the Atomic Bomb Dome. As a dome-shaped building, it was one of a few reinforced concrete buildings in Hiroshima and did not perish like everything else around it. In 1963, a plan was made to preserve the ruin of the A-bomb Dome. The decision to preserve this ruin created conflict and turmoil for survivors, who were torn by the meaning of this building, which in time became a national symbol for the city of Hiroshima.

The preservation of the Atomic Dome was announced in 1967, becoming a symbol for the world. Today, the Dome stands in Peace Memorial Park, acting as a blatant reminder of the city's atomic identity.

In my personal quest to understand my relationship to this human catastrophe, I discovered that a paternal great-uncle of mine was a renowned Japanese musician. Born in Kobe, Japan, Michio Miyagi helped to invigorate the spirit of many with his koto arrangement *Sakura, Sakura* (Cherry blossoms). This song was heard throughout Hiroshima in the aftermath of the bombing. The song musically images nature in its full bloom.

The Japanese culture is known for its reverence for nature and its beauty. *Hanami* (cherry blossoms) parties are held in the spring throughout the country where competition for the best views of blossoming trees can be fierce. Symbolically, the cherry expresses for the culture a reminder of the evanescent beauty of the floating world. As a culture, the Japanese strove to represent and bring form to the atomic experience by the building of the Peace Memorial Park and other memorials built for commemoration. During my participation in the ceremonies on August 6, the intensity of sorrow, grief, and mourning gave way to an evening of festivities symbolizing a collective, transcendent function.

As the sun set, contemporary music was played along the Ota River as families young and old gathered. Young children were dressed in traditional summer *yukata* robes. The young children followed a ritual of placing small colored lanterns around the Atomic Dome and then bowing in observance. This scene images the honoring of a painful collective tragedy, which all generations share.

In the evening, the heaviness and grief of the day gave way to an experience of transcendence. I viewed hundreds of colorful lanterns lit by candlelight floating down the seven rivers of Hiroshima. They are inscribed with the names of mothers, fathers, and young children who died in the atomic bombing.

The atmosphere of this evening can only be expressed by the Japanese expression *mono no aware,* or, the sad beauty of existence. This quality is strongly related to the capacity to transcend one's state of mind through a uniting symbol. While viewing the pink, yellow, orange, and red lanterns floating down the rivers, I had images of people jumping into the river to escape the intense heat around them or to cool their burning bodies. I found that the movement of the lanterns healed the heaviness of my heart and in this "dance down the river," I felt a sense of lightness, which merged with visions of people crying out for water as they succumbed to death. The sense of death's finality moved me into a lightness of being.

A collective transcendent event transports the survivors into the present, reuniting them with humankind.

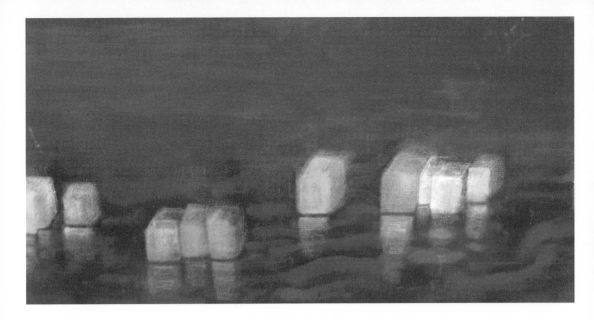

—

Hiroshima River Lights
Janice Nakao

Behind the Summer Rain

Kim Shi-Jong

I can see an abandoned chair
blurred by the rainy day.
It appears to be my proper place:
I displaced from I.
It appears as my weathering bone,
its existence long forgotten,
perhaps a thing before which I must wait.
Nothing is ever gone.
Splashing water around,
an unidentified voice sounds in the dim air.
Behind the well-trimmed hedge,
fresh green leaves breathe,
never washed away, dripping.
The constant rain falls to be cleansed by itself.
Thus people never bend backward in the rain.
I can see and cannot see.
There, I don't see the fields of muddy country,
only the voices dripping wet.
Alone, splashing, popping,
the white chair hazing over
behind the spray.

At the Heart of the Pale Blue Sky

Kim Shi-Jong

I have no voice.
I have no place to stop by
to raise a cry.
A mere mumbler, I have no choice
but to let my voice rustle with my own sigh.

I have no way to inform.
I won't belong
to any intelligence all my life long.
I have only a voice to conform
to my ear's hallucinated song.

Someday, just some other day, I will...
So I thought,
but my words always disappear as the wind,
leaving only a vestige behind.
Each time I look upon the hill,
the college oak stands mute,
though plenty of nuts fall
without hope to root.

Unutterable words
stammered
surrounded by innumerable eyes.
I do not know my confession yet.
I do not know my incantation yet
to atone for my debt.

A roaring sound blows through my ear.
Voices gather as leafhoppers in the air.
Soon sparrow flocks will appear
to drive away the sky,
freezing my winter's eye.

Word petals are strewn everywhere,
and there I am,
my ears pricking up to nowhere.
Surely I know something is there,
bursting at the heart of the autumnal sky.
Love this poor guy
who can never stop living a lie.

Poetry by Kim Shi-Jong

Oh, April, my Distant Days!
Kim Shi-Jong

My spring is always colored red,
flowers dyed by that bloody hue.

Not butterflies, but carpenter bees fly among the pistils,
and with their faint buzz,
April overflows, eyes red with distemper.
A raven on a forked branch
stirs not an inch,
impatient for the tree to meet its fate.

There, motionless,
he will become a knot of tree.
Though I have long since entered a new century,
and only with my eyes shut, I see that bird
yet survives, pecking all my memories.

At the crossroads on the hill,
we parted in opposite directions.
You have since forever changed your name.
Then April spouted forth as a beacon at twilight.
Our village, beyond the trampled azaleas, burned,
winds blown in a thick cloud of dust,
a convoy of military trucks.
On the day you collapsed, your face crushed in
silky green chinaberry,
a white dust rose through the flowering apricot.

Haze hung over the light morning glow,
spring blossoming without pause,
and yet there remained the people, trees, and a lonely bird.
Never raising voices in the glaring sunlight,
but lowering them in harmony with the drizzling rain,
trees, souls, trembling winds
inscribed a lonely waiting on earth.

Oh my memory is blurring.
That crossroad, that corner,
that hollow where my
old love shed fresh blood.
I, who should have been there, am uselessly old,
and have survived a slanted life in Japan
with the grief of flowers, forsythia and apricot.
Today the sun shines brightly, and my
April comes again, dyeing red my sight.

Oh trees,
trees, listen within to your trembling!
Thus, as if nothing had happened, my
spring returns to life,
shedding repentant tears.

For the author, April is the
cruel month that commem-
orates the Jeju Uprising
beginning on April 3, 1948,
dragging the entire island
of Jeju into desperate strife
for more than six years.
Seventy percent of the
island's villages were burned
down, and almost 60,000
people were killed in fighting
or executions among
various factions in the postwar Korean repression
against leftist activities. The
then nineteen-year-old
author participated in the
uprising, witnessed the
massacres, and finally smug-
gled himself into Kobe port,
Japan, only to live in exile for
the remainder of his life.
On the other hand, August for
the author means the
month of liberation in a glaring daydream when the war
and the Japanese occupation
of his native Korea ended.

Poetry by Kim Shi-Jong

—

From: *Lost Seasons.*
Tokyo: Fujiwara-shoten, 2010.
Translated by
Ryuta Imafuku in collaboration with
Karen Tei Yamashita.

Passing into Twilight Alley

Tami Sakiyama

There is a hand with a dreamlike touch that crawls out of the slumbering tunnel and taps at reality's wall, tsuku tsuku.

A slithering chill strokes my jaw. Bougainvillea in burgundy flames and bursts across my startled vision. Lured by the commotion of color, I bend forward and sniff. No scent. A blossoming profusion between my dreams. I am reminded of that alley.

There was a town naked to tida's aggression.[1]

The alley, coiled and anchored in silence, lay stagnating in a hollow section of the town. That alley. Whenever I stepped into that alley, I felt dizzy with nausea.

That's right. Now I remember people called that alley Akou-kurou-gai.[2] During the day the alley lay soundless and like the night without human shadows. At night, it grew noisy as if daytime, tornados of chaos swirling around silent hollows lit by grimy neon.

Everywhere in that town smells rotten.

The stink's source is alcohol, sweat, spit, urine, sex, and mold mixed and fermented. A sudden shriek becomes a scream, followed by the sound of an explosion. Yelling. Shouts. Accusations. A sound of sirens. Spasm. Mass seizure. Loud mocking laughter, like random gun shots, fire off through the dark alley, now dyed a sad blood red. The colliding stinks and sounds rip away, slide, and criss-cross the streets. Thus memories of that alley crawl out tsuku tsuku through the walls of my dream.

I cannot remember the knot of logic that convinced me to wander to that separate place outside my own neighborhood; a broken piece of memory crawls back from my mind not yet five years old.

The alley was wedged into an indentation in the peninsula's chopped and spreading coral plate.

—

1

tida

sun in Okinawan language

—

2

Akou-kurou-gai

the state between brightness and darkness;
in other words, a twilight
and *gai* is Japanese for
street

The narrow zigzaging alleys intersected, connected, dead-ended. Even in those cul-de-sacs, there were shabby human shacks, more like horse corrals than human houses. These crooked tin-roofed shacks were covered in a dust of poverty, jammed ramshackle into the island's dump.

Over the hill was another street filled with the bars and clubs and waiting soldiers who lingered on without reason; the war had ended a long time ago. Akou-kurou-gai was a second-tier district of people from the underclass trying to make a living selling their leftovers from the main business district.

Along the winding alley, to the left and right, you encountered lines of signs. Bar Texas. Yumi's Bar. Okinawan Music Bar Attchame. Chiru's Noodle Restaurant. Nmya-chi Oden. Lucky Juke. Take a Break. Only Americans. No Islanders Allowed. Dance Lessons. We Teach Karate, too. Defend Yourself. Nakasone Dry Cleaner. Tailor Hatsumi.

These signs, half-business and half-tease, were roughly painted unprofessional plucks, cheap and deceiving. Their garish colors glittered under the strong sun.

The moldy breeze carries the constant gossip from the alley.

Most of the voices belong to women. The gossip starts in whispers, as if to repress their high-pitched tongues, but eventually their talk turns bold. Their rude stories swell the belly of the alley until its surface cracks and explodes, reverberating air waves through the town.

"Damn, what's with that woman?"

"Yeah, she pissed me off."

"Who does she think she is. That bitch makes herself sound as if she's somebody."

"Somebody, nobody. Someone said her mother was a juri in Chiiji." [3]

"A juri?"

"Yeah, that's what I heard."

"I heard that, too."

"Yeah, I know that, too."

"Me too."

"What did you say you knew?"

"What've we been talking about?"

"About that monster juri woman."

"What's that?"

"About a juri woman who got a huge ten-story building. Made money, you know, from Shuri samurai and Japanese soldiers. Long time ago when Japan took over Ryukyu. Then she played those American officers for their money in the American days."

"So that monster juri woman is the mother of that woman?"

"Rumor, so people say."

"Yeah, they say she's got blood from Chiiji."

"No wonder she stinks different than us."

"Now that you say that... she's got some kind of hin."

—
3
Chiiji
an Okinawan pronunciation for Tsuji, a red-light district which used to be in Naha. The women who lived and worked there as entertainers and prostitutes were called *juri*

"Right, right, sexy with hin."

"Men are weak to hin."

"What's 'hin'?"

"Nothing to do with you."

"Ha! What is hin, hinhin, sounds like a horse rutting."

"Right. Why don't she whinny in a horse-dance procession,[4] well, if she's really a juri daughter."

"Yeah, she better put on a bingata and do up her hair."

"Here she goes, hin, hin, hin, yui, yui, yui!"

The women open their mouths wide, showing their teeth as if a bunch of neighing nags. They are so loud and powerful, they quite swallow up all the moldy air filling the alley.

The women shook their bellies drumming the ground. As they raised their voices, the ground rumbled "duh, duh, duh, duh, … ," resonating with their spattering spit raging, "puh, puh, puh, puh." Then rose another sound, "chii, chi, chi, chi, chi… ," a vexed spitting followed by a long deep almost secretive sigh of forgotten breath. Then whistles, "phii, phii," responded weakly in exhaustion.

Suddenly out of noisy chaos came someone's low powerful voice, "You, liar."

The air grew tense, and the heads quickly turned around toward where the voice came from.

"Who's the liar?"

"You. Liar!"

"What do you mean?"

"I'm saying you are the liar."

"What? What makes you say that?"

This story that should have concluded found a way to continue on.

"To tell you the truth, the truth was that… that… "

"What's *that?*"

"I mean, the inaguuya[5] of that woman was *she.*"

"Who's 'she'?"

"How could she have been a juri! *She* was a mud woman, so to speak."

"Mud woman? What you talking bout?"

"I myself have seen it."

"Oh, you the peeper. What did you peep this time?"

"I saw her sneaking out every night."

"What's wrong? Everyone in this town 'sneaks out every night.' We do it, too. That's our job."

"No, hers is different. Specially weird."

"What is so 'special' about 'sneaking out at night'? Everybody does the same thing."

"No, no. There is something definitely weird about her case."

"Hey, wait, who're you talking about?"

"Don't know her?"

"That's why I'm asking you who *she* is."

—

4

On every January 20th in lunar calendar, *juri* women walked in their district in procession, singing and dancing in a special costume with a horse-head attached to the front part of their kimono

—

5

inagu means *woman* and *uya* means *parent*, thus *inaguuya* means *mother* in Okinawan language

"Nobody knows who *she* is exactly."

"......"

"Hey, hey, you gals, the woman is *she.* How come you don't know her after all the years you've been living in this town?"

"I don't know her and won't, no matter how long, even after a hundred years living here."

"C'mon. You fathead."

"Stop! Just tell me who *she* is!"

"You know. That—I mean... "

I wonder where their megalomaniac this-and-that-spilling gossip begins and eventually ends?

Most of the women's gossip finds its source in the quiet and secluded lives of others coming to settle in the neighborhood. Those others are almost invisible and nobody knows who they are. The Akou-kurou-gai was a perfectly hidden place for those who have been shunned by the world. Diverse kinds of people—women, men, the elderly and youth with *a history*—live in this place and those huts, wandering the alley day and night. They by nature pretend to be crazy, bothering pedestrians, appropriate behavior for residents in this alley.

And *she* may have been one of them.

My memory of sorrow unchanged, I can recall the same strangeness when I first saw her. It was rather a feeling of *déjà vu* than a strangeness. It was unusual for a child of less than five years old to have such a feeling, but the sensation was so clear as if it had been engraved in my senses. Yes, I had met her in my memory, which extended through my mind just as a sandy beach in sunset. I saw her back while she was sitting on the beach gazing at the ocean. It was the feeling evoked through the memory far away in the past.

I wonder how many times I had wandered about the Akou-kurou-gai before what happened next.

I had been roaming in the alley in the twilight, all by myself, ambling without intention. As usual, I think I heard women's ceaseless gossip in whispering voices, and I remember how the rough resonances of their voices irritated my eardrums.

Shaking its head once in a while, the child kept walking.

The petals of bougainvillea over the fence were colored in blue from the evening darkness. Struck by the bright purple colors of the flowers, the child traced the line of bougainvillea along the fence until the child turned around the corner and stopped. A strange-lump like something leaking out of the twilight caught the child's eyes.

Beside piles of lumbers or junk, a lumpy shadow emerged. It reminded the child of a meditating trainee monk or a statue thrown to the side of the road. It, however, turned out to be a woman. It was clear, even to the eyes of a child from the distance, that the woman wasn't young and had a round shape. In half-sitting posture, the woman faced the road, all by herself, as if she was planting herself firmly on the ground. The image was so striking that the child couldn't help approaching her.

She looked even weirder up close. She supported her posture in a delicate balance, with the hem of her skirt tucked up in her naked thighs, arms on the knees, and bent slightly forward. It seemed she was neither meditating nor enjoying the cool evening. She was just there—all by herself. Her face was powdered thick, and the white spots from the sweat here and there on her face made her look like a clown. Her eyes were those of dead fish. So dull. She had no expression as such. None. She had no particular reaction to the child who came close to her. As if she was a museum exhibit, the woman sat there just like that. There was an assailing smell about her—a smell of some kind of burning steam or something given off from dry soil.

A strange stillness surrounded the woman's body that was giving off a smell of the soil.

Overwhelmed by these things, the child watched her, wondering if she might not be a real human. Neither tottering nor moving her half-sitting posture, the woman was holding herself so still that she looked as if she wasn't breathing. She looked like a clod of dirt.

An idea came to the child. The child felt like standing beside the half-sitting woman. The child went behind the woman, slowly lowered itself, putting its chin forward a little, stood firmly on the ground, and braced itself motionless. Then something strange happened.

As if teasing a foolish behavior of an innocent bystander, the woman started shaking her buttocks lightly and quickly.

"What?" the child asked. A voice squeezed out of the throat and tickled the child's ear: a voice that rhythmically corresponded to the woman's physical motion, deep as if crawling from the ground, and yet distant. The child got startled and was driven to come around to the woman's front. The child looked into her face. The woman, however, didn't seem to have opened her mouth. Her expression, too, remained unchanged. The child tilted its head to one side in question, went back behind the woman, and lowered its body again in a half-sitting posture close to her. Soon again, the woman's buttocks started shaking quickly and rhythmically. The voice was also heard again. As soon as the child came around to look into woman's face, the voice and her shaking stopped. The child sat low again. Then there was heard that voice. It was a kind of whistling sound like a lullaby or a wailing aria pushed out as collective disjointed sounds.

Yoooi yoooi, yoi, yoi yoi
Hohooi, hohooi, hoi, hoi, hoi
Aari yohooi, yoi, yoi, yoi
Hohooi, hohooi, yoooi, yoooi,
Aari yohooi, hoi, hoi, hoi

I think the voice was flowing like that.

The child could do nothing but listen to the voice that sounded like something calling from woman's back, which looked like a mound of soil. The child's ears were vulnerable to the voice until it finally sank deeply into hidden folds of memory.

At last, the mud woman made a clear move. She started changing slowly out of her half-sitting posture, which made her look as if she were enchanted by a spell that could never be broken or as if she were showing off her super-human mastery of not making even the slightest move. It was also as if a lump of shadow finally melted into particles of thick darkness slowly falling through the air.

She suddenly rose, pushing herself with hands on her knees and slowly bent forward. Her head was bent between her legs. She stood as if finishing her business over a squatting toilet, and the hem of her skirt—ample fabric tucked in between her legs—loosened and dropped. Then she lost her balance, dizzy, and turned around to face the sitting child.

The next sequence was obscene. Her skirt, like an open parachute, billowed in the air and fell down over and covered child's head. Underneath the skirt, the child's eyes and nostrils were hit by an intense stench. It came so suddenly that the child had no chance to cover its nose. Now the woman completely lost her balance and fell upside down. With a heavy sound of her body hitting the ground, the soft parachute skirt this time billowed inside out and covered the lying woman's upper body. The child was astounded at the sight of the woman's exposed lower body and hopped up with its eyes and nostrils wide opened.

A strange landscape spread before the child. On a white sand beach embracing an isolated island on the ocean lay two pieces of slick decolorized driftwood. This was the patter that the child read. The woman wore no under-garments. Under the naked mound of her lower waist, exposed was a slit of bivalvia. Her pubic area had no hair. There was not even the footprint of a plover, the hamachidori, chirping or sobbing homesickness.[6] Looking at the beach on her body, so simple and sorrowful, deserted and washed by waves, the child made firm fists.

Slowly turning around, the woman stood up sticking out her buttocks.

Once she stood up, the woman was rather large and tall. Her move-ments were, however, soft and elegant, when both of her hands brushed off and straightened the hem of her skirt. Scattered in the lower area of her skirt was a geometrical mosaic oddly colored in bright lime green. Every time she brushed off her skirt, the pattern appeared here and there breaking into smiles. The woman began walking unsteadily, and the movement of her hands seemed as if she was shooing away the child. But, on the contrary, the child followed her, like a stalker.

On Akou-kurou-gai, night falls with a rhythm of thick rain drops trick-ling down from the eaves. Poto, poto, poto. Night falls like the thickness that

—
6
hamachidori
means *plover,* and it's also a title of an Okinawan folksong in which a plover is compared to a young woman who was sold into prostitution sobbing in homesickness like a bird chirping. Another version of interpretation of the song compares a plover with Okinawan immigrants sob-bing in homesickness. Okinawa is well known as a community that has sent a number of immigrants all over the world since the nineteenth century.

increases as a child makes its first step, or it falls like a lullaby that makes a lost child ever more insecure.

Jiri jiri jiri jiri... jiri jiri jiri jiri...

A sizzling voice is heard. It could be made by someone trying to spread particles of insecurity and discontent. The sound may come from someone tittering on the corner end of the alley. It may not be intended to be heard, but it actually falls from the sky through an amplifier and gets on the nerves of the people, busy getting ready for the night.

Jiri jiri jiri jiri jiri jiri...

The sizzling voice continues on and on. Finally, someone who was cleaning has had enough, breaks the broom into half, kicks the bucket, and rushes out to the alley, sliding the door with a fierce sound. "Hey! You! You are getting on my nerves. Unsettling my innards. What's the matter with you making that jiri jiru jiri jiri?"

"... yat... yat . . . yat... "

"Oh god. This time 'yat, yat'? Look you're turning pale to the forehead and foaming at the mouth."

"Jiri jiri jiri... yat... yat... yat."

"Stop it. 'Cause your jiri jiri is not only your problem anymore. Tell me why you're jiri jiri-ing!"

"......"

"What happened to you?"

"How can I tell such a thing to others?"

"Such a thing or that thing doesn't matter. If you keep holding the nasty in your stomach, your belly will swell like a balloon, and you're gonna get sick."

"I'm already sick. I can't do anything about this sickness, this heartache."

"Heartache? What's the big deal? Your heart aches because you are alive. Anyway whatever nasty you have in your stomach, you'd better spit it out."

"......"

"Now, why don't you say something? I'm listening to you. I am."

"......"

"Hey, if you keep your mouth shut like this, the nasty will grow bigger and bigger in your belly until it gets unruly. Then you'll become a loony."

"......"

"Come on. Do you really wanna be a loony?"

"I tell you what... "

"Tell me what?"

"I dream... every night."

"What dream? So what? Even that dog lying there dreams."

"I wonder what kind of dream a dog has."

"Don't know. You got to ask the dog."

"Mine is about killing a man. Every night, in my dream, I'm beating a man to death."

"I know what you mean. I perfectly understand how you want to get rid of your ex…"

"No, in my case, they are strangers I never met and never touched in my life. I randomly…"

"You mean you smash and kill men randomly, one after another? What, that's just random killing, like an indiscriminate terrorism. You are evil, though you don't look like you're a murderer. I wonder you may be the type whose potential grudge against men is more intense than a normal woman's."

"Po-ten-ti-al gr-dge…?"

"Nothing. Forget what I said. No need for heartache. If you want to kill men, just kill them. Don't worry and kill as many as you want. It's not real—just happening in your dream anyway."

"……"

Their conversation carries on nonsensically, perhaps only good for getting rid of pent-up frustrations, ceaselessly discharging in the dripping darkness through a back alley where everything accumulates, even as the child drifts after the mud woman.

The woman walked slowly, swinging herself side to side. The child sensed that the woman was heading north on the alley, draped with thickening blue-purple darkness and the weight of raindrops. The season was the beginning of summer, for sure. Yet the child somehow thought the woman headed north because its arms and legs started shivering from the blowing wind as it walked on north. But the northern edge of the town ended at an earthy hill before the dump.

The woman walked as if she were dragging the bottom of the alley. She turned many corners, dragged herself through the street where people busied themselves before their night businesses, until she came to an area where there were no stores or houses. On this side of the hill where the rock surface stood close behind, there were three or four flattened roofs exposed to the sun's rays. The woman stopped at one of the houses, in front of its white-washed wooden wall. There was a sliding door, perhaps made by cutting out a part of the wall. It was barely large enough for one adult to enter. The woman slid open the tight squeaking door, gi gi, and lowered her body to enter slowly through it. When she lowered herself, she made a slight gesture of turning around. The child thought the woman might be responding to someone behind her. The woman's gesture was loose enough to let the child believe it was up to the follower to decide whether she meant "buzz off" or "come in."

The child had no hesitation. With a swiftness of a draft, it slipped inside right in time before the wooden door was shut. At the moment of entrance, the child heard behind it a shriek-like sound of wind.

There was an empty confined space. It was a tiny fortress to defend against an enemy attack, a hideaway. It seemed more like a hole than a room. There was no place to take off shoes before stepping up to a wooden floor as the entrance was connected directly to the room. Removing her flip-flops in a free and easy manner at the space only inches from the earth, the woman slowly entered the shack.

Pressing its back against the wooden wall, the child stood transfixed.

It may have been too early in the day to put on the light. The inside looked darker than dusk for the eyes just coming in from outside. The indoor space looked narrow, empty, yet somehow deep. There was only one window high on the wall to the right. A dim light reaching inside through that window and through the slit of the half-closed sliding door made a few pieces of furniture-like objects in the room visible. The dingy curtains were hung. On a low table were miscellaneous goods. These things certainly indicated that the shack did have a human occupant.

The woman did not pay attention to the child that followed her without invitation. The woman may have had an incredible sense of responsiveness to the external because her behavior hid her inner feelings, as if her disenchanted body moved regardless of her will. The woman grabbed some clothing. She looked fumbling around her front with one hand and disappeared in the next moment. She may have been absorbed into the wall.

The child was again transfixed. Its eyes were already wide-open but became more focused, trying to understand what happened. Then the child heard a sound—the sound of someone bathing. Sounds of splashing water continued at intervals. It seemed on the other side of the wall the woman was bathing. The child glued to the entrance door and listened to the sound.

Then, suddenly someone banged at the door.

Bang... bang, bang, bang!

The frightened child jumped aside, and someone with a grating voice rushed in.

"Hey! Are you alive in there?" The voice came from a plump woman giving off a greasy smell and hastily stirred up the atmosphere. Paying no attention to the child standing beside her, the plump woman vigorously yelled again into the hollow. "I brought you a supper. I cooked too much soki soup.[7] It's just leftovers, but I wanted you to have it and invigorate yourself."

So she said, impudently treading into the room. She was holding a large steamy soup bowl in her hands.

"You've been looking stupefied on the street for hours in the midday. Everyone talks about you saying, 'She shouldn't wait for a runaway boyfriend; it's no use,' or 'No, after all, she is like that because she has no guts to kill herself,' and someone even said, 'She's as good as dead.' You know the women here don't know how to entertain themselves except by gossiping, and that's why they can't help spreading half-truths, what's there, what's not. Even if you happened to hear some bad rumors, you got to ignore it, pretend you didn't hear."

Sounds of splashing water continued. The woman might not have been listening to the plump woman as she didn't respond. The plump woman went on and on as she wished. "But how long are you gonna be stupefied like

—
7
soki soup

a popular homemade Okinawan dish of pork ribs *(soki)* in broth along with vegetables and pieces of seaweed that? Some people worry about you, thinking that you will soon be melted down by the heat from burning tida. Well, we should ignore such uncalled-for gossip and worries. Anyway, eat everything, and build up yourself; otherwise you can't do your work, can you?"

The plump woman went on and on. In her compulsive talk, which she must have believed was the only way to manage their communication, there were insensitivity and cruelty in the disguise of kindness. The child felt it, but learning that the mud woman was actually not completely isolated like a pebble or a piece of dirt thrown away to the corner of the alley somehow made the child feel relieved.

The plump woman kept chattering while her hands were restlessly reorganizing the things on the table. Judging from her impertinent manner, the plump woman may have been woman's landlord or employer. The plump woman put what she brought on the table. After she spoke nonsense into the wall, then abruptly yelled, I'll be back and see you again, and took off. The plump woman seemed to notice the child crouching at the entrance, but she had no time to be bothered, and she neither said anything nor gave an inquiring look as she rushed off.

The vinegary smell of soki filled the room. The child slowly moved into the room, not attracted by the food smell but drawn in by some thickness that filled the space.

The child sat down in front of the table absentmindedly. Watching the steam from the bowl, the child realized the splashing sounds had stopped. The child turned around and saw the woman standing there, casually wrapping herself in yukata.[8] The exposed part of her skin was moist and sleek. The child hurriedly stood up.

She gave a look at the child while she was nonchalantly straightening the collar of her yukata. Her glance was not focused, but the face she directed toward the child was unexpectedly clean and handsome after the clown-like thick make-up was completely washed away. The child felt followed by the woman's loose gaze: soft, but not smiling. For the first time, the child knew how it felt being watched. The child should have felt guilty about trespassing, but instead, stared back into the woman's stagnant eyes in her featureless face that made her stout body look feeble.

A subtle smile like a twitch showed on her mouth. All of sudden the air shook. In the next moment, the woman grabbed the bowl and threw it fiercely out through the slit of half-open door. The ceramic bowl crashed against the ground and broke in to pieces. The vinegary smell of meat soup spread. The woman's sudden violence, her act of throwing back pushy benevolence, however, made perfect sense to the child.

A strange time passed.

The woman didn't gesture to force the small trespasser to leave, though the child had been occupying the space for quite a while. The woman

—

8

yukata
a cotton kimono
casually worn
every evening after
a bath

neither seemed to mind nor felt like speaking to it. The silent woman showed the next move.

She quickly took off her yukata then slipped into it again. Without tying a belt, she began to step forward slowly, dragging the hem.

She began to walk along the edges of the eight-tatami room,[9] slowly from one corner to other. She walked with her feet scuffing the floor. Bending herself backward, holding her jaw to point upward, with an expression as if she were looking up to something, she walked in the square room tracing an oval. She sometimes leaned her shoulders slowly to one side, stood upright, scuffed the floor, then dragged herself to move forward again. She had walked the same way dragging the bottom of the alley, but this time she was moving into the hollow within the house. You could say this was both abrupt and prepared. In any case, the woman's silent performance, which made no sense to the child, continued.

The woman danced for the child, her sole audience. She turned around and around and around, and her repetitive movements in the small room—dragging herself, jutting her jaw forward—caught both the performer and her audience into the depth of an inner self. The child felt repelled, frozen in a sense of isolation. The child backed away inch by inch to the entrance and, from there, watched her, the woman who turned slowly and slowly.

The lights were not yet turned on.

The time was located in darkness outside and dimness inside fading into each other. As if she herself were melting into the blended darkness, the woman abruptly stopped her movements. She slipped her yukata off and cast it away. She stripped herself naked, pearling on her silky sleek skin. She sat down limply with one knee drawn up. Her hand fumbled behind searching for a fan. She fanned herself softly. A pale expressionless open field between her legs stared out. She dropped the fan to the ground. She placed her empty hand on her knee and returned into a clod of dirt that had been stripped of her costume. Flexibly wiggling her nude body with a big belly, she performed in the dusk as if showing off her special art.

The child didn't turn away its eyes; watching was its only choice.

Nothing special, however, happened between the mud woman and the child no matter how long they shared time together. Except for a few moments, if any, moments of encounter occurred through shared lines of sight, staring incoherently at the same midair, gazes twisted, cut away, blurred.

Outside the wooden sliding door, darkness dripped incessantly.

In the rhythm of darkness tapping ceaselessly on someone's back, something like a pale blue and moist fog began to circle around the hollow lit by a stagnant light. The darkness outside invaded along with a sound. It gradually filled the hollow. It wrapped around the child, clouding its eyes. The child's eyes, however, continued to sense the sliminess of the mysterious body, open yet vulnerable and sunk in the sediment of stillness, crawling from the bottom of the hollow.

9

Japanese rooms are measured by the number of tatami mats contained in a room. One standard tatami-mat, or one *jo,* is 85.5 centimeters wide and 179 centimeters in length (about 33.5 by 70.5 inches)

How much time had passed before that moment? In the next moment, the child's open eyes caught a grimy shadow dropped there, tracing the trail from the window. There remained a flicker of the woman's silhouette, which convinced the child that in a moment of inattention she may have leaped instantaneously to the other space.

Still, I waited. I waited in the alley as darkness fell faster and faster, murmuring yet invisible stories in yet silent voices, hutsu, hutsu, hutsu, singing out like, ho-oy, ho-oy.

The darkness fell incessantly. Tapped by a heavy rhythm, the poto poto of dripping darkness, my eyes and ears were exhausted, left open for stories yet to come.

—
"Akou-kurou Genshi-kou."
Subaru, 28.9 (2006): 240–52
Translated by Ikue Kina with thanks to Karen Tei Yamashita for her contributions.

A Landscape of Words: The One in between *Appa, Anna* and *Obaa*
Tami Sakiyama

In poet Taeko Tomioka's collection of essays, *Nihon* and *Nihonjin (Japan and Japanese),* Tomioka[1] describes her attitude toward words:[2]

> *Though I understand that the language spoken in the Kansai[3] area of Japan still retains many pronunciations from old-time Japanese, I would feel it was farfetched to judge that my everyday language is the old Yamato.[4] My personal uneasiness… comes from a sense of insecurity and uneasiness when reminded that I speak such lousy Japanese when I go out of the sphere of my dialect, where I have been residing for more than twenty years.*

The "sense of insecurity and uneasiness" that Tomioka, who lived in the world of Kansai dialect, felt in the "standard" language of Tokyo might further be paraphrased as follows: "I would feel this chaos and insecurity only when speaking. My dialect would never confuse my writing."

Comparing her with Okinawan writers who have been afflicted by the issue of a "standard language" and a "dialect," Tomioka's statement is so clearcut that we Okinawan writers cannot help sighing. However, no matter how far the distance between a local place (margin) and a metropolitan area (center), whether or not one's language is standard or dialect, there is always a gap between the written and the spoken languages because there is a self-evident difference between the "spoken words" that disappear as soon as they're articulated and the "written words" that have a structure to be preserved. Dialects, then—the spoken words of an indigenous language—are fated to die out by the authority of "written words." Even when dialects survive, they are subject to constant change and transformation.

1
Taeko Tomioka
well-known Japanese woman poet, novelist, and critic, born in Osaka in 1935

2
The Japanese word for "words" is *kotoba*. Sakiyama deliberately uses the word *kotoba* in her essay as she seems to want to distinguish *kotoba*, or words, from "language" as a linguistic system, or from "dialect" that immediately presumes "standard." In this translation, therefore, I use the English words for the places where Sakiyama uses *kotoba*

3
Kansai
the western metropolitan area as well as the old capital cities of Japan, including Osaka, Kyoto, Nara, and Kobe

---

4
Yamato
the old name for Japan

5
Uchinaa is an Okinawan way of saying "Okinawa," and **guchi** means "mouth" and "tongue." **Uchinaaguchi,** therefore, means "Okinawan language," but emphasizes spoken language.

Okinawan language survives at a distance from the center and thus successfully preserves many features of the old Yamato language. Therefore, it may be possible to emphasize the special qualities of the Okinawan language and to claim the necessity of preserving and continuing it through education. The lesson we have learned through our painful history of being discriminated against gives us every right to do so. I believe our struggles for expression are the result of how we have been driven to seek our expressions in our everyday language, *shimakotoba* "island's words,"[6] after experiencing the uneasiness, humiliation, palpable untruth, awkwardness, and hollowness when forced to express ourselves in standard Japanese as if we could snuggle up to its authority.

In my case, things were more complicated. My language was *shimakotoba,* but that didn't mean a single kind of dialect. I grew up in a village community in the western part of Iriomote Island,[7] which was a colony of the immigrants from outside the island after World War II. Next to my home village was the community of coal miners who had come from Yamato—mainly from Kyushu—to settle there eventually. The linguistic environment where my *shimakotoba* was formed was, I would say, a chaotic one. Oftentimes, the villagers would laugh at each other because one would think the other was speaking a weird language. At home, I had parents who spoke in Miyako words and in the neighborhood, there were other family members who would speak in Hatoma[8] words. From the house behind ours, we would hear our neighbors speaking in high-pitched Sonai[9] words. My everyday language, which was formed in this kind of linguistic environment, was switched naturally to the formal standard language once my day at school began. Among many languages in my life in those days, I was especially attracted by Hatoma words spoken by my neighbors, perhaps because I was feeling some kind of exoticism. Their language would shake my heart sometimes, just as any foreign language will do.

Appa is one of those words. The grandmother of the Kedashiro family, called *appa* by her six grandchildren, was a pleasant person who would sing *Densaa-bushi*[10] in a nice and carefree voice whenever there was an occasion. My own grandmother, called *anna* by my parents, had passed away before I was old enough to remember. I may have seen my *Anna* in *Appa* from the Kedashiro family. Actually, a grandmother is *nma* in Miyako words and *anna* is for a mother. I was mistaken to believe that grandmother should be called *anna,* as I remembered my mother would call her own mother *anna*. The word *anna* touched my heart, perhaps because of this memory.

I have invented two written words, assigning letters to each spoken word—阿ツ婆 for *appa* and 阿ン母 for *anna*—and exchanged, intermixed, and finally started using them in my novel writing. Almost thirty years have passed since I had parted with those whom those words referred to. I do feel there is a kind of impulse within myself, which compels me to use these words in my writing. Both *appa* and *anna* had been lost phonetic sounds for a long time, and when I came to realize how significant these lost words were despite being

—
6
shima
literally means "island," both in Japanese and Okinawan. But **shimakotoba** is a colloquial expression in Okinawan, and, more precisely, should be pronounced **shimakutuba** as *kotoba* in Okinawan should be *kutuba*.

—
7
Iriomote Island
belongs to the Yaeyama Islands, located about 300 miles southwest of Naha, on Okinawa's main island. Miyako Island is located about 190 miles southwest of Naha.

—
8
Hatoma Island
a small remote island located about 3.6 miles north of Iriomote Island.

—
9
Sonai
a small community in the western part of Iriomote Island.

—
10
Densaa-bushi
a folk song of the Yaeyama Islands about the stories of old-time neighborhood communities. The song *"densaa"* means "the words to transmit," not only to the community but also to future generations.

lost, I became obsessed with the impulsive idea that I wanted to write down these words by some means or other. Now I often feel that this obsession still continues to be a source of energy when I write.

Today I don't call anyone *appa* or *anna*. Actually, when I think about it carefully, I don't recall ever calling anyone by those words. If I ever articulate any word that could equate to those two words, it would be *obaa,* which is the more generally accepted Okinawan word for "grandmother." While *appa* and *anna* have darker connotations, the word *obaa* has a more cheerful sound, as it fits the general audience's popular image of what it describes. Hoping to benefit from the vigor of the sound, I make a joke about myself these days: "I'm an *obaa* now, and I can't count on my willpower to keep myself going like young people do. If I force myself, look, I get a lower-back pain like this. Gee, I'm such an *obaa.*"

The point I'd like to emphasize by this comment, of course, is not that I am well aware of my aging in my mid-forties. I imagined myself as an *obaa* because I do want to pour the vigor coming from the sound of the word *obaa* into my poor, feeble body. The same manner of loading the words with desire, in my case, can be applied to my novel writing. Thus, the words *appa, anna,* and *obaa* in my novel do not refer to anything with real substance, but they may refer to something dead and lost or refer to the hope and love for something yet to come.

On the other hand, I want to enjoy the charm of plain Japanese language. The split desire for the words confuses me not only when I speak but also when I write, yet I guess I have no choice but to keep writing about this very confusion within myself.

—

From *The Place Where Words Emerge*
Translated by Ikue Kina

The Silver Motorcycle

Katsunori Yamazato

1

She died nearly ten years ago, toward the end of a summer when it had hardly rained at all. Like sparrows at sunset, people had flocked together and gossiped about how she had been a little strange.

That summer, everything dried up. She had been proud of the big rubber tree at her gate, its leaves covered with fine white dust. The leaves turned yellow, then gradually brown as they fluttered in the wind until at last they fell straight down with a dry, rustling sound onto the pavement in front of the garage. And they kept falling, one after another, whenever the south wind blew hard, carrying with it a vague feeling of nostalgia.

The sofa in her living room was also covered with dust. She kept the curtains drawn, but the dust that blew off the street behind her house got in through small openings in the windows.

I worked for her that summer, taking care of her yard every other week. She had enough money from what Harry left her and got a check from America once a month. She couldn't spend it all by herself and was never stingy when it came to my wages. A little patience and I could get that motorcycle. "Just wait," I told myself, "and that shining 125-cc bike will be yours." I'd found the second-hand bike at a motorcycle shop near my house. The owner, a friend of my father, said he would keep it for me until I saved up enough money. The woman I worked for knew why I had taken the job in her yard, so she always gave me more than we had agreed to. My father was going to put up most of the money for the bike.

I always avoided the woman when I went to work. I tried to stay out in the yard as much as possible because I didn't like the way she looked straight into my eyes when she talked to me. It was my mother who made me take that job. "You should feel sorry for your aunt," she told me.

In those days, I was mad at myself for being so shy. I'd get embarrassed because I couldn't quite figure out what she was saying to me and would answer her sullenly.

"Is it raining? It must be raining."

"No."

"It must be raining. You'll catch a cold if you get wet."

"No, it's not raining."

"Not raining? You must be kidding."

"Take a look for yourself."

She spoke from beside the window where she sat with her eyes shut tight. I had tried to sound mean, telling her to "take a look for yourself," but my voice had turned hoarse when the words came out. Even so, they'd had an effect, and I could see her back twitching. She knew I was watching her and wasn't about to give up the argument. Though she seemed to be searching for the words to throw back at me, she was obviously beaten, unable even to look out toward the yard. After sitting up very straight for a while without saying anything, at last she pulled the curtains shut and withdrew inside the house. Victorious, I glared at her from the other side of the curtains. "There's no way it's going to rain," I told myself. "But if it does, let it pour down on this thirty-nine-year-old woman and wash away this obsession of hers."

As I pushed the lawn mower, I wondered why I felt this strange antipathy toward her. She had started talking about rain a couple of years after Harry died.

Harry never left Okinawa and ended up dying here. After coming back from Korea, he'd moved into one of the houses built for Americans on the hilltop in Ginowan. Years afterward, he came back early from Vietnam, got out of the army, and turned into a hopeless alcoholic. He would scare little children at the local clinic where he went to the doctor. When he saw a child crying, he would dance up to the kid, wagging his hips, and blow whisky breath in the kid's face. Or sometimes he would gently bite a kid's ear and yell, "Who's giving Mama a hard time?" Of course, the doctor told him to stop drinking, but he was always dead drunk by the time he got to the clinic, making the kids bawl and their mothers worry. And when he got tired of that, he would amuse himself talking to a black man who was just as drunk, also waiting to see the doctor. One day, a nurse called the woman to complain, and after that she went with Harry to the doctor. He'd sit quietly whenever she was with him.

But now the black man got bored. A fat man with a thick neck, he would come over to wag his butt and twist his torso in front of them. The woman reached out with her left hand and tried to push him away. But he only laughed in a low voice and twisted his hips even more feverishly, dancing nimbly with his butt pointed toward them. She couldn't stand it anymore, she said, and tried to hit that big butt of his. But the black man was too quick, and her hand hit only air. Now Harry broke into loud laughter, pounding the sofa with his right hand.

And the black man laughed, too, his whole body convulsing. Soon she was left alone in the waiting room, exposed to everyone's probing eyes.

Whenever she talked about this, her eyes got a little wild and she cursed the black man.

Harry died suddenly.

She insisted he had died because of the black man. "Harry always thought he might die at any time," my mother said to her, and then added in a whisper, "That's why he told you to go to the hospital."

"No, he just didn't want that baby," she replied, tugging gently at her hair.

"I'll never understand why he had to die in Okinawa, coming here all the way from that fine country of his," said my mother as she munched on peanuts coated with brown sugar.

In those days, I couldn't tell whether the woman was sad or not. It seemed as if she were trying hard to look calm, and she came often to see my mother, but I never saw her crying. The only difference was that whenever the wind picked up or there was a slight murmuring outside, she would always ask if it was raining and didn't seem to care if her question interrupted other people.

The leaves rustling on the row of palm trees in the yard did sound a lot like the showers that come suddenly on a summer evening. But she was the only one who always mistook the wind for rain. In the late afternoon, whenever the withered banana leaves swung listlessly, her ears would be deceived by the wind. And when she realized it wasn't raining, she would stare at us intently.

Drinking coffee, she would chat for hours. Sometimes she went to see a *yuta* fortune-teller and then brought my mother the latest news. Harry had ignored the important news from the *yuta,* so now she talked about it excitedly to my mother, who was always an eager listener.

My mother, who burned incense twice a month in front of the gas stove and prayed to the fire goddess, would encourage the woman to tell her everything the *yuta* had said. And my mother often nodded with satisfaction at the *yuta's* interpretation of things that had been worrying her. "Well, that's a relief," she would say, firmly committing the *yuta's* words to memory. "It was just as I'd imagined."

But for the woman it was all just talk, and she never followed the *yuta's* instructions. Whenever my mother tried to set the day for a pilgrimage, the woman would complain that walking made her tired, adding that even if they drove, it was still a long walk to the family's tomb, a hollow carved out of a cliff surrounded by rocks. Besides, she said, the silk trees growing along the path would scratch our arms and shoulders, and she got goose bumps just thinking about those mosquitoes that were nearly the size of your fingertip. "When Harry was alive, he never let me open the screen even for a second." She could think up any number of excuses for not going. And my mother used to say that it was just a waste of money if you didn't really believe what the *yuta* said.

—

yuta
a spiritual guide, in Okinawan culture

In those days, I was rather serious about my studies and stayed home every day. When I got tired of studying, I'd have a cup of coffee and listen to them talk. I came to think of her as "that stubborn, rain-crazed woman" and tried to avoid eye contact with her. Sometimes she teased me and would say something out of the blue. "You have a nice masculine voice. The girls must like that." Then, when she stared at me, I got all flustered and clammed up. My mother winked at me, stifling a laugh, and said, "He's just shy, you know," which made me mad. Sometimes, all at once, the woman would start talking feverishly. She would speak about things from deep inside the burning core of her memory and seemed to forget about everything around her, including us, as if she were talking to herself.

"I sure hope it'll rain soon. Remember when we went to the hospital? Ever since then, I've felt the rain coming. It's strange, though, because that was so long ago. I know the rain will be heavy, and before the downpour, it will get very dark. We'll see the lightning flashes all around, and the thunder will shake everything. The rain will start far away, but I can feel it coming closer and closer to where I'm standing. I can smell the earth now as big raindrops begin to hit my face. It hurts so much that I have to open my eyes, but I can't see a thing through the heavy rain. I'll catch the thick drops in my palms, cupping them together until rain pours from my hands. Harry told me to go to the hospital, so I had to, but ever since then I've been feeling that a heavy rain like this would start any time. Well, he never came to visit me there. I guess he thought it would be all right because you were with me. It was humid that day. Now, if it rains…"

Unless my mother yelled at her to stop, she would go on and on like this, talking to herself. Whenever she started, my mother always tried to divert her attention. "Let's talk about what we did after the war," she would say. "About when we came out from hiding in the hills."

Then they would sip coffee and talk about my grandfather, sometimes cursing him, sometimes pitying him.

"By now there must be lots of fruit on the Indian almond tree behind our old house. Remember how we used to eat it? I want to go pick some now, but I feel like that old drunkard is still there."

"That's no way to talk about him. Everyone becomes a god after they die."

"That's easy for you to say, since you moved away to Koza after you got married. That old drunk was always waking me up in the middle of the night. Mother died too soon, while Seiichi and Keiko were still crawling around."

My grandmother died of encephalitis five years after the war. She died singing "coloring the flowers, coloring the flowers" in a soft, clear voice. According to my mother, the memory of that voice and her song haunted my grandfather, and he became a hopeless drunk.

After my grandmother died, the woman worked for about a year under the big radar dish at the American base on top of Mount Yae, near the town of Motobu. She washed and dried soldiers' uniforms, always noticing that Harry's was the biggest. Harry was kind and generous to her. It wasn't that she was tired of paying for my grandfather's liquor or taking care of her little brother and sister. So she didn't think it was wrong to say yes when Harry asked her to marry him.

But when she told my grandfather, he grabbed the pole he used to carry baggage and tried to club Harry with it. Then she ran out of the house, following Harry, and never went home again.

My grandfather died of appendicitis. He had tried to ignore the pain, dulling it with liquor, and got peritonitis. He died in his futon, sucking a thick sugarcane leaf. There was already a bad smell coming from his guts, and it filled the house. He wasn't really the kind of man to die miserably like that, my mother had said. She came back after his death to put away the futon while the men there laughed and drank.

These are the things I heard them talking about as that summer came to an end.

That summer had constantly betrayed the woman as the days came and went uneventfully. The typhoons that suck in all the energy and then explode off the water skirted the island many times. But the heavy rains she was waiting for never came. The ocean, dyed a dark red in the light of the setting sun, rolled on and on with a sense of promise. And the clouds skirting southward thrilled her. At night they would sweep across the sky, sucked in by the approaching typhoon. And behind them the moon shone, flickering like the giant inflamed eye of the universe as it gazed down at humanity and its puny rebellions.

But the typhoon only pretended to attack and retreated without striking. One of them could easily have landed, raping the island, yet even if it had, the woman would have just stared calmly into its face. But then it would only pass by, front paws extended, back stooped over. Or it would run out of breath and drift away, panting toward the distant southern seas.

3

She always acted bossy inside her house, except that the telephone would startle her. But if it were a wrong number, she would chew out the caller. A man with a gravelly voice dialed the wrong number many times that summer, maybe because it had been so hot.

She liked to make fun of Gravel Voice. He seemed sincere when offering a lengthy apology. But her voice, when she answered, "That's perfectly all right," sounded so phony it made me angry.

Sometimes, though, Gravel Voice seemed to learn from his mistakes. He could apparently tell by the tone of her voice whether he should apologize politely or just hang up quietly. When he didn't apologize, I would always have to listen to her bad-mouthing him. He even seemed to know that he should hang up on the days she spent manicuring her nails over and over. On those days, I would be sure to stay outside in the far corner of the yard.

I just couldn't figure her out. She would stop drinking her freshly brewed coffee to complain that the clock's chimes were too loud. She accused the clock of playing innocent while it cut everything short, ticking toward some final goal. The clock fooled everyone, she said, because it looked so ordinary. Then, grumbling about how we were all being deceived even as we sipped our coffee, she would empty her cup into the sink.

"Listen, it's a race, okay? You'll be tricked if you just keep sipping coffee. The moment you close your eyes and say, "Ah, that's good," you've already fallen way behind. Doesn't it just wear you out, trying to keep up with everything?"

"But I heard things were easier for you, living by yourself."

"Who said that?"

"My mother."

"That stupid woman."

She always talked in riddles. But all I could think of was the shiny 125-cc silver motorbike, so for me, the things she said and did were just a nuisance. I was supposed to report them all to my mother, but there was no way I was going to try deciphering all that mumbo-jumbo she threw at me.

Stripping off my undershirt, mowing the grass, gulping down water from the hose, then splashing the water on my face, neck, and shoulders all helped to relieve the oppressive feeling I got from talking to her.

Summer grass grows faster than you realize. Every other week, when I went there, I was surprised at how tall it had gotten. But she never cared about the grass. It would grow very early in the morning or very late at night, while she was sleeping. Just after she fell fast asleep or before she woke up, those blades fed off of the sunlight they snatched during the day. Or, giggling among themselves, they imbibed what they could find groping inside the dry soil. The summer grasses, too, seemed to be outwitting her.

I pushed the lawn mower hard when I cut the grass. The wilder the grass grew, the harder I pushed. The motorcycle was shining brilliantly in the sun, in a future not too far off. Stretching out my arm, I could almost touch it. Every time I pushed the lawn mower, I advanced a notch along the flow of time. The stiffness of each stem of grass only made those notches more tangible. When I cut the grass, I held my breath and felt I was controlling the flow of time. Cutting the grass was all I had to do, I thought. But now I know I was wrong. That summer, I was determined to cut down every blade of grass in her yard until I got that 125-cc motorbike, no matter how uncomfortable I felt talking to her and how quickly the thriving grass outwitted her.

Toward the end of August, when its growth slowed, she started wearing gaudy clothes in bright primary colors and letting her hair grow long. I would walk straight to her yard, pull out the lawn mower, and try to avoid talking to her.

Since it was too hot during the day, the best time to work was between five and seven in the evening. Mowing the grass on a hill in her yard, I would see the sun sinking over Kerama Island, squatting out in the ocean. A little past seven, the red-hot sun would start melting. As it dipped toward the horizon,

The Silver Motorcycle   Katsunori Yamazato

its core turned fluid and it could no longer hold its neat midday perimeter. The cloud castle towering in the western sky seemed to catch fire, and the white cement walls on the island smoldered silently. A lonely pine tree writhed as it burned, and a coral reef emerging from under the sea seemed annoyed that it had dried up. That's when I noticed that the upper half of my body, too, had gotten burned. Feeling for a moment like the whole universe was on fire, I watched the bloated sun sink into the horizon.

Seeing everything aflame as I stood leaning against the lawn mower, I repeated many times in a small voice, "Oh, gods, if we're all going to die, please let the red-hot sun burn us up."

It was around this time that her hair got really long. Toward evening, she took a shower. Then she would sit with her shiny dark hair wrapped around her slender neck, gazing at herself in the mirror. Her bedroom faced the yard, and when she pulled open the drapes, it made me uncomfortable to see her large almond eyes peering up at the mirror. I pretended not to notice her, but she insisted on talking to me. As she put on her makeup, she told me about her plans for excursions, which of course never materialized. Or, she talked about some poor heroine in an old movie whose lover pushed her off a bridge. She cursed the man's cruelty but seemed to enjoy telling his story. Then she frowned and said how she hated April evenings when the southern breezes start blowing. "After the kids run off, you can hear the *sanshin* in the dark. 'Oh, Kana, my love, how well I remember your face...' Oh, yes, even I know that song. Granpa was always singing it, playing his *sanshin*."

She went on muttering while she made herself up. "Oh, you that I love, if only you could love me." Leaning her head to one side, she slowly brushed her hair. "Please come to my village." I stopped the lawn mower, telling myself I would say something nice. Suddenly, she turned toward me, noticing that the lawn mower—Harry's lawn mower, rusty from years of use—had stopped. She pointed at me with her index finger curved slightly downward like a witch and said, "I'll get mad if you keep calling me Auntie. From now on call me Masayo, like Michiko does. I'm Masayo Kinjo, okay? Well, Masayo Thompson is fine, too. Listen, I haven't dried up like Mrs. Jones and Mrs. Scott. You know what I mean, don't you? Probably not."

Her laughter sounded rough and mean. Finding no words to throw back at her, I stood in silence as she turned again to face the mirror and began reciting a Ryukyuan poem in a high-pitched voice. "O, you that I love, if you love me, too, please come to seek my hand at the village of Ishado blooming with flowers in Nakagusuku."

4

By the end of August everything had dried up. I watered her yard furiously, but the whole island lay parched, waiting for rain. The American military seemed aloof to the problem at first, but finally the high commissioner (or some other high officer) made an announcement that a rainfall operation would be attempted over Yomitan. They were going to scatter chemicals over the clouds to make rain.

She came to our house early on the day of the rainfall operation. Her Plymouth stopped with squeaking a sound, and when she opened our front door, her eyes were sparkling. A telescope hung from her shoulders. It had belonged to Harry and was especially powerful and of high quality. She wanted to go to Yomitan with my mother to see what she called "this great operation." She wore a long, loose-fitting purple dress that looked like an evening gown. Whenever she dressed like that, my mother talked to her as if she were her dumbest daughter.

"It's not going to rain, you know. The newspaper says they're only making a trial run. Just look at the sky. They aren't magicians, after all. I'm not going."

"The military can do it, I'd even bet on it. I'm driving, so come with me. Just to watch the airplane. See, I brought my telescope."

"Hey, there are things even the military can't do. You just don't want to go by yourself. But I really can't make it. They're supplying water today, and I need it to do my laundry."

"Michiko, you only do what I ask when you need something. Well, from now on I'm not doing *anything* for you."

"C'mon, you know I'll be in trouble if I don't fill my buckets with water. Seizo, maybe you should go with your auntie. I mean, if you're not study-ing today."

Hearing this, the woman and I both frowned. But my mother started winking at me as she always does, and in the end I had to go. So I went out and got into the woman's Plymouth.

We whistled as she drove north on Highway One. Obviously in high spirits, she leveled her intense gaze at me and asked if I could whistle. It was embarrassing to listen as she soared easily up to the high notes. My whistling stayed low and somber, never reaching those joyful heights.

"I bet it'll rain."

"I wonder."

"I'm sure of it. I trust my sixth sense. Harry told me once that the air force always makes it rain in California. I know it'll rain today."

"Well, if you say so, but... "

"But what?"

"Never mind."

"You should act like a man and not be so wishy-washy. Maybe that's why you failed your entrance exams."

"Well, what are you going to do? I mean, if it doesn't rain today?"

"Now you're mad."

"No, I'm not."

"If it doesn't rain, I'll give you the telescope. I'm taking you away from your studies today, so you can have it."

I didn't answer.

"Now what's the matter?"

"But I thought you really liked that telescope."

"Hey! You're a strange kid, thinking it's already yours. Now what are you going to give me if it *does* rain?"

"I'll cut the grass for nothing and wash your car, too."

"Now you're trying to be stoic. Just buy your motorbike, and if it rains today, you can give me a ride when you get it."

She was speeding way over the limit on Highway One, and I was worried the MPs would stop us. Driving along, she whistled short, high-pitched melodies as if reminiscing about something. In the bright, transparent daylight I could see the downy hair on her rounded lips.

That morning was terribly humid. The oleanders planted along the fence inside the military base were blooming in bright red clusters. I only glanced at flowers from our passing car, but they seemed to be floating before my eyes all the way to Yomitan. Every time I thought of how the oleanders burned even redder under the summer sun, it felt like sweat was breaking out all over my body.

The sky above Yomitan was covered with clouds. Through the opening between them I could see chunks of blue sky that, with their ragged cloud perimeters, looked like slices of bitter melon that someone had shoved inside. But those clouds seemed much too high for rain.

She decided to park her Plymouth on a small hill to get a good view of the airplane. Veering recklessly off the road, she drove around in search of a vantage point until she finally came to a stop on a slope covered with rocks. Coming out of the car, she saw a boulder nearby as tall as she was, and, pulling her dress up to her thighs, she hurried into a shaded spot underneath that was just big enough for one person.

The operation was scheduled to start at eleven, and she waited without saying a word. She never seemed to think about anyone else. Whenever I saw her, she always made me uncomfortable.

A little after eleven, from out of nowhere we heard the roar of an airplane. She looked up at the sky through her sunglasses, but neither of us could spot it. The plane sounded as if it were determined to keep flying above those clouds. And, listening to that faint but persistent drone, I began to think that it might actually start raining, that maybe the American military really *could* make it rain.

The sun was right above us. There was sweat on her forehead. I could smell gasoline from her car, and the air was filled with the pungent odor of grass. Small insects flew all around, annoying us. The smell of tires. Flies. Rocks baked hot in the sun. Naked... Harry and his friends had been naked above their waists. Small bottles of beer. Strong American men pouring beer over each other in the late-afternoon sun. Clarinets, saxophones, and trumpets wailing frantically in my ears. Roaring laughter. A hairy chest. The small carton of ice cream Harry had given me that I hid under the sofa, where it melted and turned into bubbles. Harry's yard. The close-cropped lawn with the bittersweet smell. Harry's hard body conquering and taming the grass with the obstinate violence of iron. The late-afternoon sun beginning to bloat. Someone's back starting to sweat. The smell of beer. The rasping of a trumpet. A languid saxophone. "Harry, Harry! The ice cream is melting. It's all melted!" "Oh, no," she says. "I told you to put it in the fridge. I'm not going to bring you here anymore if you don't do what I say." "But if I put it in the fridge, it won't be mine any more." "What a dumb kid," she says. Harry and his friends roar with laughter. After tossing me around playfully from one to the other, they give me a big box of ice cream. But, oh no, that's melting too, and will be all gone unless I do something. Ice cream melting in the heat and changing into white bubbles. Noisy flying bugs. The scratch I got from a twig begins to hurt. The smell of gasoline. Water. She drinks from her cupped palms. The smell of burning tires. Sunglasses. Telescope. Clouds. And, oh yes, the roar of an airplane. The roar....

We waited for two hours but never saw the plane. And there wasn't even the slightest hint of rain. Apparently the operation had ended in a fiasco.

"So this is what you call an 'air force,' a 'great operation,'" she said angrily.

But she kept looking up at the sky, and I hesitated to say let's go home because she seemed to be challenging something up there. She wasn't just looking at the clouds, but at something beyond the clouds, higher and deeper.

Strangely, at that moment I could feel her strength. Then, maybe because the telescope was too big for her, I felt like laughing. It hid her pale, white face completely. I decided to tell her I wouldn't take the telescope after all and that she could ride the motorbike whenever she wanted.

The warm southern wind swept over the hill, rustling the hem of her long, loose dress. It was a beautiful sight, I thought.

The next morning the newspapers reported that the cause of the fiasco had been "low cloud density." Maybe so, but it just shows that making rain is no simple matter.

A few days later my parents went on an overnight trip. I'd caught a slight cold and had to stay home in bed. My father said he couldn't postpone the trip because he'd already scheduled his annual paid holiday. He was grumpy that day because my mother had been pestering him to go, and he had finally given in.

My parents had asked the woman to come and stay with me.

As soon as she came into my room that evening, she held her nose. I had sweated a lot sleeping in my room, which was baked by sun during the day. That night I had a fever. She had kept telling me to take a shower, and after I did, I ran that fever and my eyes got bloodshot. I knew she was upset, but I didn't say anything and just stayed in bed.

A little after ten o'clock, she told me she would be staying overnight because it looked like rain.

It was the first heavy rain in ages. After clouding up in the evening, it began pouring after ten o'clock. When the rain started, she sat on the edge of my bed and softly sang a very old song.

I could hear thunder in the distance, and streaks of lightning slashed through the darkness outside my window. Then I heard the unmistakable sound of rain hitting the ground. She had waited a long time for this rain, but she greeted it silently. Though I told her not to, she began combing my hair with her fingers. A languid feeling came over me, and I kept my eyes closed.

After that I dozed off, though I don't know for how long. When I woke up, I saw her standing next to my bed. She was drenched with rain, her large eyes shining and her lips pressed tightly together. Raindrops were dripping from her hair. I looked up at her but said nothing, and then suddenly she threw herself onto the bed. She didn't seem to care whether I got wet or not as she wrapped her arms around me and pulled me toward her. My throat was dry, and I couldn't say a word.

Holding me softly, she put her nose to my neck and called a man's name I'd never heard.

Though wet, she felt warm to me and smelled good. She reminded me of my mother, who used to lie down next to me whenever I had a cold. It was the same warmth and smell. And she felt soft, too.

Outside my window if continued to pour.

Her voice moaned as his name tumbled from her lips. In her trembling body, I felt a sadness I could neither describe nor explain. Then my body began to tremble. I couldn't help it and didn't know why, but now I was shaking and crying, too.

Apparently startled, she pushed me back down on the bed and hurried out of the room. But I couldn't stop shaking.

It rained until the next morning.

Late that afternoon, my parents returned home in high spirits. But the woman stayed closed up silently in the room next to mine.

I couldn't explain why I'd cried so much that night, but I had strange dreams later, whenever I thought of her.

She is walking toward me, about to cross the Hija Bridge from Yomitan to Naha. A man is with her. She is wearing an old-fashioned white cardigan. She starts pleading that she doesn't want to go across the bridge. Her eyes seem like a rabbit's, meek and innocent, as she peers up at the man. Despair is written on his face, but he drags her toward the bridge. "I'm doing this for your sake," he says. He is heavy-set and bowlegged with a sallow face, and he is a smooth taker. Yet he seems pathetic, too, a man whose whole life has been a failure.

Near the bridge, I see big, beautiful Ryukyuan pine trees spreading their branches. The moonlit night is tinged with blue. Yes, it is one of those April nights when the southern breezes begin to blow, making everyone restless. She is weak, going along with the man just because he yells at her. She is singing a song. I can hear your song, Auntie, if you sing it a little louder, just a bit louder. But, look, she is crossing the bridge. She fades from sight.

Next she is standing on the south end of Hija Bridge. She has draped a red cardigan over her shoulders and hides her face with a scarf. She wears black high heels. She is walking around rubbing her hands, waiting for some-one. She is chewing gum. Here he comes. He is tall with a cold, indifferent look. She is trying hard to say something to him. But he only pretends to listen. She motions that she can't go to the other side of the bridge. The tall man laughs. The night is clear with no north wind. But the white road stretching north and south from Hija Bridge looks cold. Now the man is leaving. She is left standing alone in the moonlight.

Next I see my grandfather. He is drunk and trying to club someone with his carrying pole. He makes me want to laugh, and then I really am laughing. Now he collapses on the ground, wailing in that pitiful voice. Grandpa, where's your sense of dignity? I'm sick of your crying and wailing.

Still, she stands alone, stretching her arms outward into the slashing winds of purple time that swirl around her.

5

On the last Saturday in August, I finally got the silver motorcycle. It had a black seat and a silver body that was light and sleek. Though a second-hand machine, its sturdy engine looked as though it would never stop running. And the tires were sharply notched with a deep tread that seemed sure to grip the road without slipping. This bike would run fast and proud on Highway One.

As I rubbed the machine all over with an oilcloth, the guys at the bike shop made a lewd joke about what I was doing. The owner laughed. "You be careful now," he told me. Later, when I was riding close to home, I shifted down and ran the bike for 300 yards in low gear. The heavy throbbing of the engine felt good and made me proud.

That day my father came back from his job at City Hall before noon and said something that made my heart sink.

"Well, thanks to Auntie Masayo, you can ride that bike now even if you haven't passed your entrance exams yet. We ought to go show it to her."

"Hey, he worked long and hard in that blazing sun," my mother said.

"Aw, c'mon. He's already a young man. The heat shouldn't bother him."

"Oh, yeah? It'd wear you out in half an hour."

"Hey, everybody at City Hall tells me how tough I am."

"Well, then, why don't you cut down the branches in the yard once in a while on Sundays instead of lying around the house all day."

"A section chief's job is demanding. Exhausting."

"Oh, sure. Sitting at your desk, puffing on cigarettes. Isn't that really all you do?"

"Smart-ass women. Think they know everything."

"That's right. We know *all* about it."

"Hey, why do you have to talk to me like that?"

"Well, *excuse* me. I'm *so* sorry... "

It was true that the woman they called Aunt Masayo always made me feel strange. Yet she threw herself into everything she did and seemed more sincere than either of my parents.

That afternoon, my father drove our mini-car along the highway just ahead of me riding my motorcycle. My mother, who sat beside him, kept turning around to look back at me. She was talking to my father and smiling, but he wouldn't answer and just stared straight ahead. She seemed proud of me. My father stayed in the far right lane, driving ten miles below the speed limit. It annoyed me. I told myself that after showing the woman my bike, I would drive out to the reclaimed shore land and open it up as fast as it would go. It took us half an hour to get to her place.

After making us wait a long time, she stunned us when she finally opened the door. My father grimaced, and my mother's shrieking laugh sounded almost hysterical. I felt like hugging the woman and vomiting at the same time.

She must have thought she looked "cute." She wore a white cotton shirt and red short pants covered with little pale printed flowers. She had laced her white leather boots extremely tight. She wore no lipstick but had put on thick eyeliner, and her shiny dark hair hung down her back.

My parents looked disgusted but went inside without saying anything. Meanwhile, I couldn't take my eyes off her. Under her thin cotton shirt, I could see the shapes of her breasts. If I cupped my right palm, it would just cover one of those poor little breasts. While my father spouted polite clichés, thanking her for the motorcycle, she seemed restless, walking back and forth over the tile floor in her squeaking boots. She had longer legs than I'd thought, and seeing how thin they were made me angry. Her small waist made me sad, though, and I wanted to howl like some wild animal.

Without asking anyone's permission, my mother went about making fresh coffee and was soon sipping it with my father. When the two of them started talking about old times, the woman got bored and said she wanted to take a ride on the motorcycle. Though the long downpour had ended, the island was still covered with thick clouds, and it rained off and on. But she was no longer preoccupied with rain, her interest having already shifted to the silver bike that was now mine. Before my last day working in her yard, I had explained how to ride a motorcycle. I told her how to start the engine, release the clutch, and apply the breaks. She insisted that I accept her telescope or she wouldn't take driving lessons from me. But I was stubborn, too, when it came to the telescope. So we made a compromise and asked my mother to hold on to it for us.

That day she got off to a shaky start. At first, I had to hold on to the seat from behind so she could keep her balance. She sat there, laughing happily, but looked funny because she was leaning too far backward. I kept telling her to bend forward. After driving only four or five yards, she fell off because she had accelerated too abruptly. But she didn't seem to care that her left knee was skinned and just got up and grasped the handlebars again.

We decided to take a break, and I explained again how to control her speed by balancing the clutch and the accelerator. She was so cheerful she seemed like a different person. She listened to me attentively, stroking her hair and leaning her head to one side. She looked very funny, I thought, like a high school girl. But she was so serious that I couldn't possibly laugh.

After the break she tried again. I decided I would let her drive today as much as she wanted. She went a hundred yards this time but fell again on her way back to where I was standing. She'd hit her right elbow hard on the ground and there was a lot of blood. I ran to her and reached out my hand to help her up, but she slapped it away and averted her eyes. She gazed off, squinting into the distance, as if to watch a rival who had passed her up and was now driving a motorcycle far away at full speed.

She wore the look of a young girl determined to win.

There was no way I could stop what happened after that. Suddenly she got up, straddled the silver motorcycle, and took off at full speed. The whining roar of the engine stabbed me in the stomach. In the next moment she shifted quickly from second to third, then bolted ahead.

She was racing after someone, speeding toward some unreachable goal.

Her hair fluttered wildly in the wind.

At the next curve she failed to make the turn, plunged off the road, and crashed into a stone wall. The collision hurled her down onto the asphalt in a flash of silver light.

An Exchange for Fire
The Final Pilgrimage of Poet Craig Arnold

Christopher Blasdel

On the morning of April 28th, 2009, I was settling into my workday at the International House of Japan in the Roppongi district of Tokyo. After several weeks of cold weather, it had finally warmed and the day promised to be glorious. Vivid rows of azaleas bloomed in the Japanese garden outside our office.

Suddenly, a secretary appeared with an urgent message: the police chief from Yakushima Island, a well-known tourist spot far south of Tokyo, had called, asking if we knew a foreign traveler named Craig Arnold. The police chief wanted us to return his call right away.

Such an inquiry, coming out of the blue, could not be good news, and so with a sense of foreboding I made the call. After I got the chief on the line, he told me that Craig had apparently gone missing the previous evening on Kuchinoerabu Island, a small, rugged volcanic island located about 12 kilometers west of Yakushima. Since there were no police stationed on Kuchinoerabu Island, a contingent of policemen from Yakushima made their way over to Kuchinoerabu Island on the morning ferry to begin a search for him. A card with my name and the contact number of the International House of Japan was found in the backpack Craig left at the inn. The police chief wanted to know who Craig was, how I might be connected with him and, most importantly, how they could get in contact with his next of kin.

It was no coincidence that Craig had my card. As director of the Arts Program of the International House of Japan, it is my duty to oversee a program known as the U.S.–Japan Creative Artists Program. This program, sponsored by the Japan–U.S. Friendship Commission and the NEA, sends five U.S.-based artists each year to Japan for an extended residency. Craig was chosen as one of the recipients from its highly competitive application process. The International House of Japan, also known as the I-House, facilitates the residency and provides both general and specific support to each artist during their residency in Japan. We act as the artists' entry into the culture and provide logistic, artistic and personal support.

Craig arrived in Japan on March 16, 2009, a little less than six weeks prior to the phone call from the Yakushima police. As one of the artists chosen for the 2009 program, he had written an ambitious proposal: to climb the various volcanoes of Japan, explore their surrounding countryside and research their history and geology. In his application, he also proposed to converse "with people who live in their shadows, with other travelers, other writers and record impressions of landscapes both natural and social."

Craig described this proposal as a "pilgrimage," and the experience in Japan was to tie in with a larger project, a collection of poetry entitled *An Exchange For Fire,* in which he planned to chronicle his travels through the volcanic countryside of Greece, Sicily, Guatemala, and Nicaragua—places he had already visited. Japan was to be the final stop on his pilgrimage.

The seeds of this project began while Craig was a Rome Prize fellow at the American Academy in Rome. He was there, along with his fiancée Rebecca Lindenberg and son Robin, to finish his book of poetry, *Made Flesh,* but he became bogged down and had problems concentrating. On the suggestion of Rebecca, Craig took off for a solo visit to Sicily's Mt. Aetna, in order to "find a new landscape for his thoughts."[1]

Mt. Aetna impressed Craig with its violent history of eruptions and made him acutely aware of the destructive power of volcanoes. Later, he traveled to the Greek island of Santorini, a huge volcanic caldera in the southern Aegean Sea, where he could see the ferocious remnants of eruptions. He made special note of an extraordinary, explosive eruption that occurred in the second millennium BCE. This eruption, said to be one of the largest in recorded history, destroyed the Minoan civilization that possibly inspired Plato's story of Atlantis.

Although humans from all cultures and ages share hopes and struggles, worldly aspirations pale when put in context of epic cycles of destruction and creation. These cataclysmic occurrences became a fascination for Craig, and "the volcano became an emblem of geology's indifference toward humanity." The title of the proposed work itself, *An Exchange for Fire,* comes from the Greek philosopher Heraclites, "whose mystic notions of change and impermanence comes closest perhaps, to the insights of Zen Buddhism, blurring our conceptions of what constitutes Western, what Eastern thought."

Craig continued to search out active volcanoes and climb them. Their extreme and violent landscapes were for him a kind of ritual; each step up the mountain a meditation. In this reverie, he could ponder not only the fate of history or the locals who lived close to omnipresent danger, but he could also view his own life and mull questions of artistry, fatherhood and partnership. Sauntering the rugged physical terrain became a metaphor for traversing the shifting inner geography of the mind.

Japan, as a country with a long history of violent volcanoes and a culture where the idea of impermanence is an integral part of the national aesthetic, was the natural next step on Craig's journey. Japan also has a long tradition of the pilgrimage as developed from ancient Buddhist, native animistic

—
Craig Arnold
photograph by Amanda Abel

—
1
Interview with R. Lindenberg,
Nov. 18, 2010

An Exchange for Fire   Christopher Blasdel

and shaman traditions. Pilgrims in Japan include, on the one hand, the legend-ary, hardcore *yamabushi* monks who undergo austere physical disciplines over a period of years and gain, at least in the popular mind, extraordinary prowess in both the physical and spiritual realms. There are also less rigorous pilgrim-ages, most notably the Shikoku *junrei,* where lay folk take a few days or weeks out of their lives to visit a series of eighty-eight temples located throughout the island of Shikoku. No matter what the level of difficulty, each pilgrimage becomes an outer reflection of an inner necessity to rise above the vicissitudes of the mundane world and attain understanding and peace. In this light, Craig's volcano pilgrimage became the "independent variable that everything else is tested against."[2]

2
R. Lindenberg, *ibid.*

Craig arrived at our office on March 17th for an orientation that we arranged for him to explain the conditions and details of the grant. He walked into our office dressed in jeans, a long sleeve T-shirt and a colorful cotton scarf wrapped around his neck. Tall, with shaven head and unshaven face, he was a refreshing anomaly to the formality of the Japanese office. Although tired and jet lagged from a long flight and even longer period of intensive travel in the U.S., he sat down and smiled, immediately softening the situation. Soon the conversation, which began on topics of mundane business, became vitalized with talk of poetry, travel and life experiences.

My first impression of Craig was that of an extremely intelligent and loveably engaging man, exuding an immediate, sensual intimacy. He had the power to effortlessly direct this sensuality toward anyone. This included my assistant, who later confided to me that she felt Craig was flirting with her, but I admitted to her that I felt the same thing. Such openness on a first meeting is rare in Japan, but it was perfectly natural with Craig. There was nothing forced about his familiarity, and this fascinated me.

Craig announced he planned to commence his volcano climbs as soon as he could. The first volcano he wanted to climb was Mt. Asama, in Nagano Prefecture, only an hour or so away from Tokyo. The mountain is close enough to Tokyo that on a very clear day, one can see its upper slopes shimmering in the distance.

Craig asked me about climbing the mountain. I told him that it prob-ably wouldn't be possible, for two reasons. Firstly, the peak, at 2568 meters, was still covered in deep snow, and secondly, Mt. Asama is an active volcano and climbing has been officially prohibited since 1972, although there are lulls in the volcanic activity and times and routes when it is possible to climb the peak in a minimal amount of danger. In actuality, however, the volcano had erupted just a month ago, in February, and it was presently being monitored very carefully.

As I spoke, I could see Craig's eyes widen, his interest intensifying, as if I had just given him more reason to make the climb. He seemed to think that the snow would be no problem, telling me he was used to climbing active volcanoes in extreme conditions. He must have then sensed my concern, however, for he quickly added that he was wise enough to know when to stop.

Soon afterwards, around March 20th, Craig took the bullet train up to Karuizawa and set off for the mountain. Karuizawa, located near the base of Mt. Asama, is famous as the summer home and playground of wealthy Japanese who escape the sultry summer heat of Tokyo in the town's high altitudes. During the summer months, the town is bustling and full of specialty shops that cater to the city folk, but in the winter, it returns to a quiet mountain village.

Karuizawa lies along one of the main *shinkansen* trunk lines radiating out from Tokyo. It passes by Mt. Asama, but the station is not all that close to the base of the mountain. Craig apparently thought about taking a bus from the station to the trailhead, but decided to walk, thinking that the hike would focus his "restlessness, give it a pace and a direction." He liked the idea of making the entire trek up the mountain on his own, without relying on public transportation.

Volcano Pilgrim, a blog[3] Craig kept almost up to the day he disappeared, details his attempted trek up Mt. Asama and dealing with the snow and cold. The lower slopes where he began his hike were wintry but dry. It was easy hiking and the poet made keen note of everything around him.

> *Above the town you turn off the road onto an old nature trail, sign posts with peeling pictures of wildlife, and follow its erratic switchback up and down the sides of ridge and gully. You meet no other hikers. It is still winter here, leafless and budless – the trees are some type of larch that loses its foliage in winter, and the only green thing is a globe of mistletoe in the high boughs of a tree. A few wax-pale berries have fallen on the path, and when you pick one up it pops between your fingers, releasing a sticky pearl of jelly.*

> *Every now and then you pass a gap in the bare branches and catch a glimpse of Mt. Asama, still snow-topped and glittering.*

As he climbed higher, his observations changed to reflect the increasing difficulty of the hike. There was more snow, the trail, leading deeper into the mountain, became more difficult, and even though he was still far from the summit, his wet feet bothered him. A hint of misery permeates his lines.

> *The going is not pleasant, steep and slippery... you are more exquisitely attuned to the unique sensation of dragging your ankles through snow that has fallen and melted and frozen again.*

—
3
http://volcanopilgrim.word-press.com/. The dates in his blog, for some reason, are unreliable. The dates I give here are recounted from my daily memos and receipts Craig left.

Craig often added personal haiku poetry to his blog, each one carefully following the five-seven-five syllable rule of the genre:

it is hard to feel
moved by natural beauty
when your socks are wet

Unbeknownst to Craig, a well-paved road paralleled the trail. He discovered this when the trail finally crossed the road several kilometers up the mountain. There, to his relief, he found a small store—one of Japan's ubiquitous *konbini*—and he stepped inside to dry off. While inside, he befriended a Japanese couple, Shin and Keiko, who happened to be headed to the same hostel that Craig booked. They offered him a ride, which he gratefully accepted.

the sweetest five words
to a hiker with sore feet –
do you want a ride

Serendipitous encounters were not unusual for Craig. His sense of ease and warmth with complete strangers manifested even when fatigued, troubled or lost.

Shin and Keiko took a grateful Craig to the hostel. That evening during dinner, the hostel owner showed Craig a photo of himself, as a toddler, at the summit of Mt. Asama. This excited Craig and he began, in his basic Japanese, to pepper the man with questions on how to climb the mountain and where to find the best trail. When the owner realized that Craig was seriously thinking about climbing the volcano the next day, he clearly warned Craig that it was dangerous and officially closed. The hostel owner didn't speak English all that well, and Craig struggled with Japanese, but the man made his point by saying that the mountain is a *deesu zoun* ("death zone") while making an X sign with his hands. Craig turned to his new friend, Shin, to confirm; is it really unclimbable? Shin just countered with an enigmatic smile, which in Japan can mean a number of things, but in this case the unmistakable nuance was "yes, but I don't want to tell you so directly." Craig now had all the confirmation that he needed to know that the volcano was too dangerous to climb. Shin added in English: "self-responsibility," as if he were worried that Craig might still try to make the trek up the mountain.

Still, Craig's purpose in coming to Japan was to climb such mountains, and there were many on his list. If he didn't make it up this one, now that he was so close to the summit, he might never again have the chance. In an almost prescient passage in his blog, he mulled the idea of self-responsibility versus his need to continue up to the summit.

These days you are low on self-responsibility. Only last month
Mt. Asama erupted, throwing lava bombs a kilometer from

the crater. A four-kilometer exclusion zone has been declared around the volcano, a perimeter that barely excludes the highway and the shrine of Onioshidashi-en to the north. Climbing it now would be, as with so many of your plans, a bad idea. This does not make it seem any less attractive. Whatever holds you back, it is not self-responsibility. There is also the matter of the snow. Climbing a mountain in the face of sudden fiery death has a certain romantic pathos to it, but slipping on ice and ending up in pieces at the bottom would just be embarrassing.

During his many climbs, Craig must have been intensely aware of the possibilities of falling. It is, of course, an unavoidable danger of mountaineering. But there is also a primordial fear of falling that we are all prey to. It is as if, once having learned to stand upright as a child, we spend our lives in fear of falling back down, either by accident or old age. Craig described an exercise in his drama class that was aimed to transform the fear of falling into a sensation of trust in the other.

There is a game you would play called Circle Fall. The cast forms a ring, with one of their number in the middle, close enough so that they may reach out and grasp him by the shoulders or under the arms. He stands with feet together, stiff and straight, closes his eyes. Then he gradually lets himself topple, forward or backward or to one side, like a tree the lumberjack has just given a final stroke of the axe.

Now he is in the hands of the others. As he falls, they must catch him, taking the weight of his body gently and gradually, raise him upright again. Then they give him another push, maybe in this direction, maybe in that. He falls, and is caught; he is stood back up, and toppled over again. One might think there would be the one joker in the pack who would let their fellow fall, but no one ever does. It would be more than a betrayal.

The next day, Craig wisely decided not to try to climb the mountain and instead explored the perimeter and the area around the hostel, in particular the Onioshidashi-en; a five-kilometer lava flow consisting of sharp, crystallized lava that burst forth from the mountain when it erupted in 1783. A shrine constructed amongst the lava rocks is a popular place for tourists. The area is also the closest one can get to the summit of the volcano by highway, and from here one can clearly see Mt. Asama's peak. There are no large trees or vegetation obscuring the view.

He spent the day in the shadow of the peak, watching it but unable to climb. At the end of the day, on what he thought would be an easy return to the hostel, Craig got confused in the warren of small roads that crisscrossed the mountainside and lost his way. Again, in a prescient passage, he described his mounting anxiety at not finding his way back.

> Somewhere between Onioshidashi-en and the hostel, you take a wrong turn, or several. It would not be hard to do— few of the road names are posted, and the arrows on the signs point in directions that make no sense to you, even if you could read them. You stumble on for an hour for two, for four.

> Now dark is falling, and you are nowhere near anything you recognize. At times you catch glimpses of Mt. Asama through the trees, each time in an unexpected direction. You grow frustrated, you curse the hand-drawn map you made this morning. Anger drops you into sadness, and sadness into that slow sinking that you have never learned to pull yourself out of.

There is a sense of desperation and near panic in the account of this misadventure, although being on paved roads and in the general proximity of civilization, Craig was never in any particular danger. Nonetheless, it was unnerving for him. Once again, he was "rescued" by his friends Shin and Keiko, who happened to pass him on their way to the train station. The hostel itself turned out to be just a block away; Craig had actually walked around it several times and had probably passed it without recognizing it.

Craig returned to Tokyo on the *shinkansen* on March 23rd. In order to save on hotel costs, he planned to leave for his next trek that very evening on the overnight ferry. This time he headed to the more temperate waters south of Tokyo—the island of Miyakejima.

Miyakejima lies about 180 kilometers due south of Tokyo and is one of several volcanic islands that make up what is called the Izu group. Craig described the islands in his blog:

> Miyakejima, or Miyake Island, is one of the Izu-shôtô, the chain of islands that begins just beyond of Tokyo Bay and continues south along the juncture of two continental plates. All are to some degree volcanic. Miyake in most cases means "royal estate," but here it probably remembers an older word, yake, that means "burning." Like Stromboli, the island is essentially one big volcano, Mount Oyama.

During the last century, the volcano was fairly regular in its habits. Every twenty-odd years, a vent would open and pour lava down one face of the mountain, or a new cinder cone would be thrown up. This happened in 1940, 1962 and 1983. Lava flows are not good if they happen to end up in your backyard, but they move slowly and can usually be seen coming. At the old summit, all was relatively quiet. The crater lake became a tourist site, with a visitor's center, pathways to scenic views, a gently steaming fumarole surrounded by tropical flowers.

But in 2000 the volcano broke character. The pressure in the magma chamber had built up faster than any small pressure valve could relieve, and the result was what volcanologists call a Plinian eruption—sudden, violent, voluminous, and with a bang. (There are also super-Plinian eruptions, but records of these, as well as of the populations that experience them, tend not to survive).

Between June and August, there were three such major eruptions. Luckily, they all went up rather than sideways, or the result would have been catastrophic. As it was, no one died, but authorities were taking no chances, and the evacuation began.

The evacuation of the entire island was major news in Japan when it occurred in 2000. Most of the island's 2,800 residents were elderly and had known nothing but life on the island all their years. They were relocated to a busy suburb in Tokyo, where, bereft of their normal sense of community, vocations and activities, many suffered serious physical and mental stress. Residents were not allowed to return to the island until 2005, and even then, parts of the island were off-limits. Poisonous emissions of sulfur dioxide still emanate from its fissures, and the authorities set up loudspeakers across the island to warn residents of the dangerous gasses and the wind conditions. A sudden shift in wind could bring disastrous results, and the inhabitants continue their lives under this threat. This human element of the cataclysmic aspects of volcanoes was of great interest to Craig, and one of the impulses driving his pilgrimage.

Craig set off from the small pier after the ferry arrived at Miyakejima in the early morning. He had slept very little, didn't have a chance to change clothes and was hungry. Yet at 5:30 in the morning there were no shops open, so Craig was relieved when he encountered one of the vending machines that dot every corner of Japan. He purchased a small can of hot coffee and sat down to wait for the bus to take him to the trailhead.

Craig was an inveterate chronicler of the immensity of detail that surrounded his peregrinations. As he sat on a road, he noticed a small animal stick its head out from the lush vegetation, readying to run across the road. Craig read the creature's intentions, but, realizing that a car was approaching, he made a sound to frighten the animal, causing it to dart back into the bushes and thus preventing it from being run over. This act gave Craig a small pleasure.

> *If nothing else you have saved a life today. A life other than your own, that is. Danger has a way of cutting through melancholy, the real fear blinding you to the fear dimly imagined. If you could only always just have escaped death, you would never be sad again.*

Miyakejima had none of the wintry, forbidden quality of Mt. Asama. It was warm and welcoming and appeared more like a picnic than a climb fraught with danger. Yet even in this complacency, Craig sensed foreboding and struggled to free himself from his fears. Danger, whether from a car about to run over a small animal or a sudden volcanic eruption, was never far from the poet's mind.

Suddenly, the island's loudspeakers crackled to life. Craig understood only the *ohayô gozaimasu* "good morning," and wondered if a warning for the sulfurous gasses had been issued. Since he could not understand, and no one was around to explain or warn him, he decided to ignore it. It was more important that he begin his climb.

> *But the hot coffee has helped you reach a kind of resolution. There is nothing for you to do but to walk, following the slope of the roads upward, to see how far you can get before something or someone makes you stop.*

As he began his ascent, Craig realized that the climb was not difficult. In less than an hour he found the road that circled the base of the volcano and discovered where he could follow the road leading to the summit. In Craig's experienced estimation, he imagined he could be up and down the mountain in time to catch the afternoon ferry back to Tokyo. He continued around a bend in the road, where he suddenly had an unimpeded view of the summit. However, a single glance of the gasses streaming off the peak and the havoc wreaked by the eruption nine years ago made him realize he had made a serious mistake in judging the mountain.

> *It is as if you have wandered into some post-apocalyptic science fiction movie. There is the husk of what must have been the visitor's center. There is a backhoe, resting on its side, yellow paint pitted with rust. Whatever road once went*

*to the summit is now under a lot of dirt and rockfall and dark
gray ash.*

The destructive effects of the eruption still lingered, and what was once a popular tourist path up the mountain, along with a public visitor's center and sightseeing spot, now lay in ruins. He also realized that the huge plumes of sulfur dioxide gas spurting from the peak could not have been seen on his approach from the boat, since he arrived in the dark. But the plume was towering and the danger real. He then heard another siren, loud and piercing. He couldn't tell if it was a warning, but suddenly the wind shifted and the gas bore directly down on him.

*This seems like an opportune moment to reconsider your
plans for the morning. Luckily there is another road down,
and you take it. The metal guardrails have been eaten half-
away, and they twist off easily in your hand.*

Back in Tokyo, Craig recounted these adventures to me in his inimitable storytelling technique; a way he had of relating events that made the mundane seem like high adventure and any subsequent danger like minor mishaps to the narrative. But when he related this story and its description of decay, I felt a sense of loneliness. Many years ago, when the volcano was still asleep, I climbed the same mountain, and the landmarks he recounted in his story were familiar. Yet when I climbed, it was in the company of others; happy families on picnics, young backpackers from Tokyo and industrious locals selling snacks and drinks at the visitor's center. He had seen only ruins, and I think it had a profound effect on him. In Japan, there is nothing more forlorn than coming across abandoned, derelict structures that once hosted human activity.

I also had experiences getting lost in Japanese mountains. Trail and roads are often not marked, or if they are, it is only for a few kilometers, providing hikers with a false sense of security before totally bewildering them. According to Rebecca, it was unusual for Craig to become totally lost, as he did on Mt. Asama. He was usually levelheaded and careful. Nonetheless, she did point out that he could sometimes be blasé about the inherent dangers in climbing. He had a singular focus and would only see what he wanted to accomplish. This, at times, blinded him to danger and made him seem rash, but it also provided a focused, almost visionary way of seeing the world.[4] This is the world he shared with us in his writings.

I looked forward to hearing of his subsequent adventures. He planned to travel down the length of Japan and visit the active volcanoes of Kagoshima Prefecture (on the southern tip of Kyushu) and slowly make his way to Okinawa, where he had lived briefly, years back, when his father was stationed there in the U.S. Military.

—
4
Lindenberg, *Ibid.*

In one conversation, Craig mentioned his strong interest in music and his early career as a musician. I was not surprised: his poetry reads with a definite musical cadence, and the clips I had seen of him reading his works had an element of an *avant-garde* musical performance. Since my specialty is music, in particular traditional Japanese music, I invited him to a concert I gave on April 4th, the night of his planned departure south.

The performance, at a small temple in the suburbs of Tokyo, was part of the opening events for an exhibition, *Sakura Kûkan* (The Space of Cherry Blossoms), hosted by the Japanese photographer Eikoh Hosoe, who had asked me to play *shakuhachi*[5] to accompany his photographs.

Hosoe is one of Japan's most influential postwar photographers and is perhaps most famous for his depictions of the writer Yukio Mishima in a series of photographs Hosoe directed and took, entitled *Ordeal by Roses*. The book has been out of print for many years, and Hosoe decided to exhibit large-scale digital scannings of the original photos of this and other older works in scroll-like photographs placed face-up on low tables that extended the length of the temple anteroom. One entered the large *tatami*-mat room, followed these scrolls like a story unfolding, and then continued into the main hall where the *shakuhachi* performance took place. Craig attended with writer Patricia Chao, who also resided in Tokyo on the Japan–U.S. Creative Artists' Program.

The small temple hall provided an intimate connection between the performer and the audience. Craig told me it was the first time he had heard the *shakuhachi,* and he was much interested to hear it in a temple setting.

Hosoe and his son Kenji, also a photographer, chronicled the performance and audience with their cameras. In one of Kenji's photographs, Craig sits in the audience a few feet from the music with an incredulous expression. Totally unaware of the camera, his face registers a look of extreme surprise. One wonders what kinds of tones he heard from the *shakuhachi* that occasioned this expression. I suspect that such a reaction—a look of inquisitive innocence bordering on disbelief—was not unusual for Craig, and that it demonstrated the process by which he inquired into the world, whether at the vast and dangerous beauty of nature or the soft, subtle sounds of the *shakuhachi*.

After the performance there was a short reception, after which Craig took his leave to catch the night bus. As he left, he approached and hugged me goodbye. He held very tightly and suddenly, as we pulled apart, kissed me. It was an unexpected yet wonderful gesture; a heartfelt thanks from the poet and, I felt, the yearning of a very sensitive soul for others who might share his sensitivities. It was also, as it turned out, his parting gift to me.

Craig's plan was to be away for about six weeks and return to Tokyo to do a series of public readings. Later on, Rebecca and their son Robin, were to join him from the States. He was very excited about his family coming to visit.

In Kagoshima City, located on the southwest tip of Kyushu, he visited the active volcano Sakurajima, famous for its eruptions that spew forth smoke and detritus on almost a daily basis.

—

The author performing shakuhachi for Eikoh Hosoe's exhibition "Sakura Kûkan." Photograph by Kenji Hosoe

—

5
Japan's vertical, five-holed bamboo flute. The instrument has a long relationship with Buddhism and the process of meditation. It is also very flexible and used in much contemporary and experimental music around the world.

Kagoshima is the departure point to the volcanic chain of islands that lay on the way to Okinawa, many of which are still active. From Kagoshima, Craig took the ferry to Yakushima Island.

Yakushima is one of the most idyllic of all Japanese islands and is known for its stunning scenery and biodiversity. In 1993, it was designated as Japan's first UNESCO World Heritage Site, mainly due to the presence of huge cryptomeria trees, some believed to be over 3,000 years old.

Craig based himself for about ten days in Yakushima.[6] According to the unedited and unpublished diaries found in his computer, he stayed in the local youth hostel and spent his days hiking, bicycling and, true to his gregarious nature, making friends and writing about his encounters. Underlying these entries, however, was a restlessness and need to keep moving. He seemed impatient when weather or other unavoidable circumstances stalled his journey. He couldn't sit still. In *Volcano Pilgrim,* he describes this need.

> *...it is like the shark who must keep moving, moving to breathe, moving to stay afloat, or else sink, into the dark blue depths, under the weight of endless tons of water, where even the light of the sun, if it could reach that far down, would be pale and cold.*

The true significance of a pilgrimage is not in its completion, but in the process itself.

Craig's plan was to visit two active volcanoes near Yakushima: Satsuma Io-jima and Kuchinoerabu Island, before traveling on to Okinawa. For his first visit, he chose Satsuma Io-jima, a small island of about 11.6 square kilometers and 142 inhabitants, situated between Yakushima and Kagoshima Bay. Satsuma Io-jima's volcano is classed as an A-type volcano,[7] and its steep sides soar 704 meters above sea level. It erupted as recently as 2004.

A local ferry services the island only three times a week. Craig did not want to spend any more time than necessary, so he arrived on the morning ferry, immediately began climbing and returned to the village by evening, where he spent the night and caught the morning ferry back to Kagoshima. He accomplished here what he had wanted to do on Miyakejima; a daylight climb timed to match the ferry schedule. Another reason for his haste was the lack of Internet or cell phone connection on these small islands. He loved to keep in touch with his friends and family in the U.S. through Facebook and his blogs. He had, in fact, just purchased a new iPhone and was using it for the first time on this trip. He kept in regular touch with Rebecca through his travels. Whenever he had an Internet connection, Craig updated his activities.

Craig departed Yakushima on the morning of April 27th by ferry and arrived at the small island of Kuchinoerabu at 2:40 PM. Following the same *modus operandi* as he had on Satsuma Io-jima, Craig planned to arrive in the afternoon, run up the mountain, then descend in time for dinner and leave the

---

6

The movements of Craig from this point on to his disappearance on April 28th were uncovered by the detailed investigation of the local Yakushima Police and my conversations with Rebecca.

7

The Japan Metrological Agency classifies volcanoes into type A, B and C. Type A volcanoes, the most dangerous, are ones that have been active over the last 10,000 years with high eruption activity for the last 100 years. There are a total of thirteen type A volcanoes in Japan.

next day so he could post his recent activities online, since there was no Internet service on Kuchinoerabu Island.

Craig befriended two passengers on the ferry. When they learned he had no place to stay, they offered to take him to the inn at which they had reserved, called Minshuku Watanabe, situated just few meters from the ferry dock in Honmura, the main settlement of the island. After the ferry landed, Craig went to the inn with his new friends, dropped his bags off and was informed that dinner was served at seven PM. He asked directions to the mountain, drank a vitamin drink, then left the inn with two hiking sticks.

Craig left Honmura heading toward the mountain, passing by the island's only store, the Co-op, where several people saw him. They could not but help noticing a tall foreigner with a shaved head purposefully striding out of the village with hiking sticks. A little further out from Honmura, Craig came across a small settlement called Maeda, where a local guide, Mori Kifune, lives. Kifune saw Craig walking up the road past his house. Craig initiated conversation and asked if this road was the right way up the mountain. Kifune said yes, but also warned him against climbing at this late hour. Craig answered *daijôbu* ("no problem") and started to walk on. Kifune saw that Craig was in shape and an experienced mountain walker so was not too worried, though he decided to give Craig a ride to the trailhead in his car.

In third world countries, like Nicaragua, Craig always hired a local guide to take him up the mountain. This not only helped him navigate the terrain and kept him from getting lost, but it helped him steer through the local bureaucracy and, through interaction with the guides, provided him insight into the culture. Why he didn't hire local guides in Japan is still a mystery. Perhaps because he thought that Japan, being a first world country, would be safe enough, or that the cost of hiring guides would be too expensive or the language barrier too formidable? Whatever reason, Craig was lured by a sense that Japanese mountains would not be too dangerous.

Kifune took Craig up the mountain on a narrow but well-maintained, paved road to a sand dam that lay at the head of one of the several trails up the mountain. This trail is steep but the fastest way up to the peak, Shindake (654 m), which is the island's active volcano. Considering the late hour, Kifune believed this to be the safest route for Craig to get up and down before dark.

When Craig didn't return to the inn on the evening of April 27th, the innkeeper became concerned. He took his car and made a cursory look around the village and up the road toward the mountain. When he couldn't find Craig, he called the local fire brigade. These men, including Kifune, searched for Craig along the various roads under the mountain, calling out his name, until around midnight. When they didn't find him, they notified the Yakushima police.

The police arrived the next morning, April 28th, from Yakushima to begin the official search. A total of forty-three people, including five police officers from the Yakushima Police Station, reinforcements from the Kagoshima Prefectural Police, two dogs, two helicopters and a boat, joined the search. Their standard method of operation consisted mostly of a grid (also known as rolling) search along the sand dam trail Craig ascended and areas they thought he might have descended.

After the Yakushima Police called me at the International House, I immediately contacted Citizen's Services at the U.S. Embassy, who in turn contacted the Fukuoka Consulate in Kyushu. The assistant to the Consulate General in Fukuoka called me for further details about Craig and his residency. I did not look forward to my next task, however—contacting Rebecca to inform her of the situation. No amount of mental preparation makes this job easy, and I dreaded having to tell her the bad news. To further complicate matters, I only had her Facebook contact and would have to message her. I thought long and hard about how to compose it:

> Hello Rebecca, this is Christopher Blasdel of the International House of Japan, Craig's contact point in Japan. A serious matter concerning Craig has arisen and we need to contact you ASAP. Can you give me a call in Japan? Sorry to contact you through Facebook, but this was the only way I could think to get a hold of you.

I left my phone number and instructions to call any time, day or night. At about 1:00 the following morning, she called me.

I did my best to try to keep the conversation calm and just repeat the facts as I knew them. Rebecca was understandably flustered and anxious, but she remained level-headed and thought of ways to help us understand Craig's possible movements. She provided background on his climbing experience and what he might be carrying. All this information I passed on the consulate. At the end of the conversation she told me of their method of staying in contact:

> Craig and I have an understanding that if he did not check in with me at least once every 48 hours, I would contact you to inform you that I had not heard from him – this was one of our "safety" precautions. In about five hours, that 48-hour time window will have elapsed, and I will not have been in touch with Craig.

She also gave my contact information to Craig's brother, Chris, who called me later that morning.

By law, Japanese police are required to search only three days for missing persons. This is usually enough time to rescue someone who is lost or discover their remains in the case of a fatal accident. The police rescue team from Yakushima originally planned to follow this rule and had no intention of extending the search. Furthermore, it was right at the beginning of Japan's main holiday season, Golden Week, and the police felt pressure to get back to Yakushima to oversee the safety of numerous tourists who visit during the holidays. Because of the many popular mountain trails on Yakushima, the local police spend a lot of time and resources on search and rescue.

The officials from the U.S. Embassy were, from the outset, very concerned and put a great deal of effort into trying to liaison between the family and the local authorities. It turned out the Consulate General in Fukuoka was a friend I knew from the time she was stationed in Tokyo, and I was able to talk to her directly to obtain information. She told me that she was trying very hard to get the local police to extend the search to six or even nine days, but was not having very much luck.

In the meantime, a Facebook page dedicated to finding Craig and various blogs and Internet sites sprang up to inform the literary world about Craig. Many of the blogs announced that the Yakushima police were only going to search for three days, as required by law, and implied that the Fukuoka Consulate was dragging their feet on the search efforts and implored everyone to write the U.S. Embassy or their congressman and urge the Consulate to take more action. A typical blog read like this:

> My friend Craig Arnold, a father, poet, and professor is missing in Japan and the authorities are only required to search for three days. Today is the third day. To encourage the authorities to continue the search, media attention and pressure from American authorities could help. Read the details here and write your representative here.[8]

I flung myself into the effort to coordinate and keep everyone—the family, the NEA and the Friendship Commission—informed as best I could. I did this not only because it was the obvious thing to do, but because when faced with a possible tragedy, either on a professional or personal level, sometimes the best response is just to act. At least it kept me from imagining the worst.

The embassy in Tokyo was also taking action. One of the highest-ranking officers there arranged for a number of Okinawa-based U.S. military aircraft (including helicopters) in the area on a training mission to assist in the search. On April 30th, they appeared suddenly over the island and circled for two or three hours, using infrared and other state-of-the-art devices. Around this time, the Consulate General in Fukuoka called me to announce that they had convinced the Kagoshima police to extend the search for three more days and increase the number of men on the ground.

By May 1st, Craig had been missing for over three days. For the next three days, the police widened their search area to include not only the trail Craig used for his ascent, but all areas of the mountain where he might have wandered. At this point, the number of people involved in the search included three locals, twenty-two Kagoshima riot police and seven policemen from Yakushima, including the police chief. Two police helicopters continued their search from above. For a small island with no more than 150 residents, the activity was unprecedented, and the local housewives gathered in the schoolyard to cook meals every night for the influx of searchers.

—
8
http://mamatrue.com/
2009/04/30/
my-friend-craig-arnold-is-
missing-please-help/

It soon became apparent that someone from Craig's immediate family would have to be available to take charge in the event Craig was found, so his brother Chris decided to make the trip from New York to Kuchinoerabu Island. The Friendship Commission agreed to cover my expenses from Tokyo as his interpreter and guide.

Chris arrived in Narita on May 2nd, and I waited for him outside the arrival lobby. It happened to be at the height of the swine flu scare and the authorities were inspecting every plane before allowing the passengers to deplane, so it took him over an hour to pass through immigration and customs. Although tired from the long flight from New York and the immense stress of this situation, he was ready to jump right into action. We took the bus to Haneda, Tokyo's domestic terminal, where he stayed overnight. I met him again in the morning, and we flew to Kagoshima and then changed to an inter-island flight to Yakushima.

At first, I could not get a reservation on the inter-island flight because they were fully booked due to the peak Golden Week holiday season. Again, the Fukuoka Consulate came through and somehow secured passage for us on one of these flights.

It could not have been an easy journey for Chris to make, but, like Craig, he had a single-mindedness of purpose and was determined to find his brother, no matter the costs of money, time or energy.

Around noon on May 3rd, Chris and I arrived at Yakushima and took a taxi to the ferry. After boarding the ferry, there was nothing to do but wait. Chris busied himself writing press releases, hoping that increased media attention would spur the authorities to prolong the search. I stood on deck and watched the island of Yakushima recede into the distance. The ferry turned into the open ocean and the sea became noticeably rougher, and I went inside. Also on the ferry was a squad of Kagoshima riot police who had been pressed into search duty. I struck up a conversation with one of them, a youth no more than eighteen or nineteen, just out of high school. He was reticent to talk at first, but he opened up as I pressed on. I asked him what he had heard of the incident about Craig. Nothing he said, except that he was told to report to Kuchinoerabu Island on this ferry. Had he ever been there before? No, but he had read about its volcanic activity in school. I pointed to where Chris was sitting, and told him that was the brother of the man who went missing. The young policeman regarded him for a moment in silence, then just said, Oh, really? But I could see in his expression a realization that this job had been suddenly given a face. He was going out to search for a family member. This would not be the last time I witnessed such a reaction by a local.

When we arrived at Kuchinoerabu Island, we were met by the Yakushima police who guided us on the exact route that Craig took, beginning from the Watanabe Inn, where he left his luggage, up past Kifune's house, and continuing up to the head of the sand dam trail. Together we walked several kilometers up the trail.

Since it was beginning to get dark, we returned to Honmura village where the police chief held a thorough briefing on the search situation.

We gathered in the small *tatami*-matted meeting room in the concrete building that served as the ferry office and town hall. It was the largest and most secure structure on the island. The very first thing the police chief said was that they were all searching for Craig as if he were family. He said this not in a patronizing or bureaucratic way, but in a sincere and softened voice. I was moved by his dedication to his job, but I also realized that the arrival of Chris on the scene had the effect of making the search very personal for all those concerned.

After the police chief briefed us on the search, Kifune arrived. This was the man who gave Craig a ride up to the trail, against his better judgment, and the last person to have spoken to Craig. As an expert on the island and its topography, Kifune, together with a man named Yamaguchi, were directing the search efforts.

I expected Kifune to be an older man, wizened and reserved through years of hard work in the outdoors. What I saw instead was a young man, in his mid-thirties, with a slight build and sensitive face, not unlike Craig himself. When he met Chris, he suddenly broke into tears and began profusely apologizing. He clearly felt a responsibility for not having stopped Craig from climbing.

Both Chris and I did our best to assuage Kifune's feelings. We told him that Craig was not a person who could be dissuaded from his path and there was absolutely no need for Kifune to take responsibility. Yet for Kifune there was much more at stake than just finding a determined American hiker who had become lost; there was a matter of deep pride in his island home and his sense of responsibility to visitors. Someone had been lost on his watch, so to speak, and he felt a grave responsibility, whether deserved or not. One never operates in Japan in a vacuum; there are always those around who want or have to take responsibility. Craig's volcano pilgrimage may have been an intensely personal one that led him to active volcanoes around the world, but on Kuchinoerabu Island, he had become a missing family member who garnered the concern of every individual on the island.

The police chief ended the briefing with the welcome announcement that they had decided to continue the search for another three days, for a total of nine days. The pressure from the U.S. Embassy in Tokyo had borne fruit.

In the meantime, Rebecca arranged for a professional tracking service, the Joel Hardin Professional Trackers, an NGO based in Idaho, to come to the island to assist in the search for Craig. This team was founded by veteran tracker and former Border Patrol Officer Joel Hardin.

Members of this service use highly refined methods of scientific observation of footprints, vegetation and subtle changes in the surroundings to discern and follow where and when a missing person may have gone. They have made a significant name for themselves in the arena of law enforcement, locating missing persons and search and rescue. They agreed to take on this job for expenses, but it would take another two days for the team to make their way to the island.

During the wait, I found myself beginning to wonder if Craig would be found alive. My gut feeling at this point said no, though even now I can't say why I felt this way. Perhaps it was looking at the desperation on Kifune's face every evening when he returned home from an unsuccessful day of searching, or the realization that if Craig were alive, he would have already made his way out of the mountain, even if injured. One cannot share such reservations in the middle of a search when everyone is trying to stay focused and optimistic, so I kept silent. Anyway, there was still logical hope for his discovery. For example, the island is riddled with deep volcanic vents covered over with vegetation. Kifune mentioned that someone could fall into these holes and not be able to climb out. Perhaps he was waiting to be found in one of them. The search team was methodically checking out all the possibilities.

The following day, May 4th, I stayed with Chris to translate and assist him while the police continued their search. Together with some other volunteers, Chris and I walked along the roads under the mountains to keep an eye out for any sign of Craig. It was a way to keep us occupied more than anything else, as it would have been too dangerous for us to participate in the search on the volcano itself.

The weather was perfect, and as we rounded the bends on the mountain road we were confronted with truly stunning scenery. After leaving the sand dam, the paved road climbs the side of the volcano, and from its vantage points we could see the peaks that beckoned Craig and the turquoise sea, far below, shimmering in the sunlight. In the distance, Yakushima seemed to float in the mist above the sea. Just then, Chris began to call out his brother's name, hoping that his voice might somehow call his brother back. His voice poignantly reverberated through the hills but went unanswered.

It reminded me of a dream Craig wrote about, in which he tries to save his younger brother from a mountain tragedy.

> It is not our first memories but our first dreams that make us. You are climbing with your little brother up the slope of a mountain. You lead, he follows. It seems not a particularly difficult mountain to climb. You turn just in time to see him being carried suddenly away by a river of molten lava. There is no noise, no heat, no horror: the rock seems only as hot and as liquid as your young imagination can make it. Only you look behind you and there he is, going away, beyond the reach of your outstretched hand. The expression on his face, if he even had one, has long been lost to you. What you do recall, what is still familiar and intimate as the shudder of your own heartbeat, is the shock of panic and guilt—that it is your fault, that you have failed to pay close enough attention, that you have

neglected some responsibility toward another person, that something is now irretrievably, irrevocably ruined.[9]

—
9
From "Atlantis: Prologue to a Pilgrimage," as quoted in Craig's residency application.

The roles had been reversed.

On May 5th, the trackers arrived and went immediately to the entrance of the sand dam where Craig was last seen. Rebecca provided them with a photograph of Craig's footprint he had taken while standing in the soft sand at Miyake Island a few weeks earlier. This photograph proved invaluable to the professional trackers as they tried to follow Craig's footprints. They discerned Craig was wearing a 12 ¼ inch Merrell boot with lugs on the outer rim, and this is what they looked for.

The tracking team spent about forty minutes examining the entrance to the trail, in order, as they explained to me, to calibrate their eyes and decide which of the hundreds of footprints that now littered the trail belonged to Craig. Since this was the main entrance to the mountain, most of the police and other searchers had passed this way. It amazed me that, from the myriad of footprints, they could actually find Craig's.

From Kifune, the trackers knew that Craig started up the trail at the sand dam trail around four PM and probably took about an hour or so to reach the top of Shindake, putting him there around five PM. Although most of the sand dam trail follows a river basin and is easy to hike, near the ridge one has to scramble up a steep basin of scree. The trackers spent the rest of the day following his footsteps up the river bed and climbed up to the scree below the edge of the caldera.

Above the scree basin is the Shindake caldera, extremely deep and rugged. Although one can approach the rim, there are areas that are extremely unstable and prone to breaking off. Adding to the danger are plumes of sulfur dioxide gas that continually emit from numerous fumaroles both inside the caldera and along its edges. The poisonous gas vapors were not as bad as what almost overcame Craig at Miyakejima, but they are thick enough to make breathing difficult.

Next to Shindake is Furudake, an older yet still active volcano. From the rim of Shindake it is only about a twenty minute level walk to the Furudake caldera. In contrast to the Shindake caldera, Furudake is easy to enter. It is flat and contains several interesting natural phenomena, like a bubbling pit of mud, high-pressure steam vents that make a loud hissing sound, and colorful sulfur vents. Although there still remains the problem of sulfur dioxide gas, the caldera is easily accessible, to the extent that the island schoolchildren make yearly excursions there to learn about volcanoes.

The next day, the tracking team continued their observations. They discerned that Craig went first to Shindake then over to Furudake, where he stood in the shallow caldera and, again, left his footprints in the sand.

Craig probably stayed too long in the Furudake caldera before he realized it was getting dark. In late April, there is a residual light until about seven PM, but only in the open spaces, like the mountain peak. Everything but the peak is covered in dense vegetation, so the trail was quickly darkening. In addition, the night he climbed the mountain was a new moon. Once the sun went down it would be pitch black.

From the caldera of Furudake there is a relatively short trail, the Hatake Trail, about one kilometer in length, leading down the backside of the mountain. The beginning of this trail is obvious, and from the summit it seems to lead right down to the road. The trackers surmised that Craig must have thought that instead of scrambling back down the steep sand dam trail, the Hatake trail would be the best way to descend in the waning light. Once he got to the road the darkness would not bother him, since he could just follow the pavement to the village.

Hatake Trail, however, is deceptive. Although the beginning section is easy to follow, farther down the trail is not well-marked and weaves through thick brush. To complicate matters, the native deer on the island have carved numerous false paths that crisscross the trail and lead to dead ends. At many places along the descent, it is just impossible to follow the main trail. For this reason, only the most experienced island guides use this trail.

Although one cannot see it because of the dense vegetation, a very steep cliff parallels Hatake trail about 100 meters to the left.

On May 7th, the tracking team started up the Hatake Trail on the back side of Furudake, thinking to hike up to the caldera and trace Craig's footsteps down the trail. This time I accompanied them to see how they worked. Two thirds the way up the mountain, however, they discovered Craig's footprints veering off in the direction of the steep cliff on one of the many false deer trails. They spent the rest of the day following his footsteps through the brush.

The next day, the tracking team continued their search of this area. Their painstaking and exacting work allowed them to cover only a few meters every hour. Not only did they look for footprints, but they searched for holes left by Craig's walking sticks. They also observed leaves and branches that were broken or littered on the ground. The color and rate of decay told them how many hours or days had passed since they had snapped. Fortunately, there had been no rain since Craig's disappearance so the dirt was still intact. Kifune accompanied the team to this area. It was a section of the mountain that the police had not searched and was uncompromised by other footprints.

The team discovered that Craig determinedly walked or ran through the brush trying to find the trail, anxious to maximize his time and get off the mountain while there was still light. Like on the roads on Mt. Asama, he began zigzagging to pick up the lost trail, all the while heading northeast—what he thought was the general direction of the road (though the road actually lay more to the east from this point). The trackers discovered indications that he moved generally in circles, stopping and climbing up boulders in an attempt to rediscover the trail and find his way down to the road. At one point, they saw evidence that he fell, picked himself up and continued with a limp, perhaps because of an injured leg or knee. It was at this point they noticed his footprints heading toward the hidden cliff.

Obscured by darkness and thick brush, Craig was probably unaware of the danger looming before him. When he broke through the brush, he suddenly found himself precariously balanced on the edge of a sixty-meter drop but was going too fast to stop. It seems he sat down and grabbed a branch of a dead tree to stop his forward momentum. The branch broke off and he fell over the edge. At the bottom of the cliff lay a deep, narrow valley, so forbidding that even the island's most experienced guides, like Kifune, rarely ventured into it.

Once the tracking team discerned the exact spot where Craig fell off the cliff they marked it on their GPS device and then returned to the road, found the valley below the cliff, and made their way to the spot at the bottom of the cliff corresponding to their GPS coordinates. They did not find any of Craig's remains at the bottom. They realized that the cliff was not a straight drop down; in the fall line were several ledges. They ascertained that he must have hit a ledge and gotten caught part way down the cliff. Unfortunately, the face of the cliff is overgrown with vegetation, making it impossible to visually confirm this, either from below or above.

The search team believed that if they could make it down the cliff and continue their tracking efforts they might be able to find Craig. The problem was that they did not have the necessary equipment to rappel down the cliff, and the police were adamant in not allowing the search team to do so, due to the inherent dangers. The trackers and police surmised that if Craig got caught somewhere down the fall line, he might have scrambled horizontally along a ledge hoping to find a way down. It was certain, however, that after twelve days without water and in the hot sun, Craig would have little chance of survival.

Up until this point, we prayed Craig might be found alive, even though each passing day held less and less hope. But at this news even that hope seemed to vanish. The Police Chief very gently explained the likely scenario; that we would only discover his remains. Using a great deal of tact, he also informed us what a twelve-day-old corpse might look like, adding that if a body were indeed found, the police would have to be in charge of recovery.

That evening, I noticed a subtle change in Chris' attitude as he acquiesced to the new reality. The drive and energy with which he had thrown himself into the search was now replaced with a sense of resignation as the focus of the search shifted from rescue to recovery.

Unfortunately, the police had to return to Yakushima to attend to other cases. The tracking team had done what they could, so most everyone involved in the search left the island on the afternoon ferry that day. Only Chris and a low ranking policeman stayed behind.

In the meantime, the Fukuoka Consulate located a professional rappelling team, based in the mountainous prefecture of Nagano, who agreed to search the face of the cliff. They arrived on May 13th. The next day, together with ten locals, they rappelled down the cliff to look for Craig's remains. Incredibly, they were unable to find any traces of Craig or his remains, in spite of expanding the search area to both sides of the cliff and up and down the valley. What that team did discover was that there were two opportunities, or shelves, where Craig might have landed and crawled horizontally, most probably continuing in a northeast direction. This team was not a tracking team and they cleared any evidence from the fall line so they could search more efficiently. Clearly, Craig was not in the fall line.

These results were disappointing for everyone. Not a single item was found, and subsequently, there was no closure for Craig's family or friends. It was especially hard on Chris, who left the island with a sense of personal failure to find his brother. In reality, he did the best he could. He came to a foreign land on a highly stressful mission, not knowing the language, culture or customs, and acted with grace and strength, adapting himself to a situation he could have never imagined.

Not satisfied with any of the results, the family put together another team from the Joel Hardin Professional Tracking Services to continue a search of the cliff. This team arrived in June, before the start of the rainy season, and spent a whole week searching. They scoured the cliff and other areas but found nothing. The lead member of the first tracking team, Sharon Ward, described the problems this team would have faced in trying to find evidence of Craig:

> The team was not able to find sign (evidence of Craig) over the edge. This is not surprising in the least. The mountain climbing team had clear-cut the entire fall line, erasing, in their almost 100 rappels, any evidence of where Craig may have landed. Trackers would have had to sign cut (look for evidence of the presence or passage of Craig) outside of the clear cut area and that would have been a task, at that point, that I, and every tracker I know, would have had one heck of a time sorting out. This is especially true because they would be tracking while harnessed up over the edge of the cliff. The clear cut and the time lag of weeks would have made the footprints or other evidence very, very hard to find.[10]

10
Sharon Ward,
in a personal email

The second team proposed some theories of what may have happened to Craig, and others also added their speculations. Since there were no remains, there was no way to be positively certain that Craig had perished.

Basically, there are only two ways a body could disappear on this island—either falling into a volcano or the ocean. Some suggested he made his way down the mountain and fell into the ocean or slipped away on a boat. This is unlikely as he would have crossed the road back to the village on the way to the sea, and even if he did make it down to the shore, there are only two or three places on the island where boats can safely approach the rugged shoreline. Being such a small-knit community, someone on the island would have certainly noticed a tall foreigner trying to leave. Just to make certain, however, the Fukuoka Consulate conducted a check to see if his passport had been used to leave the country, but the Japanese immigration had no record of anyone by the name of Craig Arnold departing Japan.

There was also speculation that the trackers mistook Craig's footprints and he didn't fall off the cliff but disappeared some other place on the mountain. Sharon Ward also addressed this point:

> My team followed a Merrell boot up the volcano and down the backside. It was the right size, right shape, right age, right sole pattern, right character and right composition to be that of Craig Arnold. Could it have been someone else? Yes, but that person would have had to have been there at the same time, with the same shoes, intention, etc. The footprints we followed stayed pretty much on a northeast bearing. If, after going over the cliff, he landed on one of the shelves, there is reason to believe he would have continued on a northeast bearing. As I understand the second search, northwest was the search area pursued.[11]

There was speculation he fell into Shindake's deep caldera. It is steep and filled with hidden crevices where a body might never be discovered. Then there are the numerous volcanic vents on the island. The intense search efforts of the first few days focused on these two possibilities, but they were both discounted because of the lack of clear evidence. Simply put, no trace of Craig, other than his footprints, was ever found.

Meanwhile, there was an outpouring of concern and mourning from Craig's colleagues, friends and family in the U.S. *The New York Times,* in a May 20, 2009 blog called *Paper Cuts,* published an article by David Orr entitled "There will be no more poems from him." Orr bemoans that Craig was silenced before he could leave a significant oeuvre of work, but points out that, by no means, was his short life of forty-one years without literary significance.

> It would also be a mistake to think of him as a writer silenced before his prime. Arnold's first book, Shells, won the Yale Younger Poets Prize and is an assured, fully-formed collection. In "Hot," for example, he uses smartly executed, slant-rhymed couplets to tell the story of a man burned from within by his need for hotter and hotter food. As the poem ends, the man takes the speaker's hand and

> > ... lifts it to his lip,
> > presses it for a second, the torn flesh
> > as soft, as tenuous as ash,
> > not in the least harsh or rough,
> > wreck of a mouth, that couldn't say enough.

—
11
Ibid.

However sophisticated we make our dishes, the poem suggests, those embellishments are born of simple craving and can never entirely transcend it. We want heat — and Arnold is a poet of "want," in both the word's senses. He's interested not only in our hunger for consummation, sexual or otherwise, but the lack which causes that hunger and follows each flickering moment of satisfaction.[12]

What actually happened to Craig remains a mystery, but in some ways, there is no mystery. A deeply sensitive and poetic soul, Craig had a simple craving—that of yearning for the beauty and crystal awareness found only in the cataclysmic experience of danger. This un-transcended need led him down the paths he took, and he perished doing what he loved.

As I departed on the boat from Kuchinoerabu Island, I had the feeling that his remains would never be found, and that the whole island would become, in essence, his final resting place. As I watched the rugged peaks of Shindake and Furudake fade into the distance, their vents relentlessly emitting scalding steam and gasses, I felt there could be no more fitting tomb for Craig.

Yet, my mind kept returning to the awful moment of self-awareness he must have had when he veered over the cliff, trying desperately to catch himself and failing, slipping and falling into the darkened depths. I wondered, in that moment, did he feel betrayal, or did he feel he would be caught, like in the game of Circle Fall? Or, after the rush of awareness at his fate, did he achieve a peace, finally escaping his captivity to fear?

At first the temptation is strong to catch your balance, to put one foot out to stop yourself, not yet quite believing that you will be caught. But you learn no longer to think of catching yourself, to lose yourself in a dark loop of falling and falling, feeling at every turn a pair of hands to pick you up and put you into the hands of someone else. And your memories of this game, from your mistrustful teens, are of great comfort. Now, many years later, it occurs to you that you like being talked out of these volcano-climbing adventures, a reassurance that someone is looking out for you, has your welfare in mind, if not at heart.

It was impossible to talk Craig out of a volcanic climb, but I found myself wishing that Craig could have seen how much we all, from the villagers of Kuchinoerabu Island, the police of Yakushima, Chris, Rebecca, his son, family and friends loved him and had his welfare in our hearts. But now, it was just too late to catch him.

—

An earlier photo of Craig's footprint (taken by Craig himself) that was essential in helping the tracking team to discover his trail

—

12
David Orr,
http://papercuts.blogs.
nytimes.com/2009/05/20/
there-will-be-no-
more-poems-from-him/

Walking
Keijiro Suga

1

The sea comes landing, to the shore,
The waves stand up and come walking, to the shore,
I touch a volcanic bomb in the rock beaten by the waves,
And I, too, walk on the shore, following somebody from the past.
I walk, accompanied by ghosts,
Listening to the gay songs of the seagulls (we call them "sea cats" in Japanese).
Exposed to the strong wind,
Basking in the bright light,
In an unknowable afternoon at the beginning of this autumn,
Heading towards a northern village,
Heading towards the village of the wordless shark,
On the coast where a vast grassland spreads out,
Against gravity,
Against time.
The heath bushes are dancing as if they were burning.
The sun keeps spinning and turns the world into a negative.

2

Finding our way between the mineral world and the vegetal world,
We went on, climbing the northern slope of the summer.
The path became a stream, then mud,
Then occasionally stairways hard to climb because of exposed roots.
The path was situated between the mud and the sky,
Between the light and the green.
Between the running water and the remaining earth,
Between running time and remaining images.
We climbed on, stumbling, and by the time we were
On a high rocky terrace, as dry as bones, and filled with the sulfurous odor,
The sky was clean and blue like midnight
And the heavy clouds advanced as if crawling into space.

Looking at their whiteness I reversed my heart and imagined a snowstorm.
Then an unexpected coldness penetrated our cheeks.
In the seamless white lay numerous soldiers, dead.
We could even see their words, frozen and dropping from their mouths, to the ground.

3

Perhaps there were days when you came walking on the calm surface of the lake.
Perhaps a beautiful name was blowing soundlessly in the breeze.
In the water were floating algae with plum-like white flowers.
In the shade of the trees, the voices of invisible cicadas
Sharply divided the shapeless air.
As for the shape of the mountain...
The mountain cast a triangular shadow on the plain for just ten minutes before sunset,
It was a triangle that could not be seen from the plain.
It was a triangle only dreamt by a Greek geometrician.
Now I find myself by a small pond near the summit
And on its border a tiny green forest frog is quietly holding its breath.
Perhaps there were days when you came crossing the surface here, too.
Perhaps shapeless sorrow was silently blowing in the breeze.
I want to follow you, if I could walk just like you.
There's a bird of prey, I don't know what species, gliding above my head.
I no longer understand this motion called "walking."

4

On the other coast, the western, an ancient forest is buried,
From the last glacial period, the deluge, the oblivion, the layer of peat.
Now everything is exposed at the cliffs on this shore.
After witnessing twenty thousand years of sunlight,
And twenty thousand years of wind and the continuous fall of meteors,
The tree roots, while maintaining their shape,
Ambiguously repeat sleeping and waking.
Water seeps out of the cliffs.
Water occasionally becomes streams and agitates my heart.
I never imagined that I would think here of Goethe's lament:
"Besides, what do we know? How far can we progress?"
On this coast where Hangeul and Russian alphabets are scattered
With the clear salt water of the dashing waves
I wash a damaged apple and take a bite.
In the shades of the waves foaming in white
Is the reflection of the gentle smile of Love.

5

Autumn comes walking, with the infallible feet of the wind,
Through the shallow marshland, through the narrow openings of the tall, silver grass.
We, too, are walking, speechless
With the intention of welcoming this autumn that has come too early.
Walking on this narrow wooden boardwalk, we see the shapes of the faraway mountains.
In the shade of the tall silver grass, dragonflies with cheerful knowledge dance wildly.
Hiding in the shades are the living of what past periods?
Did you break ice here?
Did you burn stones here?
Under the orange sun of which season, and under what kind of rain clouds?
Did you sing songs?
Did you play the pipes and strings?
Did you capture flocking birds?
My ears cannot reach the old melodies buried under the silver grass
But there's no need to give up your hope that's humming like clouds.
I am addressing all of you.

6

How did it give birth to itself?
What traces of growth does it retain?
The forest, ultimately, is the color of water.
It's the color of clouds, the color of granite,
The color of rain and snow, the color of rotten leaves.
Floating like an island on an enormous amount of water,
This forest, in this land, is gently swaying.
It's the color of mist, the color of ice needles.
From all the colors of water, as if following the musical scale of nature
Greens of all hues grow.
Along with the breaths and vibrations of chlorophyll
The latent greens sharpen themselves like the tails of rays.
They bloom, they flutter, they go mad.
What movement from that process could be registered by nature's gramophone?
Look, this vine is exactly isomorphic with my hair's whorl,
Strongly dancing the spiral of life, like a seashell.

7

Let's go in search of a small forest, a minimal forest will suffice,
I don't even care if we find hares or we don't witness owls.
This is the zone where life transits to death,
And where death makes many lives bud.
In the forest where the fungi are finally dominant
And where the earthworms incessantly work,
Shapes are in constant transformation
And colors and movements constantly shift.
But then, ultimately, all of these together form
A single life, the whole forest is an indivisible unit of life.
There, asking, I go on walking
Asking to various mushrooms with many shapes and colors.
The rotten woods on the ground have eyes and the moss-covered rocks have ears.
Even when a sudden shower comes,
The ground remains dry and light, and emits a refreshing scent.
Here there is no distinction between the midday and the twilight.

—

Translated by the author

C-Lit and *Yaoi* Desire
Mari Kotani

From femme fatale to homme fatale

I cannot clearly recall when I started to be plagued by the nagging suspicion that hidden in this world may be the issue of C. The first inklings of that notion may very well date back to my reading of the Keiko Takemiya manga *Song of Wind and Trees (Kaze to ki no uta,* 1976).

The basics of the story are well known. Born the product of an illicit affair, the diabolical Gilberte matures into a young man of peerless beauty while simultaneously absorbing the *ressentiment* that tortured his father. Gilberte emanates an intense sexual allure, dazzling for its destructive potential. Though the men around him may be able to disguise their desires in most circumstances, none is able to conceal them when they encounter Gilberte. He is frightening for the sexual wiles he employs in seducing all around him, and, as morals crumble in his wake, society labels him a depraved young man.

How did the artist of this manga choose to depict this young man who, like a harlot, would sleep with anyone? This young man's beauty, in fact, is represented in a manner that closely resembles the *shōjo* (young girl), a dominant trope in modern Japanese culture. It is the strong resemblance between Gilberte and such a *shōjo,* combined with the association of him with the harlot, that sets my heart pounding. Though in the logic of Taruho Inagaki, the *shōjo* dimension of his character would be effaced and his allure connected to phallic symbolism, the truth of the matter is that Gilberte is undoubtedly a creature emerging entirely from the genre of *shōjo* manga and his beauty is wholly that of the *shōjo.*

For these reasons, it is perfectly reasonable to consider Gilberte a literary descendant of the "femme fatale" that swept Europe in the nineteenth century. At that time, there were two distinct images of woman: "a domestic angel" and "a diabolical female." While the world sang the praises of the obedient and devoted "good wife, wise mother" (*ryōsai kenbo* as she was known in Japan), it was obsessed with its opposite: the archetype of the "femme fatale," the diabolical and promiscuous woman who led men to ruin. These women

yaoi
in Japan, a popular umbrella term for media (manga, anime, etc.) centered on male homosexuality, primarily for a female audience

manga
Japanese comics. The word is simply Japanese for "comics", but has entered into other languages to refer to a distinctive art form with its own conventions

were presented as running sexually amok, obsessed with men, and leading them to disastrous ends with their dangerous feminine wiles.

I believe this "discourse of the diabolic woman" is rooted in the male fantasy of being toyed with by a woman. Though their feverish pursuit of self-destruction is entirely their own doing, men cunningly deploy the logic of patriarchal society so as to pin the blame on this stereotypical image of Woman.

In time, this archetype was elevated to a thing of beauty and represented in painting, literature, and opera; over time, women themselves, seduced by the image, began to embrace and play out the role willingly.

The latter half of the nineteenth century, the point in time where this archetype took hold, serves as the backdrop for *A Song of Wind and Trees,* which is set in France. The manga features a classic femme fatale in the figure of the mother of Gilberte's lover, Serge: La Païva. In her character development and the situations she encounters, she shares a great deal with the women represented in nineteenth century operas such as *La Traviata* and *Carmen.* However, *A Song of Wind and Trees* does not slavishly replicate the archetype of the femme fatale as it appears in European patriarchies. On the contrary, the manga presents a critically daring antithesis. Having risen from her gypsy roots to the highest echelon of courtesan, the resplendent La Païva is the mistress of the aged Marquis Georges-Louis Garjolais. However, La Païva falls in love with Serge's father, Viscount Atlan Batteur, and the two run off together. Although they remain deeply in love to the very end, they fall into the depths of poverty and both die of consumption while Serge is still a child.

If one focuses only on the episodes surrounding this husband and wife, the Batteurs, La Païva appears to be a fairly conventional representative of the diabolical femme fatale that one finds in literary works. Her tale is, after all, that of a gypsy woman seducing a scion with her sexual allure.

However, woven into Takemiya's work are various subplots that undermine the negative connotations that are assigned these women as they appear in literature. Though she is eventually censured for it, in Takemiya's portrait, La Païva is a woman who dares to live boldly and proactively through an age largely hostile to women. She is beautiful, powerful, willful, and loyal to her one true love, and in this sense, the portrait of La Païva reshapes the archetypal narrative of the femme fatale into the kind of positively connoted romance so characteristic of the *shōjo* manga. Though she may face adversity, and though, paradoxically, she may betray the man who keeps her as mistress, the hero or heroine in a *shōjo* manga always has legitimate reasons for his or her behavior. The rules of romance in the genre demand undying loyalty to one's true love; it is part of the ethical code of the *shōjo* manga, which relies so heavily on romance. To give oneself entirely to pure love is proof of utter sincerity; it is the arena in which the *shōjo* may truly shine.

Perhaps because his mother was La Païva, who lived that role, or perhaps because his father was Atlan, so enchanted by La Païva that he gave up everything in order to elope with her, the son Serge becomes so enamored

Keiko Takemiya's book
Song of Wind and Trees
(*Kaze to ki no uta,* 1976),
featuring Gilberte

of Gilberte that he repeats his father's destiny. The story proceeds along this pre-destined route, bound by the rule that "the sins of the father will be visited upon the son." The character of Gilberte, for his part, ensnares Serge and, in this, seems at some level to be indebted to the tradition of the femme fatale. However, the femme fatale is here manifest in the form of a young man, and this fact alone brings an entirely new dimension to the archetype.

Azusa Noah has pointed out that characters like Gilberte emerged in the genre of *shōjo* manga in 1969, after the release of the film *If...* (directed by Lindsay Anderson), which features a diabolical, beautiful young man. This moment in history was marked by the flowering of world revolutionary movements, the increased vitality of second wave feminism, the coming of age of the postwar generation, and the disruptions caused by art movements working with pop culture in their opposition to the patriarchal mainstream engaged in the Cold War. The female manga artists of the time were attuned to the spirit of this age, and they embraced the youth-driven culture of resistance that marked it. The artists who launched their careers at this time were spurred along by the ethos of the time, and though the pop culture industry of the time was tightly bound to the laws of the marketplace, the artists brought sophisticated thinking to the genre of the *shōjo* manga. The works they created were intellectual and filled with a feminine interiority.

As part of this shift, there emerged from the discourse of the femme fatale a new type of life form: the not-yet-adult male known as the *shōnen,* the adolescent boy. This "homme fatale," a diabolic and sexual male, held the potential to transform the conventional discourse of the femme fatale, from which he had emerged.

La Païva and Gilberte

What makes it possible for us to categorize Serge's mother, La Païva, as a conventional femme fatale is, primarily, the fact that she is a woman. After eloping with Atlan, she becomes pregnant and gives birth to a single child. That is to say, she is unable to escape her female physiology. Through the course of her life, La Païva comes to look more and more like a strong, steadfast mother, and she loses her mysterious aura. She is a woman kept by a man, and Atlan keeps her much as he would an object. Nevertheless, she gives herself to this love willingly and consciously, and in that she breaks a taboo of the male-dominated society. This transgression cannot go unpunished and, as one would expect, she faces hardships that almost seem to be bequeathed to her by the heavens: her beloved husband dies, she is separated from her son, and in the end she succumbs to consumption. The family once so full of love is scattered to the winds.

Gilberte's story, however, is different. His body is not that of a woman, and it is therefore possible for the representation of him to take the femme fatale's sexual powers to an unprecedented extreme. As he will never experience pregnancy and childbirth, he will be spared the transition to the socially sanctioned gendered identity that is "mother;" he can continue to exist as an embodiment of pure sexual pleasure. Though Gilberte remains spiritually loyal to true love, his sexual corporeality is not necessarily an ideal match for his situation, and he is torn by the disjunction. He takes great pride in his mastery of erotic pleasures, which for him exist in a separate realm, but his physical attributes are such that they cannot satisfy the dictates of his heart.

Critics such as Bram Dijkstra, celebrated for his analyses of the femme fatale, posit her as one who leads men to a sad fate. Dijkstra and critics like him parse the symbolism of their case studies, including Salome, Guinevere, and the Lady of Shalott. Very often they adopt the discourse of feminist psychoanalytical criticism and treat these femme fatale figures as women possessing not "real" but rather "symbolic penises."

At times this has been interpreted to mean that these women have usurped the intellect, a faculty traditionally associated with the male. At other times, the femme fatale is understood as threatening or attacking the very concept of "male-ness" itself by causing the downfall of the male through her sexual allure. Here the vagina is symbolically transformed into an abyss, a shift that increases the sexual magnetism of the femme fatale. The vagina threatens to swallow the male, drawing him towards death (thanatos); it is the phallic symbol inverted.

The eros associated with such femme fatales has much in common with that associated today with vampires. The most mysterious of creatures, the vampire emerged in the nineteenth century in a trajectory that paralleled the rise of the femme fatale. This monster, the vampire, did not follow the natural reproductive patterns of humans; rather, with its propensity to bite, it revealed a physiology of a distinct species altogether, and as such, its sexual powers were immune to the processes that threatened such allure in humans.

In other words, the replacement of sexual intercourse with propagation through the ingestion of blood suggests that narratives of vampires represent an alternative, unfettered version of the sexuality so strictly repressed by society at that time. This was a sexual gratification that was not tied to reproduction, and it hints at the polymorphous perversity associated with homosexuality and fetishism. The vampire and the femme fatale hint at this context, and clearly they represent a radical threat to the status quo of the time, based as it was on conventional patterns of pregnancy and childbirth. They were monstrous, and in that, they were rivals of conventional maleness.

The complexity of human sexual conduct means it cannot be comfortably contained within the single pattern of a heterosexual society's family system. In fact, even within that social system one catches glimpses of anomalies—there was, for example, a vast array of brothels in operation and yet they were suppressed and the prostitutes and their occupation were scorned. The femme fatales that appeared in the literature of the time were intimately connected to this cultural context. The monsters, diabolical females, and faeries were all non-human creatures both dangerous and somehow beautiful, threatening to capture the hearts of humans. On one hand, they were glorified in literary texts and, on the other hand, they posed thorny questions to society.

We can safely say that Gilberte is related to these non-human entities. His character is formed as a young man with, quite literally, a penis, and he exists as an embodiment of sexual pleasures divorced from the process of reproduction. These factors make him a sort of femme fatale whose monstrous nature is raised to an unprecedented extreme. In this point, he is symbolically much like a vampire. He is a greater threat to phallocentrism than even the femme fatale. What are we to make of this?

What makes Gilberte such an interesting figure is the fact that his beauty is that of the *shōjo*, the adolescent girl, as she is so carefully developed in the *shōjo* manga genre. In one of my favorite scenes from *Song of Wind and Trees,* a young girl appears, looking exactly like Gilberte. They could well be identical twins, and this fact confirms my belief that Gilberte could have been a young woman. Still, as much as he resembles a *shōjo*, the fact remains that he possesses the phallus, and therein lies his exquisite charm. By donning the mask of a *shōjo*, Gilberte emphasizes that part of his nature that he shares with the *shōjo*: the female body's sexual submissiveness.

We notice something fascinating when we place Gilberte in the lineage of the femme fatale. In this context, we may consider him not a diabolic young man but rather a "*shōjo* with penis." It then becomes apparent that the essence of his sexual power is rooted in the fact that his young male body and his feminine attributes are two sides of the same coin.

The above fact may explain why the end of the story includes a scene in which Gilberte uses his reproductive organs for a male's sexual act: he has intercourse with the *shōjo* Camille. Though here at the end Gilberte resorts to acting as a heterosexual male, it is only after his long embodiment of homo-social behavior. The heterosexual act seems almost to rob him of his magical powers, and in a short time he dies a premature death. It seems almost as if he falls while just on the verge of male adulthood. With his male sexual organs, he had been separated from reproduction. And so, to understand the nature of Gilberte's corporeal existence it seems that the logic of the phallus will not suffice. We need to imagine something of an entirely different order.

P and C

Luce Irigaray, the French theorist, has published an article titled "This Sex Which is Not One." In it she critiques phallocentrism, marked by its singular obsession with the penis, by arguing that the very nature of sexuality differs for women. While men focus all sexual attention on that single point, sexuality for women is auto-erotic, making them in a sense autonomous. Her overall point is that in order to deconstruct the male-dominated power structure, women must examine more closely their corporeality and thereby re-theorize from a position of polymorphous perversity.

Though Irigaray does not express her theory in a linear fashion, clearly one of her central concerns is the symbolic value of the clitoris within auto-eroticism. It is an altogether mysterious organ. Though appearing in the fetus at the point in which reproductive organs are formed, this clitoris neither develops as a male reproductive organ nor, after birth, does it help women in relationships with the male during a life led in a heterosexual society. The clitoris exists at a remove from the work that heterosexual society values most in women and for which it honors them: pregnancy and birthing. Its purpose remains unknown and it is deemed insignificant—except for the sexual plea-sure it provides women. In a word, then, it symbolizes a "sexual organ that exists to give pleasure exclusively to women." There are numerous hypotheses that seek the cultural roots for the negative treatment of this organ in his-tory and folklore. The frequency with which this organ becomes the topic of debate, however, is surely evidence that there is a connection between the negative connotations associated with the clitoris and cultures that refuse to grant women access to autonomous sexual pleasure.

If we were to follow the lead of Taruho Inagaki in our consideration of the literary symbolism of Gilberte's erotic organs, we would see him in posses-sion of not a penis as symbol of maleness, but rather as something converted by illusion to an enlarged clitoris. Speculating further in Inagaki's vein, we might label its symbolic significance "C." Inagaki himself was thinking through German and therefore labeled it "K;" being more engaged with the feminist dis-course of Europe and America, however, I would label it "C." This adjustment is prompted by the influence of Freud evident in Inagaki's *The Aesthetics of Young Male Love (Shōnenai no bigaku).* Following Freud's analysis of sexuality, Inagaki deemphasizes the K, considering it subservient to the P. In this aspect, both Freud and Inagaki reveal how their experiences, rooted in a male corporeal-ity, limit their perspectives. In considering female sexualities and the literary works which reflect them, and particularly in the analysis of cultures based on an attention to the pleasures of women (as is the case for *yaoi* culture), we are surely better served by paying attention to cultural considerations involv-ing the C-sensibility.

What, then, is this C-sensibility? And how are we to interpret it in relation to Gilberte? We might begin by recasting our understanding of him, positing him as a conventional femme fatale—a woman made male, a woman with a penis. With his supernatural powers as a femme fatale, he has his way with those around him. However, much as his audience enjoys the specta-cle, the logic of the narrative will not permit him to threaten the social order, and he dies while still young. He does not perform the male's function in the narrative. What is radical about his character is the fact that he sexually accommodates men.

Gilberte's character is distinguished by his excessive obstinacy, his pride, his complete devotion to his personal pleasures, and his utter refusal to bend his will to others. Obsessed with Auguste Beau, his father, Gilberte attempts to compensate for his shortcomings by throwing himself headlong into a life of sexual hedonism. In these actions he is self-absorbed and egotistical. These, however, are his only faults; though he may have a twisted sense of morality that prompts his decadent behavior, he is otherwise perfect: rich, pleasing to the eye, and blessed with a piercing intellect. In these respects he is a cloistered nobleman, an embodiment of the hero of the gothic romances of the nineteenth century. The narrative is rooted in an anxiety that is indeed gothic in nature, and it reveals a longing to be liberated from restraints and free to pursue one's pleasures. There is also a desire to be emotionally protected from all threats, and this lends the narrative an air of paranoia.

All things considered, theorizing on Gilberte's body suggests that this body is driven less by a desire for male pleasures and more by the logic of auto-eroticism as Irigaray has described it. What we see is a narrative propelled by the quest for the individual pleasures of a woman. In other words, we catch here a glimpse of a narrative based on the C-sensibility. Rooted in female pleasure, committed to a philosophy of self-reliance, and aware of sexual gratification, Gilberte has reached a stable maturity. That autonomy makes it possible for him to pursue relationships of equality with others.

This ability to both pursue sexual pleasure and trusting relationships based on love—and for there to be no contradiction between them—would seem to be the symbolism of a C-narratology. While it may seem at first glance that the narrative logic behind Gilberte emerges from a P-sensibility, where the femme fatale is deemed nothing more than a woman with a penis, the fact is that the logic of this narrative is exceedingly feminine and representative of a C-sensibility.

Taking all of this into consideration, it would appear that C-type symbolism has the following characteristics: it is dedicated entirely to the autonomous pleasure of the female, it makes possible a realm of individual pleasures, and consequently, it allows for an expansive conception of a preference for a world free of restraints and oppression. Additionally, it guarantees the inviolability of the realm of personal pleasures. Collectively, these characteristics make it an important weapon for envisioning and constructing a world where there is nothing unpleasant for women.

The workings of the *seme* ("instigator")

When considering the active components that advance the P within a C-type narrative, we must somehow account for the structure of the *seme*, the instigator of the action, for this seems to represent the infiltration of phallocentrism. Or, alternatively, might it be that within phallocentric structures there lurks something of the C-type narrative logic?

Many *yaoi* works center on the dynamics between a *seme* and an *uke*, the object of the *seme's* actions. Who serves as the real *uke*, in fact, is a crucial issue. It is not simply that the inserter of the penis is the "initiator" and the individual who has the penis inserted is the "recipient;" the conception of the sexual roles is far more complex than this and has long been a topic of debate.

—

seme
attacker; the traditionally masculine member of the *yaoi* couple, who pursues the *uke*

—

uke
receiver; a stock character in *yaoi* media that is typically the younger and more traditionally feminine of the male protagonists

Various questions might be raised. For example, is the *seme* best thought of in terms of maleness as it is traditionally understood? Or, rather, is the *seme* essentially indistinguishable from those who play that role in a homosexual relationship, where it is called *tachi?*

Japan's anime culture rapidly spread abroad in the twenty-first century, and *yaoi* culture has been carried along with it. Even the International Science Fiction Convention now includes panels focused on Japan's *yaoi* phenomenon. At the meeting of this convention in Boston in 2004, I sat on a panel on Japanese culture and experienced some perplexing moments as I tried to explain the challenges of translating into English the terms *seme* and *uke.* Surprisingly, however, there turned out to be no need for concern as science fiction fans outside of Japan are themselves using the Japanese terms, accepting them as part of the discourse after having found them as untranslatable as words like *moe.* As these fans explained it to me, *seme* and *uke* are part of a unique sexuality distinct from those featuring conventional male and female roles or S & M dynamics.

A number of studies that analyze these sexualities have been published in Japan: Nobita Nobi's *The Adults Just Don't Get It (Otona wa wakatte kurenai,* 2003), Yōko Nagakubo's *Theories of the Yaoi Novel (Yaoi shōsetsuron,* 2005), and a chapter titled "Androgyny Under Patriarchy" *(Fukensei-ka no ryōsei guyū)* in my own *Techno-Gynesis: The Political Unconscious of Feminist Science Fiction (Jōseijō muishiki,* 1994). All of these studies note that while the roles of *seme* and *uke* seem at first glance to be stable, they are in fact continuously mutating. The feminist and gender critiques of slash fiction by such people as Joanna Russ, Jeffrey Weiss, and Patricia Frazier Lamb come to a very similar conclusion. The sexual roles assumed by the lovers in these works are not stable; instead they morph according to the situation, and it is clear that the ease with which they alter their sexual roles points to the existence of relationships of utter equality. The structure of these shifting sexual identities has been analyzed in the context of lesbian relationships, and there remains a need for further research.

For an understanding of these dynamics as they play out around the homme fatale *seme,* I turn now to an analysis of "When I Turn Around, There He Is" *(Furikaereba yatsu ga iru),* an homme fatale drama par excellence. "When I Turn Around, There He Is" was a serialized television drama broadcast from January to March 1993. This epoch-making drama was script writer Kōki Mitani's first venture into television screenplays. Set in a large hospital, the plot revolves around the rivalry for power between Kōtarō Shiba, a brilliant but sneaky surgeon demanding exorbitant fees for his services, and Gen Ishikawa, a physician with a powerful sense of justice. While jousting for power and influence, the two also fall in love. In classic Mitani style, the drama is a multi-layered parody. The setting alone calls to mind both *The White Tower (Shiroi kyotō)* and *Black Jack,* and Mitani's drama, full of clever twists and turns, is almost a pastiche of these tales. The juxtaposition of the arrogant Shiba and the gullible Ishikawa alone makes the drama worth watching, but the true glory

—
moe
budding; the ideal of child-like cuteness and frailty that has become an extremely influential element of character design in Japanese media (manga, anime, etc)

of the series is the homme fatale performance of the character Shiba, played by actor Yūji Oda.

This dimension is what the *yaoi* authors amplify in their re-writings of the tale. They trample on the conventions of the mainstream media's standard homosocial drama, always devoid of any sexual intrigue and filled instead with macho posturing, and by filtering the story through a *shōjo* sensibility, the *yaoi* authors turn Mitani's story into a charming romance. Like all Mitani's work, including *"Shinsengumi,"* his series about the young samurai who brought about the Meiji Restoration of 1868, "When I Turn Around . . ." is focused on an intense male rivalry and can be enjoyed without the *yaoi* spin. In fact, even the *yaoi* world did not latch onto this drama in a particularly fanatical way. That being said, there was a bumper crop of "Guys Looking Back" stories in the amateur coterie magazines, each of which presented visually striking depictions of romantic liaisons between Shiba and Ishikawa, the doctors in the original drama.

Shiba was not overtly depicted as exercising his sexual charms in the TV version of the story. Instead, he was portrayed as one with no regard for the ethical codes of the medical profession. He uses a wide range of ruses and underhanded tactics for a position of power in the hospital, and along the way the entire workplace's attitude toward money and profit spins out of control. In short, the drama presents the everyday world of greed and corruption that seems to be the privilege of a male society. What allows Shiba to ultimately gain covert control of the hospital is his brilliant ability as a surgeon, an ability on a par with Black Jack himself. Actor Yūji Oda's portrayal of Shiba renders him a beautiful man acting with such utter confidence that he seems to relate to his male colleagues almost as members of the opposite sex, attracting them with what can only be described as a sort of sex appeal. This dynamic leaves the viewers less interested in following the events and more concerned with the romantic aura that fills the workplace.

Dr. Ishikawa arrives in this environment from the United States. Appalled at Shiba's *modus operandi,* he plots ways to drive Shiba from the hospital. His presence is in striking contrast to Shiba's; Ishikawa is stoic and appears even vulnerable. In this sense, the rivalry seems to be between a femme fatale and a pure-hearted young man, with Shiba playing the role of the wicked temptress and Ishikawa cast as the well-intentioned young man. As the plot unfolds through various encounters between the two, Shiba's past is revealed and Ishikawa, once so dedicated to justice, is increasingly attracted to Shiba's world.

Then, just as it seems he will fall prey to Shiba, Ishikawa is diagnosed with cancer, and his sole hope for survival is through an operation that can only be performed by Shiba. Shiba throws himself into this difficult operation, one that will also give him full control of the stoic Ishikawa's heart.

This being the progression of the drama, it comes as no surprise that the romantic pairings of the two in *yaoi* derivations of the story most often cast Ishikawa as the *uke,* and he is usually the focus of attention on the page.

—

Actor Yūji Oda, Dr. Shiba of *"When I Turn Around, There He Is"*

This perspective alerts us to the fact that the reader engages the story from the perspective of Shiba, that is, from the perspective of the *seme*. The stories are presented from the all but omniscient *seme* perspective of Shiba, and this perspective ties the author of the work to the reader in some invisible bond—everyone appreciates Ishikawa from the same perspective. The Ishikawa that readers gaze upon, of course, is one infused by the readers with the psychology of an *uke* shaped by Shiba's attentions.

Kōki Mitani is male, but the parodies of his work that have appeared in the coterie magazines have been done by women. Both the *yaoi* authors and their readers have broken free of the commonly held belief that the passive *uke* role is to be played by women. The *yaoi* parodies distinctly place them in the position of *seme,* instigator. Shiba, the homme fatale, and the reader share the same perspective. The *yaoi* versions of the story appearing in the amateur coterie mangas are done by people who watched the original drama, but their versions present an Ishikawa that would never appear on TV. While the Ishikawa of the TV drama is stoic, meticulous, and utterly indifferent to sexual matters, the *yaoi* Ishikawa is pure, adorable, and prone to coquettish behavior as he responds to subtle sexual advances from Shiba. In these representations of the tale, cancer does not figure into the plot, and we appreciate Ishikawa for the cuteness and vulnerability that stem from the sexual aura he inadvertently exudes. In the hearts of both the authors who create and the readers who consume this representational mode there arises the possibility of a Shiba-esque homme fatale.

In the process of transforming the world of television dramas, the *yaoi* genre forcibly expels all elements that might disturb the romance, leaving a narrative structured solely for the purpose of bringing pleasure to its readers. In this we can detect a C-type narratology.

Love stories that start with the C

J. R. R. Tolkien, author of *Lord of the Rings,* collected his writings on otherworldly fantasies in the book *Tree and Leaf* (1964). According to this work, a tale of faeries (what today we would call an otherworldly fantasy) requires not only the depiction of a mysterious faerie but also the construction of a world that we imagine might be home to such living things. Structurally speaking, then, the worlds of *yaoi* and the various types of boys' love *(tanbi, BL,* and *shōnen ai)* would presumably resemble the realms of faeries as Professor Tolkien explained them. If the emergence of a faerie requires the materialization of an alternative world for them to inhabit, then the appearance of *yaoi* characters means there must emerge a world governed by rules that protect their existence.

A distinguishing characteristic of *yaoi* representation is the central role played by male characters. There is, therefore, a considerable amount of overlap with gay representation and, in fact, the difference between the two has been a topic of debate in the past. A careful reading of *yaoi* works in

—
shōnen ai

boy's love. Often used synonymously with *yaoi* though it also connotes a subgenre aimed at a younger, more idealistic audience, tending to be less explicit comparison with gay literature, however, reveals that they are not the same. The defining difference is that *yaoi* remains true only to female desire. Whatever a woman may find unpleasant is eliminated. For that reason, frameworks based on justice or ethics cannot be directly applied to *yaoi* narratives. The realities of male genitalia, too, may at times be omitted in these worlds where cultural symbolism and conventions appear only in modes that appeal to women. Such being the case, representations of maleness that dance within the pages of *yaoi* works require a new type of investigation, one based on the narrative logic of the C-sensibility. Such scrutiny would, presumably, shed light on this odd and puzzling phenomenon wherein characters that are physiologically male act only in ways that are pleasing to women.

The distinguishing characteristic of representations of maleness is the penis, the very symbol of the male. *Yaoi*, however, are distinct from the narratives that circulate in the real world, and they often replace the symbol of maleness with a narrative that is pleasing to women. This compels us, then, to examine what exactly has been changed in this shift. This will lead, I believe, to a discovery that what we have assumed was a phallocentric narratology is, in fact, a narratology that begins with the C.

The *fujoshi* may be in possession of a C-sensibility. If that is indeed the case, then we should recognize the fact that whenever one identifies a narrative as being based on a C-sensibility and labels it part of a *fujoshi* mentality, the true *fujoshi* would most likely turn away, muttering that the idea is nothing more than another weird theory that some science fiction-loving feminist is trying to foist on them. The true *fujoshi* would most likely object, claiming the idea had nothing to do with them at all. They would react this way because the ties that bind the *fujoshi* are based on the premise that there is to be no infringement on the subjectivity of another. With sexual preferences clearly being for the auto-erotic and the self-contained, they dream of bonds existing between equal, autonomous individuals. The C is a private thing and blooms finest when left alone; if not, it would once again be wrapped in a phallocentric narratology.

—
fujoshi
rotten woman; slang term for female fans of *yaoi* media

—
Translated by
James Dorsey

Tales from *Fin de Siècle* Japantown:
The Japanese Working Students of San Francisco
Takayuki Tatsumi

My late mother, Chizuko Tatsumi (1926–2009), had a deep and abiding respect for my American-raised great-grandmother, Fumiko Yamaguchi Kawase (1873–1956), one of the first female students to graduate from Tufts University at the *fin de siècle*.

Fumiko Yamaguchi was born and grew up in Asakusa, Tokyo, went to Boston in 1885 at the age of twelve, stayed with the Governor of Massachusetts, and majored in biology at Tufts. It may sound unusual that a Japanese adolescent girl went to the United States by herself. However, since the Meiji Restoration, which exposed Japan to Western civilization, a number of Christian missionaries, if indirectly, helped arouse a fever for studying in the United States among Japanese boys and girls.

For instance, Umeko Tsuda (1864–1929), another girl nearly ten years older than Fumiko, traveled to the United States in 1871 at the age of six, funded by the Meiji government. She mastered English by 1882, and when she returned to Japan, as the second daughter of Sen Tsuda, a strong proponent of the Westernization and Christianization of Japan and the inspiration for the Friends School Japan founded in 1887, she established the prototype of Tsuda College in 1900.

The success stories of the Japanese students in the United States must have induced Fumiko's modern parents to have their daughter study in Boston. It is no coincidence that the year 1885 saw Fumiko's voyage to the United States as well as the publication of a tremendously influential essay, *Datsuaron* (Escape from Asia), written by one of the founding fathers of modern Japan, Yukichi Fukuzawa (1835–1901), in many ways the Japanese equivalent of Benjamin Franklin.

Although the precise cultural background of Fumiko's parents still remains unknown to us, it is true that Fumiko was very active as a pious Baptist. According to her daughters, that is, my grandmother and great aunts, the Massachusetts governor himself had wanted a playmate or bosom friend for his daughter in the household, and especially wanted one from a foreign country. He found Fumiko perfect.

One might expect my mother to have held in higher regard my great-grandfather, Dr. Motokurō Kawase (1871–1945), a pious Japanese Anglican who grew up in Gifu Prefecture and went to the United States in 1892 at the age of twenty, earning a medical degree from Boston University in 1899, and later working at Japan's first modern hospital, St. Luke's. However, in spite of the doctor's accomplishments, our family reserves the highest adoration for great-grandmother Fumiko, who had established herself in America before him.

Allow me to relate an interesting episode from her life. One day in 1896 or 1897, when Fumiko was a junior or senior, the president of Tufts summoned her to his office, where she first encountered her future husband, Motokurō Kawase. He had just arrived in the Boston area from San Francisco, where he had studied English for a year. What has long amused my family is that at the very moment he was introduced to Fumiko, his wicker suitcase began emitting strange noises—beep, beep, beep, BEEP, BEEP, BEEP. The sound, it turned out, was coming from the alarm clock he had hidden within the suitcase.

Wedding of Fumiko and Motokurō

Thus, my maternal family could well be called a matriarchal line; the family history is one of not patriarchal but rather matriarchal dominance. In keeping with that tradition, it was only the thumbs up from my great-grandmother that brought to fruition the arranged marriage proposal brought to my father, Toyohiko Tatsumi (1916–), in the days right after the war. As it turns out, great-grandmother had been on friendly terms with my grandfather on my father's side, Kōnojō Tatsumi (1864–1931), born in Wakayama prefecture. They had been in America at the same time, and she advocated for his family by uttering the words of authority, "Tatsumi-san faced a lot of challenges in America, but he made his way to the position of manager at the London branch of the Yokohama Specie Bank, Ltd."

Founded in Yokohama in 1880 with the help of Yukichi Fukuzawa, the Yokohama Specie Bank played an internationally significant role from the mid-Meiji period through World War II. Not only did it help in the reconstruction of the nation after the Great Kantō Earthquake of 1923, but it also paved the way for the success of the Bank of Tokyo, with which it merged in 1947. This institution was reorganized as the Bank of Tokyo-Mitsubishi UFJ in 2006 and is currently the largest bank in Japan.

Though lacking a formal degree, Kōnojō Tatsumi was a self-educated man who worked hard in San Francisco between 1889 and 1892. Moving then to London, where he lived from 1892 to 1920, his continued efforts established him as a major banker. It is also well known that during his London life he both physically and spiritually supported young Japanese scholars and writers such as Kumagusu Minakata (natural historian), Shinzō Koizumi (economist), Takitarō Minakami (novelist), Yomokichi Sawaki (art historian) and others. His life shows us the way a Meiji Japanese working boy metamorphosed into a self-made man in the American style and a gentleman in the British manner.

After repatriating from England, my father's family lived on an estate in Ushigome, Shinjuku Ward, Tokyo. It was damaged in the air raids during

World War II, with all the precious papers and materials being lost when the storehouse on the property was burned to the ground. This has left us in the dark concerning our ancestors' time in America, and my father had resigned himself to never really knowing much about that period.

It just so happens, however, that quite recently I discovered, largely by coincidence, an important thread leading back to my paternal grandfather and his life in the U.S. This happy coincidence came about as I was re-reading the works of Shin'ichi Hoshi (1926–1997), one of the pioneers of modern Japanese science fiction, in preparation for writing something for the catalog accompanying an exhibition dedicated to him at the Setagaya Literary Museum. The exhibition, slated to open in April 2010 for a two-month period, was to be a rather extravagant affair, making full use of various audio-visual materials as well as offering a detailed history of this short story writer so eminent that he has even been granted the title of "god of the super short story." The sponsors went all-out for the exhibit; they even recreated the bar from his famous story "Bokko-chan" and installed in it not only a replica of the voluptuous robot bartender but also a life-sized photo of Shin'ichi Hoshi himself.

My interest, however, was drawn to parts of the exhibit that dealt with the history of the Meiji Period (1868–1912) and Hoshi's father (Hajime Hoshi) and grandfather (Yoshikiyo Koganei). In his later years, Shin'ichi Hoshi had himself researched their lives and even written several volumes of biography based on what he found. This was the dimension of the exhibit that I had hoped to explore.

My interest was rooted in some research I had done in the summer of 2009 as a Fulbright scholar based at Stanford University in Northern California. Though part of my work was connected to American literature, I also collected material on the origins of the Japanese immigrant community centered in San Francisco. It was while working with this material that, in a most unexpected place, I came across the name "Hajime Hoshi."

Hajime Hoshi (1873–1951) was another self-made man, or what we in Japan would describe as "one who hammers himself into shape." It is well known that his first step on the road to success was his journey to America in 1894 as an entrepreneur. Hajime traveled to America alone at the age of twenty, and he supported himself doing odd jobs while he studied at Columbia University in New York. In her voluminous critical biography, *Shin'ichi Hoshi: The Man Who Created 1001 Tales (Hoshi Shin'ichi: 1001 wa o tsukutta hito;* Shinchōsha, 1972), Hazuki Saishō focuses on this period and what followed. However, in chapter eight of his *The Meiji Period, My Father, and America (Meiji, chichi, amerika;* Shinchōsha, 1975), Shin'ichi Hoshi himself reveals that the initial point of entry for Japanese at this time was in fact the West Coast, more specifically the "Foggy City," or San Francisco.

As it turns out, Hajime spent almost two years in San Francisco as a working student. It was only in 1896 that he ventured to the East Coast, where he enrolled at Columbia University. It was after this initial apprenticeship that he returned to Japan to found Hoshi Seiyaku Pharmaceuticals on his road to enormous success.

—

Hajime Hoshi

My own research, however, was directed at something entirely unrelated: the "Gospel Society" *(fukuinkai),* an organization that looked after the needs of Japanese immigrants and students in San Francisco. Kōnojō Tatsumi, the paternal grandfather I mentioned earlier, arrived in San Francisco in 1889 as a young member of the Yokohama Specie Bank, Ltd., and he worked with this organization before moving on to England. Kōnojō was born in 1864; Hajime Hoshi in 1873. Because of the proximity of their ages, I associate the two and cannot help but feel empathy with Hajime Hoshi, whose incompetence in English and lack of familiarity with American culture led to a long string of setbacks during the time he worked with the Gospel Society as he pursued his studies. He ended up toiling diligently as a housekeeper for an American family.

My colleague, Professor Yoshiko Uzawa, has written a book titled *Hashimura Togo: Yellowface and the Japanese in American Popular Literature* (*Hashimura Togo: Ieroo feisu no amerika ijinden;* The University of Tokyo Press, 2008). In addition to earning her a Ph.D. degree at Keio University, the work was also awarded the 25th Joseph Roggendorf Award at Sophia University in 2009. In this study she carefully examines a series of humorous columns featuring "A Japanese Schoolboy: Hashimura Togo" published approximately 100 years ago by the American writer Wallace Irwin, who assumed the voice of a young Japanese writer *(Letters of a Japanese Schoolboy: Hashimura Togo* and other works are now available from Kessinger Publishing).

Very well received at the time, these works all feature as protagonists Japanese working students. Professor Uzawa's study was, in turn, the basis for a stage performance in 2009. Playwright Yōji Sakate wrote a script peppered with biting black humor and dealing with issues such as race and social class. The fact of the matter, however, is that the surviving records indicate that the Gospel Society and its support of working Japanese students pre-dates the Irwin depictions by more than thirty years.

What sort of organization was the Gospel Society? Though Shin'ichi Hoshi describes it simply as providing "lodgings," the documents indicate that it was not so one-dimensional: in addition to its meetings for Bible study, the society offered frequent educational opportunities in the form of lectures by renowned experts in diverse fields. These tantalizing tidbits had me traveling often from sun-drenched Stanford into murky and fog-covered San Francisco. I would sometimes speed in by car and at other times by train, and often with my wife along. I would visit Japantown, where to this day one can still find a tin advertising sign reading "Hoshi, for all your medicinal needs" *(kusuri wa hoshi)* exhibited inside New People, a brand new building showcasing Japanese popular culture and promoting the J-Pop Center Project.

Still, search though I might, I simply could not pick up the thread of the Japanese community as it had existed before the San Francisco earthquake of

1906. When my sabbatical ended, I left determined to return for more thorough research, perhaps by ensconcing myself in a library such as that at UCLA, with its strong collection in Japan-America relations.

It was sheer coincidence that on my return to Japan I realized that my predecessors had already produced a systematic body of related work. I am thinking of *Documents Chronicling the History of the Gospel Society (Fukuinkai enkaku shiryō;* Gendai shiryō shuppan, 1997) and the collection of interpretive essays titled *The Emergence of a Japanese Community in America: Essays Based on the "Documents Chronicling the History of the Gospel Society" (Zaibei nihonjin shakai no reimeiki: "Fukuinkai enkaku shiryō" o tegakari ni;* Gendai shiryō shuppan, 1997), collaborative studies coordinated by Yasuo Sakata and Ryō Yoshida, of Osaka University and Dōshisha University, respectively. Perhaps due to the "yellow peril" mood of the times, Japanese immigrants between 1880 and 1890 were portrayed in a negative light, and this seems to have mitigated against any serious research into that community—until, that is, the collaborative research organized by these men at the end of the twentieth century. It represents the first step toward understanding these immigrants. I had the opportunity to ask Hazuki Saishō, the aforementioned biographer of Shin'ichi Hoshi, about this pioneering work, and it seems that even she had not been aware of it.

—

Kōnojō Tatsumi

I acquired these books and untangled the various threads running through them. As I expected, I found various traces of Hajime Hoshi among the records and membership rosters of the Gospel Society. There is documentation of Hajime having presented for the society a lecture under the title "Commercial Prospects" in July of 1895. My own grandfather, Kōnojō Tatsumi, had himself been responsible for a lecture titled "Economic Theory" in February 1892. However, with my grandfather having sailed for that other foggy city, London, in August 1892 and Hajime having arrived only in 1894, there is no possibility that they encountered each other in America. My great-grandfather on my mother's side, Motokurō Kawase, arrived in San Francisco early in the summer of 1892. While there is, therefore, some chance that he crossed paths with Hajime, I find no record of his name in the Gospel Society rosters. It may be the case that he did not come under the care of the Gospel Society because he spent such a short time in the area. Though historical records tell us that he was in the Bay Area to improve his English, he was soon on his way to Boston University.

Nevertheless, it is an indisputable fact that these men, both of whom were affiliated with the very same society, were present at the dawning of the age of the Japanese working student, a cultural presence that prompted literary representations in the years that followed.

—

Translated by James Dorsey

Superflat Tokyo
Roland Kelts

On his first visit to Tokyo, American novelist Paul Auster remarked to his Japanese translator that the city managed to combine the density of Manhattan with the sprawl of Los Angeles—and still thrive. American poet Gary Snyder, while refusing to live here again, has claimed that Tokyo is the world's most successful megalopolis—home to millions, yet resolutely functional, clean, safe and efficient. Tokyo was reportedly the brightest city in the world seen from NASA satellites in space and is now home to the largest number of three-starred restaurants in the storied epicurean Michelin Guide from Paris. It is much darker now, of course, humbled by tragedy, but still standing amid the debris of its northern neighbors. Tokyo's public transit system is the envy of every city in the world, as are its relatively low crime rates, stable incomes and public services. Still, while it is easy to find people who are astonished by or simply respect Tokyo, it is hard to find people who claim to love it.

Quick quiz: How many songs can you name about the glories of New York, Paris or London? Now try Tokyo.

Tokyo is massive, and Auster was likely awestruck, as many of us are upon first encountering Japan's capital city, lone national center of finance, government, publishing, media and mass entertainment. Imagine New York, Washington, D.C. and Los Angeles sharing the same regional real estate, with a bit of South Beach decadence around the edges and thirty-five million people, the world's largest metropolitan population, vying for its services and attention. Now imagine trying to make that city livable, even pleasurable.

I have now lived in Tokyo for several years, after visiting numerous times as a youth with my Japanese mother. Yet I will never forget the fortieth floor view of the city I took in as a young adult from my room in the Keio Plaza Hotel in Shinjuku. Jet-lagged and bleary, solo in Tokyo for the first time, I watched the lights course deep into the distance and wondered: Does this town ever end?

Thickets of skyscrapers rise haphazardly across the megalopolis, which oozes out from the city's official center, the Imperial Palace, to Chiba in the east, Saitama in the north, and Yokohama due west. South of the city is the natural inlet of Tokyo Bay, but it, too, hosts an armada of skyscrapers and entertainment complexes in a mini-metropolis built on a landfill called Odaiba, originally a platform for a fortress of defensive cannons to ward off enterprising colonizers in the nineteenth century. Japan was officially opened to global trade by the arrival of American Commodore Matthew Perry and his so-called "black ships," a naval fleet of four vessels that landed at a rocky outpost in Izu, a peninsula south of Tokyo, in 1853. After Japan's nightmarish attempts at Imperial dominance of Asia in World War II, its cannons were transformed, not into ploughshares, but to pachinko (gambling) parlors and entertainment centers. Tokyo is ample evidence of a capitalist emporium gone mad, a postwar playhouse for your every distraction.

Natives of former capitals Kyoto (794 to 1868) and Nara (710-794) still speak of Tokyo as a callow upstart, over-Westernized and insufficiently schooled in the ways of proper cultural etiquette. I have experienced this first-hand, having lived in Osaka for a year. My friends there happily host me in their homes when I visit, but unless they are on business, most refuse to trek north so I can return their favors. "Tokyo is an artificial city," one of them told me by way of explanation and apology. "There's nothing real or Japanese about it."

True: Tokyo is not Japan, any more than New York can stand as sub-stitute for America, or London for England. Many Japanese outside of Tokyo are either deeply skeptical or dismissive of the megalopolis making decisions on their behalf, just as Americans love to decry the actions of New Yorkers or Washingtonians, and rural Britons gleefully trash Londoners. But owing to its mostly mono-ethnic population (roughly two percent of residents today are foreign-born) and financial and media pillars, Tokyo to me remains deeply Japanese. The casual visitor eyeing one or more Starbucks or McDonald's out-lets on nearby corners may not immediately grasp this paradox: Tokyo is both Japan's most global city, and a global cipher, resistant to transparency even as it struggles to retain relevance amid its fast-rising neighbors in Asia. It is a city that stubbornly defies comprehension, which may be part of its appeal.

Welcome to Tokyo—Hybrid City

In the early 2000s, I researched and wrote an article about the Japa-nese government's then nascent tourism slogan: *"Yokoso,* Japan!" or "Welcome to Japan!" A Foreign Ministry official told me that their strategy was to make the Japanese word *yokoso* ('welcome') as popular as the Hawaiian term, *aloha.* In 2010, no such luck. The banners greet you at the airport, and a few signs are still tethered to streetlamps, but no one in Japan or elsewhere is gleefully high-fiving, fist-bumping or shimmying to shrieks of *"Yokoso!"*

The same official's softly expressed concerns may underscore part of the reason why. Tokyo, he noted, has no visual icons it can claim as its own. While the Eiffel Tower *ipso facto* stands for Paris, Big Ben for London, and the Empire State Building evokes New York all on its lonesome, what do you see in your mind's eye when you think Tokyo? The most obvious marker is the Tokyo Tower, a gaudy orange (if slightly taller) mimic of the grand Eiffel in Paris. Tokyo's most emblematic skyscrapers are similarly plagiarized. The Nippon Telegraph and Telephone (NTT) building in Shinjuku is a grim, dark and windowless echo of the Empire State Building. Odaiba, the artificial island in Tokyo Bay, greets incoming ships with its diminutive replica of... the Statue of Liberty, courtesy, again, of France.

Tokyo is about mimicry and hybridization, borrowing influences and recreating them in the context of local culture. In the absence of original iconic images, Tokyo must reinvent itself visually—as a visual mash-up of all that it borrows, without becoming lost in its mirrors.

Tokyo's Impresario

No one has wrestled Tokyo to the mat more brutally than Takashi Murakami, whose artistic vision is an analog of the city. I first saw Murakami's art in the form of his sculpture called *Hiropon:* a wide-eyed girl-woman with massive breasts swinging a stream of lactating milk like a jump-rope around her skipping body. The torso and legs were lean and athletic, the breasts comically huge. The milk looked nearly lethal—more a bondage device of rippled eaves than a stream of life-enhancing liquid. *Hiropon's* sparkly oversized eyes above a pert and tiny nose at first struck me as too self-consciously borrowed from anime cliché. But upon closer inspection, I realized why they were making me increasingly uneasy: blank white orbs of reflected light sat just off-center, adding a hint of Orphan Annie inscrutability to the colorful swathes surrounding them. Viewed from other angles, their vapidity could look menacing. She was cute, even sexy by way of hyperbolic parody. But she was also, quite possibly, deranged. I was new to Tokyo then, but discovering Hiropon in an otherwise unremarkable western suburb made perfect sense. Tokyo had already become for me a city in which stumbling upon the tantalizing amid the mundane had itself become commonplace.

A few days later, I learned that *hiropon* referred to meth-amphetamines—in particular, the uppers consumed by Japanese laborers building a new Tokyo during Japan's postwar reconstruction. The word was also a street name for heroin. At the time, I was drafting a short story I had been commissioned to write. It was taking shape at least partly as an exploration of two of my frequent obsessions, delusional longing and delusional nostalgia, and I could not resist borrowing Takashi Murakami's sculpture for its title: "Hiropon my Heroine."

Murakami has since become well known internationally as a bridge between Japan's contemporary pop culture imagery, largely via manga, anime and toys, and its contemporary art and fashion scenes—largely via ample commercial success in the former and rampant commercialism in the latter. He has also become something of an impresario, presenting contemporary Japanese artists to the global art market via Tokyo and New York, and offering provocative theories in order to both explain and brand them for consumption. The Takashi Murakami who has been the subject of major shows in Los Angeles, New York and Europe is a seasoned businessman, unabashedly so. Newspapers gleefully call him "the artist as CEO," and complaints arose from the usual suspects in 2003 when he accepted Luis Vuitton designer Marc Jacobs's invitation to brand the company's famous brown handbags with the smiling colorful flower icons of earlier Murakami paintings.

Murakami has also almost single-handedly opened Tokyo to the buyers, critics and fans of the global art circuit. With his own aesthetic whims as guidance, he selects and helps to cultivate the careers of Japanese artists such as Chiho Aoshima and Mr., both of whom now work in the newly constructed artists' studio space in Queens. Through his Geisai Art Fairs in Japan, Murakami hopes to open the Tokyo art world to the ambitions and achievements of the city's native artists. "In the West, you [already] have your galleries and exhibitions," says one of his New York staffers. "But in Japan, it's much less rigidly defined. Takashi's fairs are to stimulate buying and selling, and to get young artists exposed. He's trying to establish an art market for less established figures."

So who is the real Takashi Murakami, emblem of Tokyo? A skilful huckster, spinning shallow art and consumerism into a capitalist enterprise and shoving it back at the West at inflated cost? A middle-aged postmodern hipster with a native knack for blending high and low in the name of the now that rivals Madison Avenue's brightest? Or a bit of both—plus a genuinely serious trained craftsman who is able to convey today's Japan in all of its cartoonish identities and show the West what it wants to see in today's Japan? Those of us who have lived and worked in Tokyo may see less reason to begin asking these questions or even raising debate, for Murakami is very much of and about the city in which he still spends most of his time. His most oft-cited boilerplate theories—"superflat" as a culturally specific aesthetic style and "little boy" as a culturally specific historical pathology—are better personified in the city of Tokyo than anywhere else in the world.

Superflat is hardly new, but it is handy—a single word to summon images of sleek computer monitors and flat panel television screens while suggesting a historical lineage (pun intended) of respectability and mystique. Japanese artists' relative emphasis on the manipulation of the line, or the outline of shapes and forms, for effect over the shading techniques (classic *chiaroscuro)* of depth perception and perspective pursued by Western artists is an example of superflat that can be traced back to the *emakimono* picture scrolls of the twelfth century. The Japanese have always seen and conveyed the world in this way, according to Murakami, and now, with our addictions to streaming Internet videos, computer games, cell phone and LCD screens, so do the rest of us.

When I was forced to describe the contrasting views of New York and Tokyo from above (my airplane porthole window) in my book *Japanamerica,* I used the following metaphors. New York, with its rising stone skyscrapers and falling avenue valleys in grid-like order, its shapely rivers and natural contours and stolid burnished lights, appeared to me as a jewel below, elegant and sturdy, clearly defined as it reached up toward you, beckoning calmly. Tokyo, by contrast, with endlessly circuitous patterns seeming to follow their own

Byzantine logic, an uncertain relationship with the sea (an artificial island in the middle of the bay?), and red lights and neons blinking neurotically and sleeplessly, looked more like a computer chip, a tangled mass of somehow interlocking devices that never revealed a start or a finish, pulsing on with perpetual data.

From above, New York is all about rising and falling, foreground and back, the space between the Empire State Building's mighty spire and the broad dark magnificence of Fifth Avenue at its side. Gazing down over Tokyo, I can rarely identify a single street, building or neighborhood. Instead there is the seemingly endless, and very flat, expanse of the urban.

As above, so below. Stroll down Broadway from upper Manhattan. Unless you are a native, and thus too frenzied and focused to pause, you will be taking time out to view the balconies and turrets, the forceful thrust of buildings like the Flatiron, or the cavernous gaps of courtyards behind iron gates. The contrast of light and shadow lures you in.

In Tokyo, the casual visitor is awash in light. Buildings assert themselves, to be sure, surrounded by narrow alleyways that are barely visible in the glow. But it is hard to notice them amid the action on the street— flashing signs inviting you to all-night *izakayas* (food and drink bars), karaoke bars, hostess clubs, fast-food counters and noodle shops. They envelop every train station, so where you are matters less than the fact that you are there. Wherever you alight in the city of Tokyo, this is what you expect—and this is what you get. Superflat.

Is it any wonder that Murakami greets us with the proliferating mushroom clouds of the only nation struck by nuclear bombs, that he sends us flowers of power with quizzically broad smiles, that his drugged up, dazed and giddily mindless Hiropon has vast breasts, mammoth milk—and an unnervingly aggressive desire to please?

Superflat is a clever word for an artistic approach that may well have been historically amenable to Japanese tastes. And Murakami may be at least partly right in suggesting that an accidental convergence is taking place in the twenty-first century, making manga, anime, fashion, high-and-low and East-and-West more blissfully confused and connected than before. To paraphrase English pop band the Vapors, maybe we are, in this manner, "turning Japanese."

Murakami's "little boy" theory—that his nation has for sixty years learned to become servile to Western interests, and developed the appropriate resentments and related irreverence—is a psycho-historic aesthetic of wounded pride and disfigured ambition. To pursue, but not embrace, his positing of America, and the West, as Big Brother, I still think it is helpful to look directly at Tokyo.

I have a personal stake in this vantage. While my mother was born in Tokyo, she was raised in northern Japan, first in the village of Esashi, later in the small city of Morioka. If you visit either Esashi or Morioka today, you will find little of the combined deference, worship and disenchantment with the West that colors Murakami's vision. Despite harsher economic conditions than

those in Tokyo, local citizens in those communities act with sincere benef-
icence—and also sincere difference. They do not expect non-Japanese to
behave like the Japanese do, hence they seem more provincial to the international traveler. At the same time, they do not harbor the vindictiveness or
self-loathing inherent to Murakami's best work. They were neither buried in
Western icons nor brutalized by American soldiers. No wonder.

Where else in the world would a capital city boast as its landmarks
crude copies of other cities' landmarks and leading artists whose grasp of cap-
italistic reproduction exceeds that of their primary sources? Tokyo's identity
is rooted in its postwar history—a hybridized, post-industrial megalopolis of
the twenty-first century, an urban center that questions the value of original-
ity through its native acquisitions, its astute borrowings of what symbolizes
other cities, even as it reinvents itself out of necessity.

In short, Tokyo is a mashup, a remix, a postwar matrix of temples to
spirituality (Buddhism and Shinto, the national faiths) and capitalism (skyscrapers and statues appropriated from Western models). As such, Tokyo has
emerged as a distinctly contemporary city, sprung from obscurity via Western films like 2004's *Lost in Translation* and native anime masterworks like
Akira. Tokyo is a real town full of real people, mega-millions of them. But after
decades on the world's stage, it remains as much of a cipher as Hello Kitty—
tantalizing and expressionless, massive but hidden, an empty vessel you can
fill with your densest dreams. Oh, what a town.

All illustrations by
Kentaro Sasaki

The Art of Passing Through Walls
an excerpt from *Jet Black and the Ninja Wind,* a novel
Leza Lowitz and Shogo Oketani

Rika was awoken by birdsong at the precise moment of daybreak. As if the birds had been waiting for dawn, having spent a restless night between sleep and wakefulness, mindful of foxes. Rika had never slept so soundly in San Francisco, with the clanging of the cable car bell and the trucks rattling down the steep hills. She had come from California to the mountains of Aomori to meet her grandfather for the first time and had slept for about fifteen hours straight in his old house deep in the mountains. She felt rested and happy. It was her mother's present for her high school graduation. Satoko said she wanted Rika to know more about her heritage. To discover her roots. Her grandfather would never get on a plane and come to America, so if she wanted to meet him, she had to fly there. At first, Rika was puzzled, but when her mom handed her the choice of a plane ticket or a summer job at an ice cream parlor and the next year filling out college applications, the choice was clear. So here she was.

Rika went into the kitchen. Masakichi was already up.

"We'll have a Japanese-style breakfast with fish, pickles and miso soup with *nameko* mushrooms, fresh from the mountain. Is that okay?" her grandfather asked. He was wearing a flannel shirt and work pants. His face was bright, and he seemed relaxed and happy.

He handed her some dishes to put out on the table. She set the table quietly.

Masakichi took a bunch of small mushrooms from a bamboo basket, shook the earth from them, cut off the dirt-soiled roots and put them into the miso broth.

"Rika, there's something I need to ask you," he said, looking up at her seriously. "Takao told me you used the art of *sozu* when you met him at the Fujin waterfall yesterday."

"*Sozu?* What's *sozu?*" Rika asked. She was still learning Japanese.

Masakichi grinned. "You hid your presence. You disguised your energy by muting your aura. Takao was surprised. Even Aska couldn't detect you."

"Oh." Rika smiled, remembering how she had disappeared into the bushes when she sensed the boy's presence. "Mom taught me how to do that when I was a kid."

"She did?" Masakichi looked sideways at his granddaughter.

"Yeah. She taught me lots of crazy things like that. She called it my 'life training.' I had no idea what she meant. I used to hate it, but it forced me to get strong."

Masakichi seemed excited. "Life training, eh? I want to hear all about it."

Rika had never told anyone about it before and was happy to be able to talk to her grandfather.

"When I was young, she'd take me to the desert or deep into the mountains at night. We did all these strange things. She trained me to walk on wet toilet paper. 'Try to walk on it without tearing it,' she told me. Even though I put every ounce of concentration into my feet to make them light as a feather, the wet paper tore at my first step. I remember it exactly." Rika shook her head.

"But mom wasn't easily satisfied. 'Rika, you misunderstood me,' she said. 'Even if you walk as carefully as possible, the paper will tear. So the important thing to remember is not to walk carefully but to breathe as if your body is as light as a feather.'"

Rika had never understood why her mother had made her endure such harsh training. It wasn't until she was ten years old that she realized not all kids had to learn how to tread water with weights on their ankles and turn somersaults in the air.

"Sounds like my daughter," Masakichi shook his head, laughing.

"I always wanted to please her, to prove to her that I could do what she expected. So I tried harder until I did. Finally, she said, 'Okay. Let's back up. Let me explain. To make yourself light, first you should breathe in a little bit of air, then spread it through your entire body.'"

Rika showed her grandfather how she inhaled slowly, filling her belly, diaphragm, lungs and chest with air, then sent it into her whole body to make it float.

"But you see, it didn't work." She sat back down. "I felt light-headed, but my body still felt like a ton of bricks. Mom said, 'That's the way. Keep working on it. Once you learn to use your breath, you can make your body light as a feather or heavy as lead. You'll see.'"

"And? Then what?" Masakichi asked. His face was flushed.

"After three years of training, I was finally able to walk on wet toilet paper without tearing it. It was amazing!" Rika remembered how proud she'd felt when Satoko said, "Wonderful! You're as stealthy as a cat."

Rika swallowed, hoping Masakichi didn't think this was all a bit too strange. Maybe he would just chalk it up to her American ways.

"Why don't you tell me how you did what you did yesterday?"

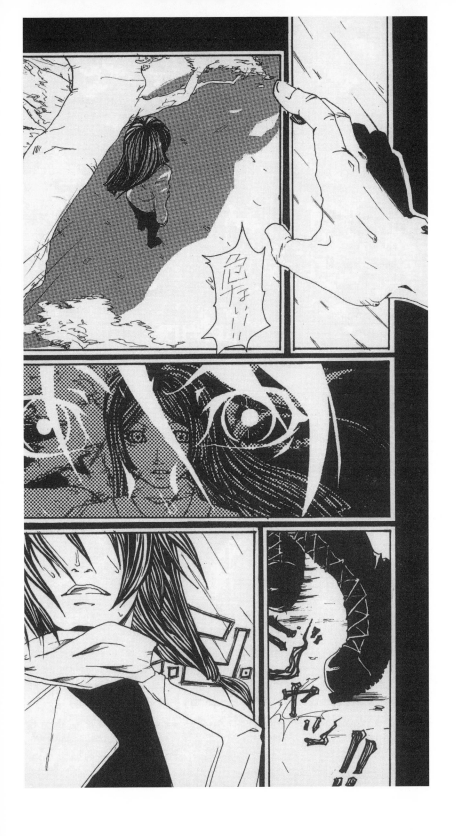

"Oh that? It was easy. You see, when the birds flew out of the bush, I took advantage of the commotion. I used the confusion to empty my backpack and throw my stuff to the bottom of the waterfall. Then I caught one of the birds in my hand, put it in the backpack, and threw the backpack over to the branch on the other side of the cliff. The strap caught on the branch."

"And then... ?"

"The bird moved inside the backpack, and Takao mistook the movement for me. That's when I jumped into the bush and held my breath so that I was barely moving at all."

"That's a lot to do in a few seconds!" Masakichi grinned proudly.

"Well, I was scared. I didn't know who he was or what he wanted. I didn't even think about it. I guess that 'training' paid off," she said. "Anyway, was that *sozu?*"

"Indeed. *Sozu* is the old Japanese word for scarecrow. When a warrior wants to conceal his presence, he decreases the length of his inhalation and exhalation, subduing his *ki,* or life force. In *sozu,* he stops breathing and stays completely still. He becomes one with nature, just like you did."

"I'm comfortable in nature," Rika said. "It's like my home."

"I can see that. You're a very unusual girl." Masakichi's face softened. "Anyway, this art was used mainly in battle, when a warrior was surrounded by enemies and had no way to escape. He lay down and pretended to stop breathing until the enemy retreated. *Sozu* was especially effective when hunting dogs were around—even they were tricked."

"Like Aska!" Takao's Akita hadn't even detected her.

"Right. The hardest thing is to stop breathing. See, you exhale completely. Then you hold your breath," he demonstrated, holding his breath for what seemed to Rika like a very long time.

"Okay, Grandpa. You can breathe now!"

Masakichi exhaled. "I could have held my breath for a lot longer," he chuckled.

"That's amazing. You must have special powers," Rika said, putting the cutting board on the kitchen counter and wiping her hands on her thighs. A smell that reminded her of dried wood rose from the pot. It was the mushrooms.

"Not so. It's just the result of practice and hard training. Anyway, since you've mastered the art of *sozu,* you'll be able to master the magic of passing through walls quickly enough," Masakichi said, taking a ladle of miso and stirring it into the pot of boiling water, using a chopstick to break up the honey-colored paste in the ladle's bowl.

"Passing through walls?" Rika's eyes lit up. "Is that what you said?"

"Yes, the art, and the *magic,* of passing through walls." Masakichi's blue eyes were half-closed, and his smile made him look more like an elf than a warrior. "Let's see, where's a good place to try it?" He looked around the kitchen.

"Right now?" Rika couldn't believe it. She had been expecting her grandfather to be an old country bumpkin.

"Sure, let's give it a go!" He turned off the gas. He walked across the room and stepped up onto the wood floor and took off his *zori* sandals. The wood floor was almost a foot higher than the dirt floor.

"Watch closely. I'll go in and close the closet door." Masakichi opened the door of the pantry and stepped in.

"Then what?" Rika called out.

"I'm going to escape by passing through the wall. If you watch from the kitchen, you'll see that I won't open the door to get out."

"Okay. I'm watching." Rika fixed her gaze on the door.

"But first, I want to show you this is not just some magic trick. Come on into the closet. Look around. Check the inside for trap doors and whatnot, if you like." Masakichi opened the door and beckoned for her to step inside the closet.

Rika peered inside. There were some wooden boxes and old jars, and it smelled a bit moldy. She knocked lightly on the walls, floor and ceiling. No trap doors or trick exits.

"Did you find anything?"

"No, not at all."

"Okay. Here we go! This is real magic." Spreading his arms like a magician, he entered the closet and closed the door behind him. Rika stood on the dirt floor in the kitchen, keeping her eyes on the dark-grained wood of the closet door. There were no sounds from inside it. Total silence.

Rika shook her head. It was impossible to pass through walls. There must be some trick. She listened carefully. No sound of moving floorboards or a section of the wall. She closed her eyes and concentrated. She still felt his presence inside the closet.

Almost thirty seconds went by. There were still no sounds. Then, all of a sudden, she lost the sense of Masakichi's presence. Where had he gone?

Rika stepped up to the wood floor. She stood in front of the closet and called out for her grandfather.

"Ojiisan!" Rika called again and tried to open the door. Then she heard Masakichi's voice behind her.

"*Oi!* Here I am!"

Rika turned around. Masakichi was standing outside the kitchen in the bright sunlight, wearing the *zori* he'd taken off when he'd stepped up to the closet.

"Those are the shoes you left on the edge of the dirt floor!" she said.

"That's right," he nodded, grinning like a child, his eyes twinkling pleasantly.

"When did you make your escape?" Rika asked, perplexed.

"Just now. When you noticed that I disappeared and stepped up to the wood floor, I opened the closet door and walked right past you, across the room to the dirt floor."

"You walked right past me?" Rika was shocked, even slightly annoyed. She prided herself on her keen perception. There was no way he could have walked right past her unless he was invisible.

"Yes," Masakichi said. He was clearly enjoying her confusion.

"But I didn't see you pass me. And I was watching, believe me."

"Yes, you did watch everything carefully, but this magic is something you can't see."

"But…" Rika wondered if *ojiisan* was crazy, senile, or both. But his blue eyes twinkled, and he looked amazingly cogent.

"Let's say you *forgot* that I opened the door and walked past you. Wouldn't that be like not *noticing* me open the door and walk past you?"

"Yes, I guess so," she said, skeptical.

"Well, that's what happened. Think about it."

"Do you mean that I lost my *memory* of seeing you open the door and walk past me?"

"Yes. That's exactly it!"

She nodded, finally understanding. "I got it! You hypnotized me!"

"That's right! The minute you noticed that my sense of presence disappeared, your breathing became slightly irregular. I used that moment to open the closet door and give you a little hypnotic suggestion. It's called *saiminjutsu.*"

"But there wasn't even enough time to blink!" Rika blurted out. She hoped she hadn't hurt his feelings.

"Well, it wasn't much time, but it was enough. This isn't ordinary hypnotism. The human brain is such a mysterious thing, you know. People can remember or forget something in the blink of an eye."

Rika hated to spoil her grandfather's fun. "Well, I remember once when I was in junior high, a student fell off the roof, got a concussion and lost consciousness. Fortunately, he regained it soon, but had absolutely no recollection of anything that had happened that day. When he came to, he thought it was the day before," she said.

"Yes. Everyone thinks he remembers what happened yesterday, or even earlier the same day. But if you ask someone to remember what he did a minute or even an hour ago, most people won't be able to remember."

She considered her grandfather's words. What was I doing an hour ago? I was….

"Hmmm," she said. "I guess you're right."

"It's not because people have bad memories. You see, the memory center of the human brain has two functions—remembering and forgetting. By tapping into the forgetfulness area, I can make you lose your memory."

"But it's so specific. How can you tap into only that part?"

"I didn't say it was easy. These warrior arts are just like any magic; every form has its tricks. This one helped a warrior safely venture deep into enemy territory, and he had to subdue guards in order to break through. This was before smelling salts."

The Art of Passing Through Walls   Leza Lowitz + Shogo Oketani

Smelling salts. When was the last time I heard that? Rika had to laugh. And what was all this talk about battlefields and strategies?

"Grandpa..." She wanted to ask why he was teaching her all this, but suddenly, it all started to make sense. Maybe her mother was a warrior, too. And maybe that's why Satoko had always made Rika train so hard in the forests and deserts. Which meant that maybe Rika was a warrior, too. Had this been what her mother meant by 'discovering her roots?' A shiver went up Rika's spine. Maybe they were even ninja!

"There are always battles to fight," her grandfather said, as if reading her mind.

"You mean the people who want to make the mountain into landfill?" Her cousin had told her about them before.

"Yes. They used to come here a lot, trying to dump waste from Tokyo onto our mountain, but we refused to let them. So they hired some thugs to harass us. But, sorry to say, we fought back," he laughed a hearty laugh. "And they haven't been around for a while. But they could return any time. Those kind of people are very persistent."

"I hope not," Rika said. The thought of the beautiful mountain being used as a garbage dump made her angry. After all, it was her mother's homeland.

"Me too," Masakichi said, wiping his hands on his pants and stirring the soup.

"I'm back!" Takao called out from the doorway, where he knelt down, wiping Aska's paws.

"Welcome home!" Masakichi said, setting the food on the table. "Anyway, there are always threats to peaceful people who live close to the land. If you stay here a bit longer, I can teach you *taijutsu,* just like I taught Takao. All you need to know is how to protect yourself, right?" He put his hand on Takao's shoulder as they sat down.

Takao nodded his head, petting Aska as she lay beside him. The dog seemed to be in heaven, peaceful and serene by Takao's side.

"But I hope he never has to use those skills. What good are these small skills against all the destruction in the world today?"

"I guess you're right." Rika peered inside the soup bowl, but could barely contain her excitement. The *nameko* mushrooms smelled like wood. When Rika swallowed, she noticed they had a thick texture, probably from the fungus that covered them. A smoky taste spread in her mouth.

"Do you like it?" Masakichi asked.

"Delicious," Rika said, pretending to enjoy the strange taste.

Masakichi shook his head. "You're not very good at lying, though."

Rika laughed.

"Your mother loved this kind of miso soup when she was little. As soon as fall came, she used to go hunting for *nameko* mushrooms in the forest. She was a good hunter."

Masakichi looked from Rika to Takao contentedly.

Then he leaned forward toward Rika. "Around here, people like me are called *matagi*. We're just hunters. If anyone asks you, that's what you should say. Okay?"

Rika nodded.

"Actually, the name of our town, Kanabe, means 'bear' in the Ainu language," Takao said knowingly, his chest beaming with pride.

"That's right. Many families here hunted bear to survive. To the Ainu, the bear was a gift from God. They respected this enormous, powerful creature. He gave them his meat, his fur, his medicine. They gave him their gratitude and respect. He kept the Wa away from the mountains. The Wa are afraid of *kanabe*, you see." Masakichi's eyes twinkled.

"And we are just as happy to have them stay away. Because as long as there is a mountain, there will be a forest. As long as there is a forest, there will be bears and mushrooms and *yakuso*—medicinal herbs—and the village will survive," Masakichi said.

"Anyway, the reason I taught Takao *taijutsu* is so that he would get to know himself better. The main thing you need to be aware of in *taijutsu* is your own state of mind. Whatever you're feeling will be embodied by your actions. If you're afraid, your actions will be controlled by fear. If you're confident, they'll be strong. This is one of the fundamental principles of the way of the warrior. The real battle is always with oneself. So you have to understand and accept your strengths and weaknesses and work with what you have. That's what makes a real ninja."

"Ninja! Did you say ninja?" Rika jumped up, spilling her soup.

"I said the real warrior has to emerge from within," he said, nodding.

Rika sat down. Masakichi poured the water over the fragrant green leaves in the teapot. Then he handed Rika a blue and white teacup and poured her a cup. "Only by strengthening your weaknesses can you be whole."

Rika took the steaming cup between her hands.

"We knew you'd come back one day, but we didn't know how much Satoko told you."

"What he means is, we're so glad you came back," Takao said. "If more people come back to the village, it will come alive again."

"That's right. It's completely self-sustaining. As long as the mountain and rivers remain, the village will thrive. That's why we stay here on the mountain," Masakichi said. "I hope you will stay for a while and learn our customs and arts."

Rika took a sip of the rich, roasted tea. It went down her throat, and she felt a warmth rise up her spine. So she would stay and learn magical things, like passing through walls and flying over rooftops.

"Yes. All the young people went to the cities, and this little village is like a ghost town. But it can't stay buried forever. Like all roots, it has to emerge. It's our destiny. It's yours, too," Masakichi looked thoughtfully at his granddaughter.

"Hai," Rika said, looking at her grandfather. A breeze blew through the old wooden house. Rika felt the brisk coldness of the wind that was coming down from the mountains, and she suddenly felt alive. She could smell the fragrance of nuts, grains and seeds in the air. She knew why the people loved the mountain so much. There was something magical about it, beyond time.

As they were clearing the dishes, her mother called from San Francisco.

"Was it your plan to make me come back to the mountain and stay here for awhile?" she asked. Satoko always had a trick up her sleeve.

"What did your grandfather say?" her mother replied.

"Grandpa said he wanted to teach me many things. So, tonight he taught me how to pass through walls," Rika reported.

"Wow. He must really like you. I didn't get to learn that one until I was twenty!" Satoko's laughter rang out across the ocean, all the way from San Francisco.

"Thanks, Mom," Rika said. "I think I'll stay for a while."

She understood that she and her mother were more alike than she'd realized. And she also understood why her mother could never tell her just how alike they were.

They were female ninja, *kunoichi.*

But Rika knew that their secret would be safe in the mountains, where the birds and the trees and the vast sky had kept their own secrets alive for thousands of years.

Dream Corridor
Stewart Wachs

Dreams say what they mean, but they don't say it in daytime language.
— Gail Godwin

When people ask why I came to live in Japan, I sometimes tell them that Japan first came to live in me; that my physical journey here in 1984 was merely an overdue affirmation of this.

It all began in 1980, when I was twenty-nine, with the first of a series of vivid dreams. These occurred at dawn and continued through four summer mornings. I would find myself in an unfamiliar yet comfortable foreign land, with men, women and kids whom I cared for, yet could not upon waking recall ever having met. In these dreams, whole days would go by. I was happy, in love and engrossed in my work—a far cry from my waking hours, where a founder-ing marriage and indecisive career were all I seemed able to manage.

It's long ago now, and details of those daybreak dreams have faded. At the time, though, they were compelling for the clarity with which I recalled them. After all, for most of us most of the time, dreams are fleeting, fugitive things. These were noteworthy for one more reason. In them I often conversed, if haltingly, in Japanese, a language I had seldom even heard.

When the dreams ceased, a yearning grew within me to leave Cali-fornia and travel to Kyoto, which somehow I knew had been their setting. But my American life, for all its shortcomings, had its trappings as well. I indulged myself instead by talking with friends about a future journey and became a Japanophile—Kurosawa and Ozu films, *koto* concerts, *otsukimi* moon-view-ing in the city park, books on *bonsai* and history, cherry blossom festivals in San Francisco's Japantown. I ate *yakitori* and green tea ice cream, and eve-nings after work I even took a Japanese language course. Then one summer afternoon, three years into all this, while grilling chicken at a barbecue in my friend Jim's backyard, I was blathering as usual about going to Japan when Jim, who had studied Chinese at Beijing University, unexpectedly grew sullen. "Stewart," he said in a tone of exasperation. "Just answer me one question, will you? Just one?"

Stammering, I said that I would.

"Do you even have a god-damned passport?"

A sheepish week later, I did, and its blank pages now beckoned invitingly. Even so, it took another year to plan my departure and go. A few days before flying, I phoned up Stephen, an old college friend I hadn't seen for a year or so. To my surprise, he implored me to meet him; he had something to show me about past-life regressions. I needed, he said, to learn about one of my own.

During our lunch at a busy Chinese restaurant, Stephen flipped through a two-inch stack of index cards that held, he said, notes of his own past lives. I listened skeptically, but intrigued by how my erstwhile stockbroker pal could ever have gotten himself wrapped up in something so cabalistic. After the meal, we walked back to my house, sat down in a pair of sofa chairs and got started on me. I was relieved there was no "New Age" ritual. Stephen began by asking whether I had recurring dreams. I recounted the two most frequent.

In one, I'm surrounded by pitch darkness, trying to get to a distant building that is all aflame, but my feet are leaden. The near-paralysis fills me with anguish. In the second dream, it's a sunny day and, in a seated position a foot or two off the ground, I whisk myself anywhere I wish to go. This hover-flight seems natural. Whenever I awake from this dream, I'm bewildered that I have somehow lost what so unmistakably felt like an inborn ability.

"For now," Stephen instructed, "enter the space of that second dream." Closing my eyes, I did so, surprised by the ease of a technique it had never occurred to me to try.

"Now open your eyes; look around you there. What do you see?" Almost immediately, a bare, tanned shoulder moved before me, part of an entire virtual scene that was somehow superimposed on my living room, also still clearly visible. In this waking dream I was riding inside a basketwork palanquin, borne by two nearly unclad men, my seated form moving along a foot or two above a flagstone path, heading toward a Japanese-style building that appeared to be a temple. I told this to Stephen. Answers to his questions appeared at once.

"Where are you?" In Kyoto.

"When?" Thirteenth century... around 1248, or '49...

"Who were you then?" On this I drew a blank.

"All right, keep moving along that stone path."

I did so another few moments.

"What now?"

The two men in loincloths had carried me to the temple entrance. I climbed out of the palanquin and slid the front door open myself, all of this happening in pictures while I sat motionless, facing Stephen.

Entering, I found an austere, shadowy anteroom decorated mainly with a pair of very tall, slender vases of blue and white porcelain. One had a cracked portion at the top where repairs had been made, on the rim.

"Now draw your attention away from yourself just far enough to look back and see your own face." This peculiar request was also easy to carry out. I now saw a man with high cheekbones and a feathery moustache, whose mournful face conjured up painful grief and a montage of recollections.

"I was an aristocrat who became a priest... unable to be with the woman I wanted... caught between my devotion to life in the worship hall and another life that I yearned for in the performing arts, where this woman lived hers... I'm watching her dance now at night on an outdoor stage, by torchlight... but all this longing is out of the question for someone like me." Then I peered straight into the eyes of that man. "I took my own life, some years later," I said. Stephen nodded knowingly, which rattled me, and the whole *mise-en-scène* simply vanished from view.

Stephen then pulled out a card from his stack and let me read its penciled notes, about a life he said he, too, recalled from thirteenth century Japan.

Within a couple of ebullient, eye-opening weeks, I had settled into a small *tatami* room near Kyoto Station, made some friends, joined an expatriate theater troupe and found a teaching job that left my daytime hours open for exploring. I'd also met Sue, a warmhearted painter ten years my senior who had come from L.A. to Japan to study techniques for restoring ancient painted scrolls.

I would spend the night at Sue's occasionally, and once, a few hours after we'd fallen asleep, I abruptly awoke from a tormenting nightmare: I'd been enveloped in roaring flames, within which emerged serene faces with eyes like thin crescent moons.

"You were shouting," Sue told me, "'Sanjusangen-do!' over and over."

I had no idea what the word meant. Sue explained that it was a temple not far from her place that sheltered a thousand statues of Kannon bodhisattva — deities of compassion. Would I like to go there in the morning? Yes, I answered, and we drifted back to sleep.

Rain clouds spread over Kyoto, dimming the interior of the worship hall as we shuffled inside in our stocking feet. Turning right to skirt what looked like the side of a grandstand, with the hall's paper-windowed *shoji* glowing softly at our backs, we were suddenly face to face with an immense crowd of time-weathered, life-sized golden figures standing in rising ranks ten columns deep and seeming to stretch on forever.

Each Kannon had dozens of arms, with delicate hands that nearly all held objects—a vial, an arrow, a set of rings, a bell, a scepter, a lotus bud. Two hands were joined in front, palms pressed together in prayer. The eyes in their tranquil faces were barely open. And each figure was crowned with several smaller heads and a halo.

I gazed at their faces, awestruck, lingering longer on some than on others. "Familiar?" Sue asked in a whisper. And yes, she was right, they were, but not only from my dream: A few of the faces—each was distinctive— reminded me of people I knew back home. Folk belief holds that anybody can find such faces in the throng.

The androgynous, serene Kannon brought to mind the myth from Plato's *Symposium:* that humans were hermaphrodites until split in two by God, since which time, mere halves, we have wandered the world in search of a partner to make us whole again—the root of the longing we know as love. The Kannon here seemed enviably peaceful legions beyond desire.

As we made our way slowly along the worn wooden floor, down the deep hall, coming before the large, principal Kannon seated centrally on a lotus blossom seven petals high, I was increasingly torn between feelings of reverence and a resistance based in a core precept of my Jewish upbringing: the ban on worshipping idols. But the reverence was overpowering, and as I let go and inhaled the incense smoldering near this largest statue I also felt, welling inside, an achingly mournful sadness.

I paused to gather myself at a counter nearby where booklets, cards and amulets were sold and purchased a picture book guide. An hour later, over a bowl of rice, I would read that this massive temple, founded in 1164, had burned to the ground in 1249. Priests had risked their lives by running into the flames to save as many of the thousand Kannon as they could. In all, 124 had been spared. The rest were reduced to ashes and cinders, and it had taken a team of Buddhist sculptors led by the master Tankei seventeen years to carve and gild anew the figures which have stood in the rebuilt sanctuary ever since.

Sue flew home. By now divorced, I stayed on in Kyoto, and then met Etsuko, urbane and gregarious, born in the rice-growing town of Sasayama. We married and soon had a daughter, and I grew ever more devoted to family, friends and students in Japan. I wrote for newspapers and magazines, took up photography, poked around in rustic villages. And I seldom gave further thought to the strange occurrences told above. They seemed immaterial now, except perhaps when I'd take a visiting friend or relative to view the marvels at Sanjusangen-do.

Years sailed by. Then one morning in early spring I awoke from a dream that I hungered for more of, yet could not even recall—a total blank, aside from knowing that this was the day to visit a well-known Kyoto temple I hadn't yet gone to see.

We were in an open corridor linking one temple building to another. My wife, Etsuko, had meandered ahead while I was looking intently at a folding screen covered with ancient, fan-shaped paintings. When at last I turned to move on, I saw her standing in profile peering into a glassed-in display. I approached but still was unable to make out what was inside, for the angle was acute and the floor-to-ceiling panes reflected the sunny Zen garden outside. Yet as I drew closer, I felt a painful tightening in my chest, and it took a moment to comprehend that here again was that grief and anguish, which seemed to have no reason at all for congealing in that moment.

I reached the display; it held a palanquin, basket woven and faded to a dirty gray. I was startled, confused, in pain, but didn't want to break the quiet flow of our outing by blurting out my dubious, self-centered tale, most of which I had never yet shared with my wife. So I steadied myself and asked her to read the little wooden sign at the bottom.

"This priest's *kago* dates back to the thirteenth century."

Silent but reeling, I stepped away toward another display nearby. And there inside were a pair of tall, slender vases of blue and white porcelain, one with a crack repaired on its rim. My knees buckled. I started to sob. Etsuko wrapped an arm around my shoulders and urged me to tell her what on Earth was the matter. We retreated to a tearoom in the temple, where, still stunned, I did the best I could.

That was eight or nine years ago. I've often thought since about the path I have followed through a corridor of dreams, sometimes looking backward to the distant past; at other times, ahead to the future. While inside of these dreams, however, the time for me has always been *now*.

Some suggest that we each have immutable souls that pass from one life on to the next. We have, they say, mistakes to correct, lessons to learn and to teach. Others assert that we're given but one precious incarnation in which to do our changing and learning. Somehow, in light of my experiences, I feel both of these standpoints hold truths partially clouded by illusion, that neither has it quite whole. For while spirit seems to pass on, nothing—not even this—is immutable.

It is change itself that makes everything precious.

Paradoxically, the more I have felt the life and death of that sad Kyoto priest echo through my days and nights, the less have I sensed any claim to him. Tasting his grief, coming face to face with artifacts from his life, I've begun to see instead that I do not own *this* lifetime either. I'm grateful beyond measure for this borrowed existence. But, like the priest's, my life will end. And like his, mine may well reverberate someday in the heart of another. After all, this happens every day between friends, enemies, students, teachers, family and lovers whose lives overlap in time. Why, then, should eras stand as barriers between us, if truly there is unity of the one and the many? As a dreamer, perhaps I have simply needed more sleep than most to awaken to the illusion of the separate self. I take heart in the words of the Dalai Lama, who says that sleep is the best meditation.

Small Fish
Iona Sugihara

Shizu was about to pour the packet of fish stock into the boiling water when the phone rang. At the second ring she turned off the gas and, with the packet still in her hand, she shuffled five steps into the next room and picked up the receiver.

"Grandma?" the voice said. She was going deaf but Shizu could still pick up a sense of urgency in Ellie's voice. Perhaps it was a motherly instinct, something that old age and hearing aids couldn't quite muffle. She answered with the usual spirit she had for when Ellie called.

"Ellie-chan, when did you get back? I thought you were still in America. I was just making the soup for dinner. The Shuzenjis, you remember them, came back from Oita with fresh spinach. I was just thinking of you, I know you like spinach in your soup." Shizu was just about to follow up with a how-are-you when Ellie spoke.

"Grandma, I need your help."

"Oh? What's that? What happened?"

"I need to borrow some money. Please don't tell Dad."

Shizu was silent for a moment. "Of course I can lend you some money, Ellie-chan, how much do you need? Are you all right?"

"I need 180,000 yen as soon as possible. I promise I'll return it as soon as I can. I need it by the end of this week. Don't worry, I'll be fine, I just have to sort something out. I need it in my account, not Dad's. I'm so sorry, Grandma."

Shizu wrote down the bank details on the back of a catalogue brochure as the receiver grew heavier in her hand. "You'll get it by the end of this week, I promise."

As she put the phone down she wondered whether she should have actually asked her granddaughter what the money was for. But there are some things better left unquestioned, and though this idea had given many people the impression that Shizu was disinterested in their trials and tribulations, it was her way of being polite, her way of expressing that she understood more than anyone that there are many places to hide things. She went back into the kitchen and slipped her hand under the microwave.

There are many places to hide things. Stashed under the microwave was her bank book, but folded away into the creases of her selective memory was a secret that Shizu had kept for sixty years. By now she was an expert at keeping secrets. The key was not to run away, but to walk down the same steps, take the same shortcut through the same forest, to get used to the smell of cigarettes. This way her memories became minimized, shrunk, the print so small that it got overlooked in the history books and photo albums.

It had happened when she was eighteen, the war just over, the "Meri-kan" soldiers occupying the small harbor town. The base-camp was yet to be completed and sailors were everywhere, too big and generous for doorways and roads. Shizu had seen them with their yellow hair, throwing out gum and chocolates to little children in the street. The children had learned American songs. They'd grown up in air-raid shelters, taking refuge for days at a time in the dark, mosquitoes buzzing and stomachs rumbling. When they should have been learning math, they had learned that bodies curl up into fetal balls when burned, that the best way to eat crickets was to fry them in hot oil. Now they serenaded the marines with garbled renditions of "You Are My Sunshine," begging like dogs for candy treats. Unlike Shizu, children were never good at keeping records. They didn't understand humiliation.

One evening Shizu was walking back from the women's college, taking a shortcut behind the school and through the deserted park and woods back home. She could see a shadow sitting and smoking on the swings, white sailor hat just visible in the moonlight. Shizu bowed her head as she hurried past him to the makeshift steps leading into the woods. The Merikan got up from the swing, calling to her in English, and she started to run. He started jogging after her as Shizu reached the steps and climbed up, two at a time. But the soldier had long legs and he caught up with her swiftly. She lost her footing on a wet leaf and fell. She screamed as a large pair of hands grabbed her by the waist and bent her back down over the wooden planks and onto the pine needles. He pulled her skirt over her head and pinned her down with it. The golden haired man with tobacco breath proceeded to teach her how to please a man. When he finished he threw a handful of coins onto the ground and hurried off, suddenly afraid of consequences. Shizu sat on the step, waiting for the pain to subside, spitting on her knees and rubbing off the dirt. She dug a hole and buried her underwear before picking up the coins and heading back home.

Several weeks later, when Shizu's periods stopped she only vaguely knew what had to be done. So she relied on old maid's tales, from washing with vinegar to walking over suspended bridges, but nothing happened. She had heard of a woman who had succeeded by massaging her stomach every day with a bamboo stick. But that didn't work either. Eventually Shizu got out the money that she hid in an upturned cup buried in the woods above the park, and caught the bus to the doctor in the next town, who sat her on a bed and shoved a set of cold metal clamps inside her with a familiar brutality.

Her punishment came in the form of an arranged marriage to an older man and two sons born feet first. After the broken plates, hurled frying pans and snapped baseball bats, she thought she had atoned for her sins, until the eldest came home one day with a white woman in his car and a baby in his arms. Shizu realized then that perhaps life is not so forgiving, that you can spend a year of mornings praying for sun and still get rain if rain is what is needed. And so she surrendered.

The bank book was tattered; everyone used cards these days but Shizu liked to keep the records. Ellie-chan needn't pay her back; Shizu was happy to help her out, it's what grandparents do. The poor girl needed a mother figure after her own mother left when she was a toddler. Shizu had known that marriage would never last. She never trusted the blue eyes. Ellie had done well, though, gotten into a university in America all on her own. Still, she needed someone to look out for her. She shuffled about the kitchen, collecting her hat, handbag and coat from the backs of various chairs. She checked that the gas was turned off one last time before locking the door, taking a shortcut through the woods, down the steps and into the small harbor town.

The money arrived in Ellie's account two days later, and she withdrew it all in cash from the convenience store, quickly slipping eighteen notes with eighteen faces into one of the pale blue envelopes provided. She placed it carefully in the bottom of her shoulder bag, under a bottle of jasmine tea and a shawl for good measure. She hurried through the crowded streets of Umeda, bumping into people occasionally, as she passed by shops full of young girls in ruffled mini-skirts and mustard berets. She tried not to look at anyone lest they look right back like mirrors. She found her way to the clinic, and at the entrance she changed into slippers and sat down in the waiting room with her bag on her lap. She'd worn too many layers and her armpits were damp. The receptionist came over and handed her a leaflet. She felt a sudden urge to pee.

She'd come back because here at least it was legal. Or it was illegal but there was a way around it. She knew how and why it had happened. They'd spent a particularly cold weekend in a single bed, working themselves up to fever-pitch until eventually, both of them did get a fever. The antibiotics had no effect on Leon, but they counteracted the pills Ellie was taking. When her period was late, she bought a test, and somehow feeling it was a private and personal affair, she took the stick out in the college toilet and peed. For two weeks she convinced herself that it usually took several tries for people who *wanted* children, but already her bra was getting tight and there was a small pulse in the bottom of her stomach. She booked her ticket back to Japan and told no one.

There were news stories, TV debates, magazine articles with pictures of a fetus floating in water like a tethered fish. Suddenly, children were all over the place, boy, girl, girl, boy, sticky fingers, snotty noses, screaming, running, falling, jumping. Since when did H&M have a maternity section? She tried to distract herself by turning on the TV only to find that Discovery Channel was running a whole series devoted to pregnancy and childbirth. She browsed through her father's bookshelf for something to read and found *Our Baby's Memory Book,* half finished, bleached at the spine. Everything spoke to her. Everything was giving a voice to the one voice that could not be heard. *Color of eyes: blue. Day twenty-three, the heart starts to beat. Expressed pleasure by cooing: three months. Day fifty, the fingers start forming, four days before the toes. My husband kisses my belly at night before we go to bed. Week eight, all essential organs are in place, now called a fetus. It's an amazing feeling, to think that you've created a life, to see the face of someone who has lived inside you for nine months.* Baby's first tooth, baby's first visitors, baby's first haircut, the packet of the condom through which baby was miraculously conceived. Or the pill that baby's mother forgot to take. She pulled the petals off daisies. She gambled with everyday life: miss the plane, *yes.* Rain tomorrow, *no.* Pro-life, pro-choice, pro-life, pro-choice. But what choice did she have, what life could she give as a mother, age twenty, a student, broke, drunk grandfather, estranged grandmother, unreliable father? She'd spent most of her own child-hood cooking and washing and cleaning, she wasn't about to do it again. *Only three out of ten healthy women in the U.S. get pregnant at their first try.* The unfairness of it. *Pro-life* but *no choice.* She'd picked up the phone and called her grandmother, because she'd spent all her money on the ticket back, because now more than ever she needed a mother.

Her name was called out and a nurse came clad in pale pink, smiling politely as she showed Ellie the way through. She stood up and held her bag in front of her to hide the sweat marks. She followed the nurse through the door and then through a room of yellow curtains that stopped at the bellybutton, where she was instructed to strip from the waist down. *Eight weeks, the eye-lids close.* The nurse left, and Ellie could hear her conversing with the doctor on the other side of the curtains. *One out of six pregnancies in the U.S. ends in miscarriage.* She slowly peeled off her leggings and then her socks, shoving one under each of her arms to soak up the moisture. Then she took off her pants. *Day forty-four, the ears swivel from the shoulders to the side of the head.* The chair was low and resembled a specialized dentist's chair, covered in a paper sheet with two separate footrests. *Recognized parents: October 1988.* She sat down slowly and placed one leg on each. The nurse asked if she was ready and after four seconds she said yes, at which point an automated voice from above gave her instructions to sit deep and lie back. *My husband kisses my belly at night.* The chair slowly started to move, spreading her legs further apart, turn-ing around and rising higher until the bottom of the yellow curtains sat limply on her stomach. She could see two pairs of feet underneath the curtain, both in white medical slippers. *Nine weeks, appearance of genitalia in males and females becomes more apparent.*

"Just lie back and relax, it won't take long," the doctor said. Ellie had had both hands covering her mouth to prepare for the pain, but propelled by fruitless instinct they quickly moved down to cradle her abdomen as a cold instrument was pushed inside her with unfamiliar force. The water in her eyes blurred the curtains and she realized that they must be yellow so that it didn't matter whether it was a boy or a girl.

The moth that looked like a leaf fluttered away from where it was perched on a leaf that looked like a moth. Duane Duppenthaler watched with interest from his wheelchair in the sun. The distracted nurse had parked him dangerously close to a rogue branch, a strong breeze and it would slap his forehead. But now there was nothing to look at and Duane was alone once more. He had just complained about not wanting to be in the same room as those other creaky fools, huddled around the television in various degrees of immobility. He pitied the nurses, who ran around changing old men's diapers as if they were babies. Never was a man's job. Duane checked that the nurse wasn't watching and carefully pulled out a packet of cigarettes and a lighter from the inner pocket of his jacket. He knew a thing or two about hiding things.

A soldier smokes because he knows that lung cancer is not the only way to die, that there are many ways to kill a man. He is always on the edge of the plank when bargaining with death. He's seen it up close; bloated stomachs floating in the water and charred bodies curled like babies. He's seen fragments of it too; bones, nerve endings and shreds of muscle hanging like fishing lines from a torn elbow, orphaned street children begging for candies. He's felt it personally, sticky blood getting in between his fingernails while retrieving the dog tags. Neville Cowie, Ben Shiffman, Josh Driskill. Duane Duppenthaler never understood that trend of wearing dog tags as part of fashion. Didn't they know what the things were for? Even his grandson came home one day wearing a pair around his neck. He'd been infuriated and thrown a plate at the floor, suffering flashbacks of chains dug so deep into skin that they sliced throats. That was back when he could still stand, before the stroke, before Leon had gone to college. But these are the small deaths men die, unworthy of history's net that catches only the big fish.

Duane Duppenthaler dropped the stub of his cigarette onto the deck and deftly extinguished it with his wheelchair in three small maneuvers. He dusted himself down, and then slowly made his own way back into the common room, where vacant faces were staring at the television. He wheeled himself over to the coffee bar and bought a twenty cent cup of coffee but stalled at the soft, gum-friendly cakes. The bar was the last shrapnel of dignity they were allowed: you can't wipe your own ass but you can buy your own coffee. He decided that the cakes and muffins looked the same as yesterday, and with his cup carefully balanced on his crotch, he slowly made his way over to the television, where the rest of his care-home comrades were watching a program on fishing. Duane knew a thing or two about fishing.

After Iwo-Jima the U.S. Marine Corps Fifth Division landed in Southern Kyushu. The U.S. Fleet Activities Sasebo was established in 1946, the base camp was completed a while later. One day, a local fishing boat had set off on a bad morning at sea, the beginning of April marking the start of the season. Each man, some as young as fifteen, prayed for good luck and offered gifts of dried squid to the shrines before setting off to cast the nets. Sailors and fishermen know that the sea does two things only, and it does them very well: it gives or it takes. Most of the crew members were in the cabin when a rogue triangle wave lifted up the rear and snapped the rudder. The boat broached and capsized on its left side, tenderly and in slow motion like a child being put to bed. The accident happened during a brief period of transition between the former Japanese Imperial Army and the newly formed Maritime Safety Agency of Japan, leaving only the U.S. Marine Corps to go out and search for survivors. They separated into three patrol boats and spent half a day looking for signs of life, a raft, a float, some debris, but could find nothing. When they returned, wet and exhausted, they found the families waiting outside the security fence. When the families saw that the marines had come back empty handed, they started screaming. Pressing themselves against the wire netting, they shouted incoherent abuse, spat, slumped to the ground and cried. The guards eventually came and dragged the families away but Duane couldn't shake off a sense of injustice at their ungratefulness. That night, he went into town and had a few glasses of Jack. During the war, there would be designated brothels in every port, but things were different now. He made his way to a small park where he grabbed the first young girl he could find, pushed her on to the wooden stairs and pounded her from behind.

Those were not his best years. Duane returned to North Carolina where he married Sarah Bromige, a skinny blonde whom he had known since he was a boy. They bought a house by Lake Norman and he started to earn a decent living selling electrical equipment, mainly to schools and universities. He was looking forward to becoming a family man. But Duane's luck ran out when Sarah died of severe blood loss while giving birth to Joe, who came out screaming, the umbilical cord wrapped around his neck like a noose. As a result, the boy would grow up with a vague sense of guilt which would manifest in a rebellious childhood and develop into an explosive adolescence. He left home at eighteen and came back three years later, jaded and broke, holding the hand of his two year old son, although the boy's dark eyes, caramel skin and corkscrew hair bore no resemblance to any Duppenthaler Duane could remember. Joe left the same night, leaving the boy in Duane's care. But Leon was not an injustice. He was a second chance, something given, not taken. For the first time, Duane would look into a pair of brown eyes and find no accusation, no fear, only trust. And in the sunlight, he could see that the ends of the luscious curls were dipped in gold.

Nurse Mannerheim came back from the telephone and spotted Duane sitting in front of the television.

"Mr. Duppenthaler, I thought I left you outside. Why are you back here?"

Duane was annoyed by her voice.

"Too cold. Nurse Cernikova helped me back in." He lied.

"But Judy's not in today."

Duane pretended not to hear and continued to watch the TV where a man in sunglasses held up a big black bass. Nurse Mannerheim gave up and started to walk over to help Sheryl out of her chair, when suddenly she twirled around.

"Oh, I almost forgot. Your grandson called, Mr. Duppenthaler, he's coming to see you tomorrow morning. Going to the airport he says."

With as much reflex as an eighty-five-year-old man can manage, Duane turned his head around and looked at Nurse Mannerheim.

"When?"

"In the morning. He's on his way to the airport or something, I didn't quite catch." She grinned. "He always brings a smile to your face, Mr. Duppenthaler, no matter how crabby you are with me."

Duane did not appreciate this sentiment but quickly forgot about it. With renewed energy, he wheeled himself to the open window, clunked onto the deck, and counted the butterflies until Nurse Mannerheim came and covered him in a blanket.

For the two weeks she was gone, Leon smoked. She'd made him give up, but he'd popped one between his lips and flicked the lighter on the way back from driving her to the airport. He didn't actually need to smoke anymore. He'd weaned himself off nicotine long ago. Instead, he continued for the two weeks because smoking is very often a lonely person's habit, and he was lonely. So he sat, night after night on the small chair on his small balcony, counting the stars and planes until Ellie's return. He hadn't wanted her to go; she'd booked the ticket and flown back without much notice. He had planned a little road trip for the two of them, visiting friends in Atlanta, now that it was getting warmer. But she said she had to visit family so he let those plans slide and decided to save them until the summer.

Leon could never quite grasp the concept of visiting family. He visited his grandfather once in a while, but he had never really known his parents. His father used to call him on birthdays but for the most part, Leon grew up without a mother or a father. Correction: he grew up without a mother. For all his shortcomings, his age, his military bark, Leon's grandfather was a better father than Joe could ever be. But still, Leon would sometimes go to bed with this unexplainable ache in his chest. He would run through all the familiar faces in his life, instinctively knowing that it was because he was missing something, trying to figure out who it was. Most of the time he fell asleep before he'd gone through the list, but occasionally it would keep him awake. The absence of a mother does take its toll. Not immediately, but later in life. Until he met Ellie his reputation among girls was a long and explicit list:

- Jerk(2001, Claudia Colton)
- Asshole (2003, Rita Klapste)
- Fucker (2005, Aisha Momtazi)
- Fucking Cheat (2005, Fiona Turner)
- Gay-Ass Fag (2006, Emily Whitmore)
- Motherfucking son of a fucking bitch fuck (2007, Layla Momtazi)

But back then he was under the impression that, the longer the list was, the more of a man you were. Then he met Ellie. She was different. She made him laugh, she made him wince, she made him come, she made him cry (after their first fight, though she never knew). He enjoyed watching her sleep as much as he enjoyed watching her suck. The aching stopped.

"Ayo, dude." He'd called his friend Kortney after two weeks.

"Wassup man, why so early?"

"I'm in love."

"Naaaaah."

"I'm serious."

"No way."

"Dude, I'm not joking. I'm telling you, I'm in love."

"Are you high?" He could hear Kortney lighting a cigarette at the other end of the line.

"No way, man, I've even given up smoking."

"For how long?"

"Three days and counting."

"What the fuck, man. Are you serious? Who's the girl?"

"Ellie Kawabata. She's Japanese. Half."

"Kawamata? Sounds like a samurai. Does she have one of those wooden sword things? Cut your dick off? *Kawamata-san! Wheeeeesh, whacha, hai!*" Kortney choked on his own wit.

"Nah man, she's cool. She's the one."

"Hey, wait a minute, aren't Asian girls meant to be slit sideways? Like their eyes?"

"Whatever, man." Leon was already regretting the phone call.

"Okay, sorry, sorry. So how long have you known each other?"

"Two weeks."

"Sheesh. You can't tell nothin' in two weeks, you moron."

"I can, though, that's the thing. It's amazing. It's like being high. I don't see no other girls, I just *don't see them.*" Leon closed his eyes, as if to emphasize his own point.

"What about that Lauren chick?"

"Forget about her, man, that's over. I'm a one woman guy now."

"Do I get to meet her?"

"Yeah, man, anytime you want," replied Leon, mentally giving it another two weeks.

"So I guess the next step is meeting the grandfather. Did you tell him?"

"Why would I do that?"

"Do you have anyone else?"

"No."

"There you go then. Meet the granddad, buy a house, wedding in Vegas, make babies. Pop pop pop." Leon didn't comment, although the idea wasn't entirely unsettling.

"Shit duuude. What the fuuuck. I can't believe this. You were always the man. Leon. Lady-killer. Pussy-licker. Whore-monger. Five a night." Leon could hear the squeak of Kortney's antique wheelie chair as he reclined. "So I guess the big question now is: is *she* in love with *you*?"

But that wasn't the big question. The big question was *how much longer?* Another thirteen hours and she would connect in Detroit. Twenty hours to go. She would be tired; she was tired before she left. He didn't get why she had been so bad-tempered, he put it down to PMS or PTA or MVA or whatever. As far as he knew, she only had her dad in Japan, and he was supposed to be an alcoholic. So why would she go back in such a hurry? Leon never quite understood the concept of visiting family. The ache was back. Maybe it was time he went to see his grandfather.

He spotted Duane in his wheelchair on the deck, covered in a plaid fleece blanket.

"Grampa?"

Leon was surprised at the speed with which the old man turned around, the wrinkled skin on his neck twisting like a wash cloth.

"Grandson," Duane replied, their running joke.

Leon dragged over a collapsible chair from the corner of the terrace and sat down.

"Sorry I haven't visited. Been busy. Coursework..."

"No problem," said Duane, lying. "You're the only one in the family to go to college. Work your ass off, young man. What have you done to your hair?"

Since he couldn't exactly run his fingers through them, Leon lightly patted his dreadlocks.

"It's been like this before, you didn't notice?"

"I never knew what to do with that hair of yours when you were younger. The kind of thing your mother would have taught you, I guess. Had to go ask Mrs. McKenzie down the road, remember? Cornrolls, she told me."

"Cor*nrows*. Yeah, I remember."

"And all these people saw me, old man with this little corn-rolled boy all those years, and thought, Jesus. Grandaddy's been showin' the maids a good time!" Duane laughed. Leon didn't. He ignored the two sentences worn threadbare over the years and changed the subject.

"How's the food? Getting better?"

"Terrible. Mush. Even you cooked better."

They were quiet long enough for a brown butterfly to do a full circuit around Duane's bald head.

"Look here, I've been wanting to tell you that I'll make sure the house, it goes to you, if. If some thing happens." Duane merged the last word with a cough. "You'll get a wife. You'll have a family. You'll need somewhere bigger than that apartment you got now." Duane looked at his grandson.

"Thanks, Grampa."

"No problem son. Just name the first-born after me." Duane laughed a smoker's laugh, all wheeze and spittle. "So. I hear you are on the way to the airport. Picking up a girl?"

Leon's heart skipped. "Yeah," he grinned, white teeth popping. "My future wife."

He left an hour later, getting into the car warmed up from the sun. Two more hours. She hadn't replied to his emails so he allowed himself extra time to find the right gate. He could actually feel his armpits getting damp. He tried not to think too much about the long sweaty night they would have ahead of them, besides, she was probably exhausted from spending hours on the plane. He didn't mind; he would let her sleep. He'd stroke her face until she dozed, watch her eyelids flutter like butterfly wings, listen to her small moans as she rolled over and hold her close, so close, as she curled up like a baby into the curves of his body. He lit his last cigarette to try and control his nerves, opening all the car windows so she wouldn't notice the smell. There would be no need to smoke once he had a family, a house, a kid, two kids, once Ellie was back. No weird aches. He pulled out of the car park and followed the road signs to CLT. At one point, the wind blew ash into his eyes and he blinked furiously, tears welling up and threatening to spill.

Disaster Memories
and other thoughts on the Fukushima nuclear reactors,
the Military Industrial Complex, the Ainu, and National Sovereignty
Hiroshi Fukurai

It is the irony of ironies that the only country on Earth ever attacked by the nuclear bomb is now facing the peril of massive radioactive contamination from another nuclear crisis. The country bombed by both the Enola Gay and Bockscar, the country that experienced deadly "black rain" and massive human annihilation at the end of WWII, is now confronted not only by the outcome of the natural catastrophes caused by earthquakes and tsunami waves, but also the man-made disaster of massive radiation leaks from nuclear reactors in Fukushima.

As of today, nearly 30,000 people are reported dead or missing due to the destruction caused by the earthquake and tidal waves. Most of these deaths and structural damages occurred in the Prefecture of Miyagi, the prefecture being Japan's geopolitical jurisdiction equivalent to statehood in the United States. On the other hand, the nuclear disaster in the nuclear plant in Fukushima, south of Miyagi, has yet to kill anyone. Nonetheless, the massive radiation leaks will threaten the lives of tens of millions of people in the northern and central region of Japan for many years to come.

Natori City, tidal waves, and the destruction of local farming and fishing traditions

I was born and raised in Sendai and lived in the Haranomachi Ward of Sendai City. My family included my parents, grandmother on my mother's side, and younger sister. When I turned fifteen, my father, Yoshikichi Fukurai, built a new house in Natori, a neighboring rural city located in the south of Sendai. Natori was still a small town with a population of barely 30,000 people. The house was built in the middle of the rice-paddy fields and we were still able to see locomotives from our house.

Back row *left to right*
Kaori Sakurai, eldest daughter
of author's cousin, Tsutomu
Sakurai

Yoko Sakurai, wife of author's
cousin, who was trapped
on the second floor by the
tsunami and rescued next day

Yoshiko Kamo, author's
father's youngest sister who
lived with his father in
his house for a month or so

Rie Sakurai, second oldest
daughter of author's cousin

Mieko Sakurai, mother of
author's cousin, his father's
younger sister who is
currently living with his father

Yoshikichi Fukurai,
author's father

Front row *left to right*
Takato Sakurai, author's
cousin's youngest son

Yuki Fukurai
author's eldest son

Haruka Fukurai, author's
youngest daughter

Mihoka Fukurai, author's
eldest daughter

My sister and her family still live in Sendai. It is truly impossible to describe the sadness I felt when I first saw pictures of destroyed landmarks and buildings in many places I know personally. I still have many friends in Sendai. As of today, I have yet to hear from some of my closest friends and old classmates from elementary and junior high school.

My father now lives in Natori City, just south of Sendai. This sleepy town was hit hard by tsunami waves that destroyed my cousin's house and his entire business, including his family farms. My father's house was, fortunately, spared. However, four cousins in Natori were not as fortunate. Hiromichi Sakurai and his wife were found dead in their car. They were on their way to Natori to pick up their elderly parents who lived near the Natori beach. The car was swallowed by the tidal wave and they drowned together inside it, and the elderly parents were found dead after the seawater subsided.

Geographically, Natori is surrounded by the Natori River, which extends from the north to the west, and another river, Masuda, which runs from the north to the south. Natori, in other words, is located in the middle of the fertile deltas created by both the Natori and Masuda rivers. The samurai feudal lord named Masamune Date moved to the area, built the castle, and claimed its lordship in 1601. Natori then became one of the major granaries of the Date feudal lord.

After the Meiji Restoration in 1868, the feudal system was abolished and replaced by the new modern government that introduced the western conception of township and cities. The town of Natori was originally established in 1955 by annexing two small towns and four remote villages, and it received city status in 1958.

After we claimed our Natori residence in 1970, the city began to grow. Today it holds more than 70,000 people. It is often cited as a "bed-town" of Sendai City, which is a municipality with a population of one million, the largest in northern Japan. Many residents of Natori commute to Sendai to work or to attend schools. Natori also has a large agricultural farmland. Nonetheless, only seven percent of Natori residents continue to work in agricultural sectors, while some are also employed in fishing industries.

My cousin, Tsutomu Sakurai, lived in the coastal Kitagama Ward of Natori, and came to be known as the last full-time agricultural worker in the entire Prefecture of Miyagi. Right after he graduated from the Miyagi Agricultural High School, more than thirty years ago, he decided he would become a full-time farmer and take over his father's agricultural business. The local newspaper ran a big story about him, because becoming a full-time farmer and taking over a traditional agricultural business was not considered a popular thing to do among many Japanese youths at that time.

The name Natori has its origin in an indigenous word, *Nutatori,* representing the meaning of wetlands. Until quite recently, the indigenous people of Japan inhabited much of the northeast region of Honshu, the largest of four major islands that constitute most of Japan's geographic territory. These indigenous people were called *Ebishi,* more widely known as Ainu. Despite many years of governmental discrimination against the Ainu, the Japanese government never publicly acknowledged the unique history or ancestral heritage of the Ainu. The Japanese government also insisted on its denials of any predatory policies aimed against the territorial rights of the Ainu people.

Since the Japanese government has stressed the importance of ethnic homogeneity and public solidarity under the reign of the imperial family, the presence of the Ainu (or any other ethnic minority) has not until very recently been recognized. Any open, public discourse about ethnic minorities and their histories has also been considered a taboo. The human rights movement to support the Ainu people, their identity, and national heritage has been largely silenced by the repressive public policies of both regional governments and national bureaucratic institutions. Nonetheless, because of a strong grassroots movement and prominent legal cases brought on behalf of the Ainu to reclaim their indigenous land rights in Hokkaido, the Japanese government was finally forced to acknowledge in 2008 that the Ainu people were indeed the original indigenous inhabitants of the islands of Japan.

Even when I was small, we had always known unique folk stories and local tales about the indigenous people living in nearby mountains. Many of them had blue and green eyes, one of the distinct physical characteristics of Ainu people. The fact that I was born with very distinctly light colored pupils may reflect some of the physiological residues of Ainu blood that my family inherited from our ancestors. Indeed, my family's ancestral roots, from both sides, are firmly grounded in this region for many centuries.

The indigenous people had called the land of Natori a wetland, and sure enough the city represents a territorial municipality that is largely flat and thus suitable for the agricultural cultivation which was promoted by many settlers, one of the reasons that the Ainu, a fishing and hunting people, were forcefully driven out of this area into the mountains. Just like with the colonial predation of many indigenous populations in North America by the British forces or in Mesoamerica by the Spaniards, Ainu people who resisted colonial policies were eradicated and some who accepted new ways of life had been forcefully made into farmers and assimilated into the settler-state social system imposed by new migrant populations in the region. I sometimes wonder what my Ainu ancestors went through in the colonial policies of forced assimilation imposed upon their ways of life.

First recorded in Japanese history as a distinct group of inhabitants in 660 A.D., the Ainu had long developed trading contacts with various neighboring people in different regions, including settler populations (or the Wajin) to the south, the Manchurians to the west, the Orok and Nivkh to the north in Sakhalin, which is an island north of Hokkaido, and the Itenmi in Kamchatka Peninsula (part of Russia) to the east and northeast.

As the expansion of Wajin populations began to incorporate the Ainu into its nation-state project, many resisted such an imposition of colonial policies from the south. There were three noted wars between the Ainu and the settler populations of the Japanese islands. The most significant conflict was the Shakushain War in 1669, as a war of independence against the powerful Japanese authority, which led to the defeat of Ainu leader Shakushain in 1672. Nonetheless, he later became a famous Ainu cultural hero.

Today, the Japanese governmental census reveals that there are only 25,000 people who identify as Ainu, most of whom reside in the northern island of Hokkaido. Other studies indicate that the population of Ainu is much greater than what the official statistics indicate, because many people still refuse to identify themselves as Ainu, fearing discrimination against their families. I always wondered what would happen if I reclaimed my remote ancestral connection to the Ainu people and identified myself as an Ainu who once lived in Natori and adjacent areas for thousands of years. Using the one-drop-of-blood theory, my family members who live in California are all Ainu descendants.

Before the settler populations moved into Natori, there were no known distinct permanent residential areas near the coast, nor any substantial rice-paddy fields to grow the huge amount of rice necessary to feed the settler population. Ainu had no huge boats to engage in industrial fishing and no international airport to transport people or commodities.

I wonder, if people had followed the indigenous ways of the Ainu, how many would have been affected by the recent earthquake and/or tsunami? How much do the naturally occurring seismic changes and oceanic activities affect the populations who follow the indigenous ways? I am not romanticizing the Ainu culture, but it still makes me wonder how much our blind submission to the western conception of civilization led to the loss of human lives in the last earthquake and tsunami disaster.

In the city named after the Ainu term for wetlands, my father's current house is located nearly five miles from the shore of the Pacific Ocean, but its foundation lies only five meters above sea level. The large flat areas of fertile ground allow the huge rice fields to extend on the west side of my father's house. I've always liked to run through the open paths between the rice fields since my adolescent years. I studied metallurgical engineering at the National College of Technology in Miyagi, which is located on top of Medeshima Mountain on the western side of Natori City. I watched and observed the rice field from my building on the college campus for five years. When we pay pilgrimage to my father's house and stay there for many weeks every summer, I still love to run or walk through the rice fields with my children and wife.

Nonetheless, for many Natori residents, the flatness of this geographical landscape was a curse, allowing the powerful tidal waves into the interior of the city, destroying many farmlands on the east side, carrying with the waves many automobiles, farm equipment, and residential buildings, and pushing them to the higher ground on the western side of the city. Tsunami waves also engulfed the entirety of the Sendai International Airport and stopped just short of reaching the Tohoku Japan Railway track, which is only half a mile from my father's house.

I need to mention my cousin now. I literally grew up with my cousin, Tsutomu Sakurai, and his little brother, Tsuyoshi, both of whom were born and raised in Natori. Even when my family lived in Sendai, I visited my cousin's family every summer and spent much time playing, swimming, and fishing with them. My cousin's house became my second home and we spent much time fishing at the nearby Teizan Bori canal, which was built 150 years ago. It extends nearly sixty kilometers from the Matsushima Bay in the north to the estuary of the Abukuwa River in the south.

After we moved to Natori, I frequented my cousin's house even more. When I was eighteen years old, I spent one summer working for another cousin, Hiromichi Sakurai, who, as I mentioned earlier, was found dead with his wife in his car. He needed an extra hand on their farm, and I stayed with and worked for him, picking watermelons and taking them to a local market. I would then play with my cousins in the afternoon.

Many of my friends commented on the horrifying videos they saw on American television, showing the black waves of the tsunami moving up the Natori River in the north, while swallowing and eating up much of the farmland and buildings, including my cousin's house, in the process. Now my cousin's old house, where I spent many summers, no longer exists. It only exists in my memory. My cousin, Tsutomu, also lost his entire collection of family photos and videos. The visual proof of their existence now exists only in memory as well.

On March 11, at 2:46 p.m., when the earthquake struck, Tsutomu was at work at his construction site. Ten years ago, the income he earned as a full-time farmer was no longer sufficient to support his growing family. He decided to work as a part-time construction worker for a contracting firm started by one of his friends who lived nearby. They themselves are also farmers, but still needed extra income to support their families as well. So they created their own construction company and my cousin decided to join them. However, the construction work is still not a steady job. Many part-time farmers in the company only get paid when local customers decide to build new sunrooms, fix the leak in their roofs, add new bathrooms, and so on. My father's living room was refurbished by this company, and my cousin did the actual work.

When the earthquake hit, Tsutomu's eldest son was working in Sendai, and his two younger daughters and youngest son were at school. His mother was away, running an errand. The two living souls in the house belonged to his wife Yoko, and the family dog. In the nearly thirty minutes from the time of the earthquake to the first wave of tsunamis to hit the coast, Yoko was busy getting things together to escape. She then realized that the huge waves were hitting the house and tried to escape to the second floor, while the rising water rushed up every step of the stairs. When she reached the second floor, she instinctively closed all the windows. She said that trapping the air inside led to the entire house "being lifted," and it began to float, rotating slowly. She also realized that her family dog had somehow managed to enter the room. She and her dog floated for nearly an hour while trapped inside the room on the second floor. Right before the house stopped moving, she realized that the house had suddenly begun to rotate "vertically." She hung on to whatever she could to maintain her balance while still holding her dog. When the whole structure stopped moving, she maneuvered to get outside and searched for her cell-phone. Miraculously, the cell phone worked and she called her husband. Her shattered house was stranded in the middle of debris surrounded by water, and she spent a freezing night without dry clothes, holding her dog close.

My father's house and piano

When the earthquake hit, my father was sitting in his living room. He had just taken a bath after playing a recreational game with his elderly friends in the nearby park. The game is called gateball, which is a golf-like sport extremely popular among the older generations in Japan. The earthquake suddenly knocked down the 32-inch TV, and the tiny residential Buddhist shrine was about to crash to the floor. According to my father, the huge piano in the entry hall literally "walked" for about one meter. Two huge Japanese cabinets full of clothes that used to belong to my deceased mother and grandmother crashed to the tatami floor. If the earthquake had occurred in the night, my father would surely have been killed by the weight of the fully loaded cabinets.

Once the tremors subsided, he checked the safety of his long-time neighbor, Saito-san, and a new neighbor, Watanabe-san. Both of them responded that they were okay, though they also said that the insides of their houses were a complete mess. They also told my father that the radio had just warned about the danger of potential tidal waves in the coastal areas and residents were being asked to prepare for immediate evacuation.

My sister rushed to my father's house, located near the main artery extending from the Natori Japan Railway Station to the Natori Cancer Hospital, where many cancer patients receive life-saving treatments. Many cars and motorcycles could be observed heading toward the mountains, and drivers were shouting about the danger of the tidal waves coming this way. My father, sister, and neighbors decided to evacuate to the nearby evacuation center, which happened to be the gymnasium of Masuda Nishi Elementary School. My father brought with him bank deposits and family seal stamps (used as a signature for contractual purposes, called *Hanko* or *Inkan),* among other important documents.

This is the same school where, when my children were small, my wife and I enrolled them during the summer in order for them to learn Japanese culture and language. When they grew up, we enrolled them in another nearby junior high school called Natori-Daiichi Junior High School. The gymnasium of this school was also designated an evacuation center for Natori residents who lived in the north.

My father, sister and neighbors waited there patiently until night fell. By this time, hundreds of people who had escaped tidal waves and lost their homes started to pour into the school gymnasium. My father and sister then decided to return to the house to see if the waves had reached his home. Realizing that the house was safe from the tsunami, they started cleaning up the place, while listening to a portable radio, which my father had bought nearly forty years ago, but is still operable. He lucked out, he said, because he had purchased a new set of batteries for the radio the previous week. He always listens to it when he goes to bed. My father and sister also discovered that there was no electricity, gas, or running water at the house. My father then brought out an old Japanese charcoal brazier from the back house and started to cook rice and boil water to make an instant miso soup to get warm. My father told my sister, "It's like a war-time experience."

Later in the evening, my cousin, along with his mother who is my father's younger sister, came over and told him that his wife was stranded somewhere in the middle of debris, alive with their family dog. My cousin soon left, picked up his three small children, and stayed at his friend's house. Meanwhile, his mother decided to stay with my father along with my sister.

Next early morning, when rescuers brought my cousin's wife to my father's place, everyone was there to greet her. It was an incredible moment of emotional eruption and joy. They also shared the sad news of many neighbors and friends whose whereabouts were still unknown.

It took another ten days to find a suitable apartment for my cousin's family. My cousin's mother decided to stay with my father. Another younger sister, who lived in Sendai, also decided to join and help out her older brother and older sister. My father says that now he is "being treated like a feudal king," as his two sisters help him cook and clean up the place, while sharing the whole life stories of their children and grandchildren. My father said that it was like "living in the same old house where we all grew up" in Aikuma town, which is also near Natori.

Nevertheless, their relationship has been all but peaceful or civil for a long time. When my grandfather died nearly twenty-five years ago, a huge inheritance, mostly farmlands, was left behind and a bitter dispute emerged among the six siblings. It continued for many years until the court was asked to intervene and decide on the equitable apportionment of the land estate and other inheritance. For many years, my father and his two brothers and three sisters did not talk to one another. None of the men wanted to break up the estate, insisting that it all be left for the deceased's widow, my father's older brother's wife, who supported and lived with her father-in-law until he passed away. It is generally accepted as the Japanese tradition that the eldest son takes care of his aging parents.

My grandmother on my father's side died when I was small, but my grandfather lived until he reached eighty-two years of age. His eldest son went to war and became part of the Japanese imperial army that reportedly killed nearly three hundred thousand Nanjin residents in 1937. He was able to survive the deadly war and returned to his home in 1945. But he carried with him many psychological scars, traumas, and tropical diseases, including malaria, and he passed away when I was small. Ever since he died, his wife, Taeko Kamo, had taken care of his husband's parents until they passed away. My father and his two brothers insisted that all the inheritance be left to the widow who had taken care of the aging parents and their grandchildren.

All the women insisted on their entitlement to the rightful share of the inheritance. Fifteen years ago, the death of the widow created the opportunity for all siblings to get together and share their emotive feelings against each other. The death of his sister's daughter also brought them together. Gradually, their wounds began to mend. Nowadays, they've become so close to one another that they hold an annual "brothers and sisters reunion" at the nearby onsen (hot spring). My father's two sisters moving in to help him out was a sign of their genuine concern and caring for the welfare of their sibling. If this earthquake could be said to have brought out any positive human element, I would say that it created the opportunity for the bonds and feelings of caring and loving that my father's siblings have for one another to solidify.

My old classmate in Sendai and his tears

Masaki Goto was my classmate in both the fifth and sixth grades in the Haranomachi Elementary School in Sendai. We were in the same class again three years later at Miyaginohara Junior High School. After graduation, I moved to Natori and had not seen him until five years ago when he suddenly emailed me, asking whether I was interested in participating in the first ever reunion of our elementary school classmates. In June of that year, twenty men and women who had shared the same class some forty years ago got together at a pub in Sendai. Since then, he and I have begun to exchange emails across the Pacific.

On March 13, two days after the earthquake and tsunami waves swallowed the coastal cities of northern Japan, he emailed me about the condition of the disaster areas he witnessed when he joined the rescue team and traveled to the Sendai Port. His house was badly shaken but remained structurally intact. As it was built in a hilly area, he was able to escape the tidal wave, though the deadly tsunami found its way nearly seven miles into the interior of the Wakabayashi District of Sendai City. His family has always lived in the same house, as far as I can remember.

He has had a very interesting, up-and-down career. He worked for a large multinational corporation and had to travel a lot. Many years of work-related stress, however, finally precipitated physical ailments and psychological distress and disorder. By his wife's urging, he decided to quit his job in his mid-forties and came back to Sendai. He then began to observe his body and mind starting to "recover." But he says that he still needs to take "tons of medications and many pills" to combat the effect of corporate-related stresses. Nonetheless, he is finally free from all those work-related obligations and mental pressures.

After he decided "not to go to work" any longer, his wife started a beauty salon to support the family. He helped refurbish his house and partitioned it to create a new hair salon for his wife. Much to his surprise, her business has flourished. Meanwhile, he became more involved in local grassroots activities and community services. Last summer he worked as a member of the volunteer community patrol team during the annual Sendai festival. He has also enlisted as a volunteer fireman in his district.

While his house was still a mess, he decided to help out the survivors in Sendai Port areas that had been hit hard by the tidal wave. One afternoon, he and his men rescued two people from the wreckage. He was very proud of himself, while, at the same time, he observed numerous dead bodies lying on the street and inside wrecked cars and commercial ships. When he saw them, he said that tears began to trickle from his eyes. Once, the Sendai port was one of the most efficient ports in northern Japan, but it is completely destroyed and will take years to get back to normalcy. Today my dear friend still serves as a volunteer fireman, collecting bodies and searching for survivors in the hardest hit areas of Sendai. His latest email, nonetheless, has begun to express more concerns about multiple explosions at the Fukushima nuclear power plant and the potential effect of radiation leakages in Sendai and its adjacent cities and towns in the region.

Fukushima Nuclear Power Plant and Tokyo Electric Power Company (TEPCO)

It is ironic that the firm that has been accused of professional negligence in causing the death and injury of its workers and fined repeatedly for millions of dollars for falsifying safety reports was still allowed to manage and operate one of the most sophisticated and sensitive machineries that humankind has ever created. TEPCO, which operated the Fukushima Daiichi Nuclear Plants, has a long, checkered history. And the Fukushima Daiichi Nuclear Plant has had a series of radiation leaks.

In 2002, the TEPCO president was forced to resign after taking responsibility for suspected falsification of nuclear plant safety records. TEPCO was also suspected of twenty-nine cases involving falsified repair records at its nuclear reactors and had to stop operations at five reactors for safety inspections. In late 2006, the Japanese government ordered TEPCO to check previous data after the firm reported that it had found falsification of coolant water temperatures at its Fukushima Daiichi plant in 1985 and 1988, acknowledging that the tweaked information was used in mandatory inspections at the plant. In 2007, TEPCO also admitted that it had found more past data falsification.

Shortly before the March earthquake, TEPCO also admitted that it had failed to inspect thirty-three pieces of equipment inside the plant's cooling systems, including water pumps at the Fukushima plant. The company also missed safety checks over a ten-year period up to two weeks before the March 11 disaster and piled up spent uranium fuel rods inside the forty-year old nuclear facility. TEPCO also arrogantly turned down U.S. offers of help to cool the reactors shortly after the disaster and waited too long to pump dangerous seawater into the stricken reactors.

People also wonder why the Prefecture of Fukushima, which is in the northeastern region of Japan, houses six nuclear reactors whose sole purpose is to supply electricity, not to the residents or industries in Fukushima, but to the population, commercial interests, and industrial sectors in Tokyo and its neighboring regions some 150 miles down south. Fukushima also houses TEPCO's four additional nuclear reactors in its Fukushima Daini Nuclear Plant located ten kilometers south of the Fukushima Daiichi Nuclear Plant.

What's so surprising is the fact that these reactors at the Fukushima Daiichi Nuclear Plant are some of the oldest nuclear plants ever designed by General Electric. GE held the intellectual property rights of the nuclear power plant and supplied the reactor for Unit 1 along with Units 2 and 6, while Toshiba supplied structural materials for Units 3 and 5 reactors and Hitachi for Unit 4. All six reactors were based on the GE design and built by Kashima, another multinational Japanese corporation. With GE nuclear experts, the Unit 1 nuclear reactor was built in 1968, commissioned in 1971, and has been operating ever since, more than forty years.

It was supposed to be decommissioned last January after having operated for forty years. Nonetheless, Japan's Nuclear and Industrial Safety Agency (NISA) gave TEPCO an approval to extend its operation for an additional ten years. This is despite the fact that on February 26, two weeks before the earthquake, many grassroots organizations, including the Fukushima Environmental Protection Organization (Fukushima Shizen Hogo Kyokai) and the Green Fukushima of Future (Midori no Mirai Fukushima), submitted to TEPCO a petition to disclose information on numerous safety checks and inspections on the Fukushima plant that have been kept from the public.

With new nuclear technologies available, TEPCO continues to rely on the ancient plant to generate electricity. Just imagine how strange you would look if you were driving your automobile which had been designed some fifty years ago. It has no seatbelts or airbags because the installation of those safety conditions was not required in the original car design back then.

The safety of this old reactor plant design has been questioned since 1972. Japan is forbidden to engage in nuclear power research and Japan itself does not produce any reactors. In 2007, the GE-Hitachi joint venture company was created in the U.S. to collaborate on the development of the new generation of nuclear reactors. Nonetheless, existing Japanese nuclear plants have been based on designs produced by foreign companies, including GE.

The design flaw of the GE nuclear plant in Fukushima had already been pointed out by many nuclear experts, including the U.S. Nuclear Regulatory Commission (NRC), which said in 1972 that this design should never have been licensed. In 1985, the NRC said that there was a ninety percent chance that in a severe accident, the spent fuel-rod containment would fail. In 1976, three GE nuclear scientists also blew the whistle on the structural flaw of the nuclear design used to construct the Fukushima Daiichi Nuclear Plant, stating that, in case of disaster, the practice of putting the spent fuel rods pool on an upper floor of the reactor building, not at a ground level, would make it nearly impossible to fill it with the water to cool and stop them from melting. They were later forced to resign for their public statement.

On March 16, one of the three scientists said on CNN with tears in his eyes that the condition of the Fukushima plant was worse than what we had warned nearly forty years ago. The difficulty of cooling the fuel rod and the breach of its containment was evident, because for the first couple of days after the earthquake, TEPCO was using Japanese helicopters to scoop seawater, dumping it from the air to try to fill the pool at the Fukushima plants. The effort was obviously unsuccessful and the lack of cooling water facilitated the continued meltdown of fuel rods and released the steam that contained dangerous radioactive substances into the atmosphere. Meanwhile, two weeks after the earthquake, GE publicly stated that the design was not flawed and it has been used in the construction of twenty-three of 104 nuclear reactors currently operating in the United States.

Governmental manipulation of Japanese media and the corporate complicity

From day one, the Japanese government and TEPCO have efficiently operated to suppress the transmission of crucial information on the status of nuclear reactors and the safety of spent-fuel rods at Fukushima Daiichi Nuclear Power Plant. As results of the coordinated corporate and governmental efforts, the Japanese and international communities were not given the correct information about the level of radiation leaks in Japan and potential contamination of regional residents in various prefectures.

First, the foreign media were effectively shut off from attending the government press conferences, and much crucial governmental information was not released to the international media. The Japanese TV and newspaper media are also complicit in their failure to ask TEPCO engineers and government officers any of a number of emerging questions about the status of nuclear reactors.

TEPCO is the largest corporate sponsor of TV and radio programs and newspaper advertisements in Japan. It is also important to realize that the main sponsor of the ruling Democratic Party of Japan (DPJ) has been the Federation of Electric Power Companies of Japan (FEPC), in which TEPCO continues to play a major political and financial role in influencing policy in Japan's nuclear programs. Consequently, TEPCO successfully took charge of the Japanese corporate media and influenced the release of information on the status of the Fukushima power plant.

Chief Cabinet Secretary Yukio Edano has been the main spokesman for the Japanese government and provided crucial information of radiation emissions supplied by TEPCO scientists. Edano has been insisting that the situation at the Fukushima plant has been steadily improving and that there is no "immediate" effect of radiation exposures, while deliberately ignoring the longitudinal effect of radiation exposures to the Japanese public. Even after the hydrogen explosion of Unit 1, Edano said that the nuclear reactor was intact, and there was no sign of significant radiation leaks in the plant, which was later found to be false.

Many of his Edano's of physiological effects of radiation were reportedly based on physiological consequences of the radiation impact upon healthy adults, not on small children, infants, or pregnant women who will be adversely affected by the exposure to radiation.

My brother-in-law who lives in Koriyama in Fukushima, sixty kilometers west of the Fukushima Daiichi Nuclear Power Plant, asked me to purchase and send him a Geiger counter in the U.S. so that he can correctly measure the level of leaked radiation in his area. Nearly all radiation instruments have been sold out in Japan. Having no confidence in any reports issued by TEPCO, the Japanese government, or the Japanese media, he decided to send his two daughters from Koriyama to my house in Santa Cruz, California, until an arrangement is made for their new school transfer in another Japanese prefecture. My sister in Sendai is also extremely skeptical of the government reports on the level of daily radioactive activities in the city and surrounding regions.

Despite the government's effort to downplay the extent of radiation leaks, Japanese people are more intelligent than the government expects them to be and are clearly aware of the government's maneuvers of the Japanese corporate media in the censorship of crucial information. Many progressive people in Japan learned very hard lessons from their failure in not detecting lies or inaccurate information on the war. Japanese historians have estimated that several million Japanese citizens were killed by the misinformation given by the Imperial General Headquarters during WWII.

Foreign nuclear experts were also skeptical of the Japanese government reports and decided to conduct their own independent investigations. For example, they have issued very different interpretations on the effect of radiation leaks in Fukushima. Immediately after the explosion, the International Atomic Energy Agency (IAEA) issued the evacuation warning to Japanese residents who live within an 80 kilometer radius from the Fukushima nuclear plant. Even the Nuclear Regulatory Commission (NRC) Chairman Gregory Jaczko warned that the nuclear meltdown and subsequent contamination was "extremely high" in the Fukushima nuclear plant and much wider evacuations were absolutely necessary. On March 18, the NRC also warned that the containment pool at Unit 4 had already ruptured and could approach the apocalyptic stage unless there were immediate strategies to cool down the spent nuclear fuels. NRC scientists also recognized the Japanese government's failure to provide accurate information and timely warnings to its own citizens.

The Japanese government and TEPCO have mobilized their resources to pacify the public and counteract any negative foreign or domestic publicity about the danger of the radiation leaks. The government even asked Emperor Akihito to visit the evacuation centers and urge the people to pull together in the aftermath of the earthquake and tsunami, though he failed to mention the effect of the nuclear radiation and radioactive leaks from the Fukushima plant.

The Japanese government has also been quite busy in its legal maneuvers and in trying to change the legal standard of nuclear-related government regulations. The government first changed the scale of the earthquake magnitude from 8.9 to 9.0, and such a change was only applicable for the extraordinary earth-shaking event. The Japanese government has then decided to allow it for the first time in its history. The international independent earthquake experts have estimated the magnitude of the March 11 earthquake to be a mere 8.3 or 8.4, much less than what has been reported in the Japanese media. The special application of the extraordinary scale will likely downplay the man-made components of catastrophes and help replace them with the natural disaster of earthquake and tsunami. This substitution will further help exonerate the extent of the man-made components and the criminal and financial liability of both the Japanese government and TEPCO in the future.

The Japanese government also changed the upper limit of workers' nuclear exposures from 100 millisievert to 250 millisievert, elevating the legal limit to extend the activities of the workers at the nuclear plant. For the agricultural crops, the Japanese government also tried to change the legal limit of contamination, but was persuaded to maintain the pre-earthquake standard.

The most unique effort to pacify the public was the use of cartoons, in which the boy-like character called "Pluto-kun" was used to dispel fears of the effect of plutonium produced by the nuclear power plant in Japan. Pluto-kun explains that he is not a monster and wants the people to understand how peaceful and safe he truly is. He says that he will not pose any danger as long as people use him peacefully and will be a reliable friend who can provide an endless source of energy to Japanese people for many years to come.

Just like my brother-in-law, sister, and many progressive thinkers, independent and young freelance Japanese journalists have also been extremely critical of the Japanese government and its information on the radiation leaks and contamination of regions close to the Fukushima Plant. Their consistent inquiries to TEPCO scientists and press spokesmen finally revealed that the Japanese government agreed to TEPCO's requests to dump more than three million gallons of radioactive water into the Pacific Ocean on April 4. The decision was carried out without any consultation of the fishing industries, local authorities, or foreign governments of adjacent countries in the region. The Japanese government also failed to take into critical consideration the possible violation of international law on environmental pollutions.

Legally speaking, the mass dumping of highly radioactive water into the Pacific Ocean is a clear violation of the 1972 Convention on the Prevention of Marine Pollution by Dumping of Wastes and Other Matters. The act of this illegal mass dumping of highly radioactive water has also shifted the perception of Japan in the world community. The illegal dumping transformed the position of Japan from the victim of inevitable, naturally caused catastrophes to the criminally liable nation-state which knowingly released tons of toxic water into the ocean, causing potential massive contaminations of oceanic resources and causing health hazards of their consumers in the world.

Last summer, I sponsored Dr. Sunsul Park from South Korea and supported his research for one year at UC Santa Cruz. He has since told me that he is amazed by the extremely pacified responses of Japanese people to this nuclear disaster. He says that if the same nuclear disaster would have happened in Korea, people would have engaged in massive demonstrations to pressure the government and the power company to rectify the situation by any means necessary. Many progressive scholars and grassroots activists would be swarming the residence of the top CEOs and government bureaucrats to demand the immediate solution to the problem.

In Japan, up until now, the collaborative effort of the government and the corporate media has successfully eradicated the potential tsunami of public condemnations and protests. The near-perfect control of the Japanese corporate media may not last forever, just like the complete media control by the Imperial General Headquarters during WWII. Independent Japanese journalists and critical thinkers like my brother-in-law and sister have begun to rely on the use of social networking devices like Twitter and Facebook to mobilize grassroots movements.

In the near future, it is possible that computer-literate populations may bring about the necessary changes to the traditional top-down system of media informational dissemination. What happened in the social networking revolution and resultant mass demonstrations in Tunisia, Egypt, Yemen, Syria, and Thailand may happen in Japan. This new nuclear disaster may bring about much needed changes in Japan's democratic movements.

International lens on the survivability of the nuclear industrial complex

A French nuclear fuel company, Areva, produces the uranium-plutonium mixed oxide (MOX) fuel, so called, used at the Unit 3 reactor in Fukushima. Areva has been commissioned by TEPCO and other Japanese electric power companies to process MOX fuels. Its use has been much criticized by nuclear experts, as it is considered one of the most dangerous nuclear fuels because of its lower melting temperature. The phenomenon of fuel melting due to the failure to cool it can facilitate the release of plutonium into the environment, threatening public health and increasing the chance of developing fatal cancers. Immediately after the earthquake, the French government decided to send five nuclear experts to Japan to offer help with the crisis at the crippled Fukushima plant. President Sarkozy also visited Tokyo on March 31, along with Areva CEO Anne Lauvergeon to meet the Japanese officials who offered the technical expertise in disposing the contaminated water that began leaking into the ground and the sea. Their visit is significant because nearly eighty percent of French electricity is generated by French nuclear power plants.

Any significant disaster may threaten the French government's nuclear policy in the future. Meanwhile, international communities have been watching the Fukushima disaster, as if it were an American and French nuclear disaster taking place on Japanese territory. The Government of India, which has been negotiating with GE for the construction of nearly 150 billion dollars worth of nuclear plants, is now reconsidering the agreement and has decided to redraft its own governmental nuclear program. Up until now, GE's nuclear investment had been greatly promoted by the American government as part of its foreign policy to export its proprietary nuclear technology to the overseas market, especially in countries in the Third World.

The current contractual agreement signed between TEPCO and GE, in the event of disasters at the nuclear plant, places the liability squarely on TEPCO as the operator of the nuclear plant. As is regularly practiced in nuclear industries around the world, TEPCO also carries insurance that amounts to over one billion dollars in coverage, with the guarantee that the Japanese government pays for the remainder of any future compensation.

The only exception from this binding responsibility may be that the original design of the nuclear plant must be proved flawed, thus shifting the liability to the designer of the nuclear plant, GE. Upon the showing of proof, GE may be liable for the payment of billions of dollars to compensate for millions of disaster victims in Japan and other affected people in different parts of the world. Regardless of the legal strategies or maneuvers, it is possible that TEPCO and the Japanese government may bring a lawsuit against GE, which drafted the original design of the nuclear power plant in Fukushima.

Ever since the earthquake and tsunami led to the shutdown of the nuclear plants in Fukushima, the American government has been extremely eager to offer logistical help, though the initial offer was rejected by TEPCO. Because of TEPCO's inability to deal with the crisis at hand, the Japanese government stepped in and took charge of much of the publicity efforts on the disaster and instituted new operation protocols. Many people believe that the offer of help from the U.S. government and its military personnel stationed in Japan comes from their genuine concern about the health and social welfare of people in Japan. Nonetheless, the potential liability of GE and the nuclear policy promoted by the U.S. government also make many people feel suspicious of the sincerity of their original motives.

Meanwhile, "Operation Tomodachi" (Operation Friends) mobilized fourteen U.S. Navy ships, more than one hundred aircrafts, and nearly twenty thousand U.S. service members stationed in Japan to provide much needed support to disaster victims in remote areas and islands. Military nuclear experts have also been invited to join the emergency committee to deal with the breach of both fuel containments and possible nuclear core reactors at the Fukushima nuclear plant.

Certainly TEPCO, GE, Avera, and both the Japanese and American governments expressed their concern over not only the extent of potential nuclear contaminations in the region in Japan and other countries around the world, but also possible legal liability, economic loss of corporate profits and revenue, and potential compensatory payment to millions of disaster victims. The radioactive contamination could become so severe that, just like the Four Corners area of the Navajo Nation and the Black Hills of South Dakota are designated as "National Sacrifice Areas," some of Fukushima and its adjacent regions might become Japan's national sacrifice region due to permanent environmental damages through radiation.

A nuclear power plant's main purpose is to boil water and create steam, which is then channeled into turbines whose high-speed spinning motion generates electricity. In other words, the primary purpose of a nuclear power facility is to boil water. This time, the cost of burning the fuel rods to boil water was extremely expensive, as it also collaterally burned the economic and financial foundation of millions of people's livelihoods. Their culture, their regional identity, and people's connections to ancestral lands and memories have already been destroyed by the forced evacuations.

It is also important to mention that the TEPCO nuclear plant was not built in the middle of the Tokyo-Shinjuku area, but in the tiny towns of Okuma and Futaba in the Futaba District of Fukushima Prefecture. In a country without many natural resources, the construction of nuclear power plants was sold to the public as a matter of national security, as well as a necessary and essential government program to secure future energy sources for millions of city dwellers and support commercial and industrial sectors in metropolitan areas.

Fukushima became the ideal and preferred site for the construction of nuclear power plants because of its high unemployment, poor economy, and its record of low educational achievement and competencies among younger students, standing at the bottom, only better than Okinawa. Though the aforementioned issues of corporate legal liabilities are important, epic natural disasters could result in apocalyptic radiation leaks with permanent and horrific effects in Japan and in the world, and make GE's liability issues wither in comparison.

Kamikaze, nationalism, and the "Hyper-Rescue" team

In the past, when a collaborative project between the state government and giant private corporations failed and led to a national disaster like an unwinnable war, the Japanese government exhibited the tendency to promote the nationalistic sentiments to call for sacrificial contributions from individual citizens to help save the nation from the disaster. Currently, in dealing with the nuclear crisis at the Fukushima power plant, a special group called the "Hyper-rescue" team of the Tokyo Fire Department was summoned in order to restore normalcy at the crippled nuclear power plant in Fukushima. The top bureaucrat of the fire department made a patriotic speech imbued with a passionate, nationalistic tone, asking the members to sacrifice themselves to deal with the crisis "for the sake of the country *(kokumei o kakete).*"

His strong nationalistic expression resonates with many speeches given by military government leaders to many patriotic soldiers, including young Kamikaze pilots at the end of WWII. As the Japanese imperial force engaged in predatory military actions against other Asian neighbors in order to secure material, natural, and human resources to feed Japan's military-industrial complex and its modernization, an army of soldiers was recruited from all over Japan, Korea, and Taiwan to participate in the imperialist project, which ultimately resulted in the death of millions in the imperial process. At home, nearly 700,000 civilians were incinerated by America's aerial raids over two hundred cities, towns, and villages from late 1944 to the morning of August 15, 1945 when the Japanese government finally signed its complete, unconditional surrender to the U.S. and its allied forces.

In 1942, at the age of thirteen, my father was conscripted to work in a Hitachi-owned bomb factory in Mito, a sleepy coastal town north of Tokyo. His job was to weld wing-metals to bombs. He began to talk about his war experience in detail only recently. He painfully talked about his attempt to help resuscitate his roommate whose stomach was blown away by bomb shrapnel. He was once so hungry that, during a U.S. air raid, instead of running to his regularly assigned bomb-shelter, he ran towards a potato field, lay down low, and started to use his fingers to search for potatoes to eat. He soon realized that he could have made a life-threatening mistake when he saw many telephone poles being chopped into pieces like match sticks by the sharp shrapnel of exploded bombshells.

He said his life in the Hitachi dormitory was a hell, as he was beaten every day by older roommates for no reason. It is ironic that nearly seventy years later, my father found himself in a similarly helpless situation, in which the nuclear reactor built by the same company, Hitachi, is endangering his life once again.

The nationalistic rhetoric given by TEPCO CEOs in encouraging their employees, rescue workers, and subcontracted workers to make collective personal sacrifices for the sake of the company, and ultimately, the Japanese people, sounds extremely hollow. In past nuclear accidents, the majority of the workers exposed to radiation have been subcontracted workers who were hired for brief periods to do the most dangerous work at the nuclear plant. These subcontract workers are called "*Genpatsu* Gypsies" (nuclear gypsies), and they move from one nuclear plant to another throughout the year, making up eighty-nine percent of employees in the industry and receiving more than ninety percent of all radiation exposure.

Many of them come from *Burakumin* and other ethnic minority backgrounds and lower classes who have difficulties in finding jobs in more stable primary labor markets. These workers are recruited from predominantly minority areas and city slums such as Sanya Ward in Tokyo, Kamagasaki in Osaka, as well as *Burakumin* residential areas throughout Japan. With more jobs at nuclear power plants in recent years, additional workers, including poor farmers, fishermen, day laborers, and even homeless have been recruited to work as temporary employees, to supplement their incomes or simply to get by. They find themselves working at dangerous nuclear fuel facilities, such as waste burial and storage facilities, mopping up radioactive water, scraping out shells and sludge attached to drains, inspecting and repairing operative equipment, and removing radioactive dust from mechanical parts inside nuclear reactors. They are attracted by high daily wages and sent into the plants with hardly any knowledge of the danger of radiation. The fragmentation of subcontract workers and their diverse backgrounds also contributed to the utter failure to form a union to improve their working conditions. In many plants, subcontract workers are required to make formal apologies to the nuclear power company if they get injuries. They have no medical guarantees for their job-related illnesses or injuries.

A similar scenario is played out for "foreigner squads" who are sent from the U.S. by GE and Westinghouse, another nuclear plant manufacturer, to work at the plants they built in Japan. It has been reported that Americans subcontracted by GE to work at the Fukushima plant have been largely African-American.

It is ironic that those who are asked to restore the operation of the nuclear power plant by the leaders of the company and the Japanese government officials who use the nationalistic and patriotic rhetoric and encourage them to sacrifice even their lives on behalf of the company and, ultimately, millions of Japanese residents are the very people who have been subject to social and economic discrimination in society. The ultimate fate of TEPCO, the lives of millions of Japanese residents, and even the survival of nuclear industries in Japan and elsewhere now depend on the sacrifices of nameless subcontract workers who themselves are victims of the very systems that they are asked to rescue.

Libya and depleted uranium ammunitions

While those subcontract workers were struggling to restore the nuclear power plants and battling the effects of radiation at the nuclear plant site in Fukushima, it was reported that in the Mediterranean Sea, French jet fighters had just taken off on the nuclear aircraft carrier, *Charles André de Gaulle,* named after the renowned French president, to bomb the tanks, armored vehicles, and military command centers inside Libya. American and British jet fighters also joined the aerial assault and attacked the Libyan army with special, anti-tank depleted uranium (DU) missiles, spreading the radioactive materials all over the battleground and adjacent areas.

While Japan's subcontract workers were working frantically at the nuclear plant to save millions of lives from potential radioactive contamination, NATO forces were trying to neutralize Libyan armies in the name of democracy, while spewing the deadly depleted uranium and its radioactive dust, potentially endangering millions of lives over the wide regions of Libya. The armor-piercing ammunitions were made of depleted uranium, which is a radioactive and toxic waste.

In the aftermath of the first Gulf War in 1991, both U.S. and British jet fighters dropped more than 290,000 kilograms of depleted uranium, thereby contaminating military equipment, food and water, soldiers, residents, and the soil on the battlefields of Saudi Arabia, Kuwait, and southern Iraq. Today, many veterans and civilians have been exposed to DU contamination and are suffering from serious health problems, including kidney damages, cancers of lungs and bones, non-malignant respiratory disease, skin disorders, neuro-cognitive disorders, chromosomal damage, birth defects, among many other diseases and sicknesses.

The governments of the United States and Great Britain, fully aware of the potential danger and highly toxic nature of radioactive contamination to people in the areas for many years to come, nonetheless continued to manufacture and employ the dangerous ammunitions against foreign enemies on foreign soils. In 1999, the UN sub-commission determined DU hazardous enough to call for an initiative, banning its controversial use worldwide. Nonetheless, the initiative was blocked by the U.S. government. In Basra, Iraq, numerous studies showed the exponential increase of birth defects in the region, from eleven per a population of 100,000 in 1989 to 116 per 100,000 in 2001. Similarly thirty-four people died of cancer in the area in 1988, while in 2001 there were 603 cancer deaths.

Dr. Jawad Al-Ali, a British-trained oncologist, found similarities to the birth defects that followed the atomic bombings of Hiroshima and Nagasaki after 1945. The most dangerous weapons, with the potential to cause serious health and reproductive hazards for many future generations, have always been used against people of color and of non-European origin, in non-European regions.

If massive radiation leaks spread over northern Japan, what happened in Basra, Hiroshima, and Nagasaki will await a future generation of Japanese children who will be adversely affected by the radioactive contamination found in mother's milk, drinking water, baby food, soil, and the atmosphere.

Last remarks and Haitian President and the Tsunami of love

One week after a deadly tsunami swallowed many of the cities and towns on the northeastern coast of Japan, another powerful tsunami hit the coast of the Island of Hispaniola in the Caribbean nation of Haiti. On March 18, former Haitian President Jean-Bertrand Aristide finally returned to his home country and was greeted by tens of thousands of enthusiastic Haitian supporters who welcomed him at the airport and followed him to his residence. "Tsunami of love" was the word used by Aristide to capture the tidal wave of warm welcomes expressed by the Haitian people. In 2004, President Aristide was kidnapped by a U.S. special forces unit and dropped off in the Central African Republic. Despite the U.S. threats against him and his family, Aristide finally returned to Haiti with the support of actor Danny Glover, lawyer Randall Robinson, U.S. representative Maxine Waters, and many other humanitarian activists and Haitian supporters in the U.S. and around the world.

The name of his political party is called *Lavalas,* which also means the "tsunami" of a cleansing flood in Creole. This time, the huge tidal wave of love and affection has literally poured down out of the Haitian streets and slums and stormed out of the city toward the airport and his residence, with the expectation that former President Aristide will help reconstruct the earthquake-devastated country of Haiti. Haiti suffered the deadly earthquake on January 12, 2010 and more than three hundred thousand people died. More than ten thousand Haitians have also lost their lives to the recent cholera epidemic which was ironically brought by United Nations peacekeeping members who came in to provide assistance to Haitian people.

What Former President Aristide plans to accomplish is quite similar to what the Japanese people and its leaders must do in their effort to reconstruct the socioeconomic foundation in northern Japan. Many volunteers, American military forces and personnel, and rescue teams sent by many other countries poured their "tsunami of love" and support on the victims in northern Japan.

The question still remains whether or not Japan's new tsunami, after having killed nearly thirty thousand people and still threatening millions of Japanese residents through a potential nuclear meltdown, may be morphed into the tidal wave of love, affection, and the goodwill of many international organizations and governments.

Until then, the fates of the Japanese people, TEPCO, the government of Japan and other crucially connected organizations such as GE and Areva are hanging by a thread, all hoping that this tragedy will not lead to an even greater disaster.

The Hiten Project: Zero Gravity Dance
Setsuko Ishiguro, Choreographer

—

Title
Hiten (Flying Apsara)

—

Leader
Setsuko Ishiguro

—

Description
Flying Apsara on wall paintings in Dunhuang
and Horyuji Temple will be recreated by JAXA
astronauts in orbit.

The motion of human beings on earth is completely governed by gravity. Thus scenes of astronauts floating in space can be surprising and refreshing to see. Released from the restriction of gravity, human motions produce beauty that can't be imagined otherwise.

Hiten are regarded as celestial beings who fly through the air to praise Buddha's dignity and guard his world. More specifically, they rejoice over Buddha's doings by performing music, showering flowers and wafting incense as they fly through the air. *Hiten,* while part of the Buddhist tradition, actually have their origin in Europe, through India from whence they were brought to China and Japan over the Silk Road. The most beautiful images of them are found in the grottoes of Dunhuang (China) and the murals from the Horyuji Golden Hall of Nara (Japan), the oldest wooden temple in the world.

This dance, the first to take place aboard the International Space Station, is a prayer for world peace.

A Reader's Guide
Mona Moraru

Nagasaki. And Scattered Islets of Time
by Ryuta Imafuku

How can a single moment in time—captured in a stopped watch or a photograph—acquire meaning? Can Tomatsu's photographs chronicling the lives of people in Nagasaki after the atomic blast be considered independently or are they inevitably monuments to the "subsequent span"?

Imafuku investigates the relationship between time, light, images. What role does text, such as this essay, play?

What was gained and lost in Tomatsu's transition to digital photography?

Blast
by Goro Takano

What does Takano achieve with the echoing motifs in this narrative?

What is the effect of introducing a Western story (the Grimms' fairytale) as a sense of inspiration for the writer?

The Diary of Noboru Tokuda

How do the images and text support each other to build a broader understanding of Tokuda's experience?

What sense of the war is derived from this diary?

Last Time I Saw You
by Kentaro Yamaki

Is the character of the woman a significant aspect of the story or is she most helpful in framing the narrative?

What role does the war itself play in the narrative's tone?

Poetry by Kim Shi-Jong

How does Shi-Jong use sounds to enhance his poems "Behind the Summer Rain" and "At the Heart of the Pale Blue Sky"?

How does knowledge of the uprising in April and liberation in August change the reading of "Oh, April, my Distant Days!"?

The Deleted Line
by Deni Y. Bechard

How do Ai's drawings relate to the perceptions of war related by Matt and the *karateka*?

How do the philosophical discussions at the conference contribute to the narrative?

The Emperor and the Mayor
by Stephen Woodhams

Could the mayor's perspective ever be reconciled with the aspect of an older Japanese consciousness, or is it dependent on the change that he saw coming?

How important is it that Japan take responsibility for its role in WWII in order to move on?

Don't Arrogate, Hiroshima!
by Hitoshi Motoshima

What might Mayor Motoshima be considering in arguing that an apology is crucial for the future of Japan?

In what other ways could the World Heritage Committee's decision to recognize the Hiroshima Peace Memorial be considered?

Park City
by Masataka Matsuda

How do the three levels of reality in this play compliment each other?

Why do writers often deal with terrible events using humor or the absurd?

The Atomic Bomb Survivors
by Janice Nakao

How do the psychoanalytic principles applied by Nakao—through Jung and Lifton—propose approaching survivors of the atomic bomb?

What, if anything, sets the survivors of the atomic bombings up for a different post-traumatic experience than that of survivors of other events on that scale?

Poetry by Ben Takara

Gama
What does Takara achieve by mixing aspects of war with different facets of nature?

A Matter of God
How does the punctuation affect the mood of the poem?

Passing Into Twilight Alley
by Tami Sakiyama

How does Sakiyama use sensory details in this story?

How does modern Okinawan history inform the story?

A Landscape of Words
by Tami Sakiyama

How are the written words that Sakiyama invented for *appa* and *anna* different from their oral counterparts?

Everyone has an early childhood landscape of words. Discuss yours.

The Silver Motorcycle
by Katsunori Yamazato

The narrator distances himself from his aunt by calling her "the woman." What effect does this have on the narrative?

What do the narrator's dreams at the end of the fourth section contribute or change?

An Exchange for Fire
by Christopher Blasdel

What sense do the quotes from Craig's blog give about his approach to this leg of his volcanic tour?

What does this piece convey about Japan?

Walking
by Keijiro Suga

How does the emphasis on movement transform the natural settings?

C-Lit and Yaoi Desire
by Mari Kotani

How does manga work as a socially acceptable medium through which to expand definitions of sexuality?

Why do male characters figure so prominently in representing this C-derived narratology?

Tales from Fin de Siècle Japantown
by Takayuki Tatsumi

What image of *fin de siècle* Japantown and the Japanese attitude towards the United States arises from Tatsumi's family history?

How does gender factor into the author's understanding of his ancestors?

Superflat Tokyo
by Roland Kelts

How does the sculpture *Hiropon* play into or against Murakami's concepts of "superflat" and "little boy"?

In what ways does Murakami interact with Kelts' view of Tokyo?

The Art of Passing Through Walls
by Leza Lowitz and Shogo Oketani

How does Rika's knowledge of her family's magic alter her perspective?

Dream Corridor
by Stewart Wachs

To what degree were the narrator's dreams translated into "daytime language"?

What is this article's view on the significance of dreams?

Small Fish
by Iona Sugihara

What role does family history play in the reading of this story?

How do the multiple perspectives shown affect the narrative?

Disaster Memories
by Hiroshi Fukurai

What effect does the narrative gain from the author's perspective?

How does this essay support a political stance?

The Hiten Project led by Setsuko Ishiguro

While the International Space Station allows for a weightless performance, what other implications, if any, does the juxtaposition of traditional Buddhist Hiten with space technology convey?

Acknowledgements

Many people have contributed to the making of this book. We would like to thank Karen Tei Yamashita for the encouragement and support she provided from the start, Dr. James Yamazaki for his interest and generosity, and Carl and Kyoko Nommensen for their warm welcome and friendship.

Before our departure Dale Johnson, Sakae Fujita and Naoko Yamamoto introduced us to the Japanese language, while Margaret Mihori, Donka Farkas, and Karen Joy Fowler introduced us to colleagues in Japan. The sister city committees of Shingu and Santa Cruz extended their hospitality as well.

For guidance in Tokyo, we are grateful to Christopher Blasdel, Ryuta Imafuku, Manami Maeda, Leza Lowitz, Yoko Sugioka, and Katsuo and Masae Matsuyama; in Kyoto and Osaka, Penny Sugihara, John Einarsen, Stewart Wachs, Jen Teeter, Taka Okazaki, Tracy Slater, Mariko Mori of *Marebito-No-Kai* and Mineo and Sanae Tokuda; in Nagasaki, Dr. Shunichi Yamashita, director of the Atomic Bomb Disease Institute, Haruko Ito of the Nagasaki Prefectural Art Museum; in Okinawa, Ikue Kina.

Syed Afzal Haider, founding editor of the *Chicago Quarterly Review,* brought his enthusiasm and vision to this project. We thank Nick Forbes, Mona Moraru and Stuart Woodhams for editorial assistance, and Hillary Geller, who as designer shaped this book into an object of beauty.

To all the writers, translators and artists who have shared work with us, we thank you immeasurably.

Finally, this collection was made possible with the support of the Japan–U.S. Friendship Commission, the National Endowment for the Arts, and the *Bunka-cho* of Japan.

Contributors' Notes

Deni Y. Béchard was born in British Columbia to French Canadian and American parents and grew up in both Canada and the United States. He has also traveled in over forty countries and done freelance reporting from Northern Iraq and Afghanistan. His articles, stories and translations have appeared in a number of magazines and newspapers. His first novel, *Vandal Love,* (2006, Doubleday Canada) was published in French and Arabic, and won the 2007 Commonwealth Writers' Prize, both for the best first book in Canada and for the best overall first book in the British Commonwealth. In 2012, Milkweed Editions will publish *Cures for Hunger,* his memoir about growing up with his father who was a bank robber. Also forthcoming with Milkweed is *Empty Hands, Open Arms,* a book about conservationism in the Congo.

Christopher Yohmei Blasdel (born 1951, Canyon, Texas), is a shakuhachi performer, researcher and writer specializing in the music of Japan and Asia. In 1972, while on foreign study in Tokyo, he was introduced to the Kinko Style shakuhachi master (later designated "Living National Treasure") Goro Yamaguchi, whom he studied with until Yamaguchi's death in 1999. In 1978, Blasdel entered the Musicology Faculty at Tokyo National University of Fine Arts *(Geidai)* with a scholarship from the Japanese government. Blasdel graduated from *Geidai* with an MFA in 1982. In 1984, he received his *shihan* master teaching license and professional name, Yohmei, from Yamaguchi—the first of only two non-Japanese ever accredited by Yamaguchi. Blasdel began working part time at the International House of Japan in 1988 as advisor to the arts program and curator of the Japan–U.S. Friendship Commission Creative Artists' Exchange Program. In 2005, he was promoted to Artistic Director of the International House. Blasdel is the senior artistic advisor to the annual Prague Shakuhachi Festival. He has added shakuhachi music to live readings of such distinguished poets as John Logan, Kenneth Rexroth, Sam Hamill, Makoto Ooka and Leza Lowitz. His publications in English include *The Shakuhachi, A Manual for Learning* originally published in 1988 by *Ongaku no Tomo-sha* (later re-written and published by Printed Matter Press in 2008). In 2006, *Ongaku no Tomo-sha* published the Japanese version of this manual. In 2005, Printed Matter Press published *The Single Tone, A Personal Journey into Shakuhachi Music.* His Japanese publications include *Shakuhachi Odessei—Ten no Neiro ni Miserarete,* translated and adapted into English as *The Single Tone).* This work was awarded the Sixth Rennyo Prize for Nonfiction in 1999. To date he has made a total of eight CDs of classical and contemporary shakuhachi music.

James Dorsey is an associate professor of Japanese at Dartmouth College. His published work includes a monograph on the Japanese critic Hideo Kobayashi (Harvard University Press, 2009) and an edited volume of essays on, and translations of, Ango Sakaguchi. He is currently working on a manuscript dealing with Japan's wartime culture.

Sakae Fujita was born in the city of Hiroshima, and raised in the city of Osaka. She is a Lecturer in Japanese Language at the University of California, Santa Cruz. Her areas of expertise include second language acquisition, language teaching pedagogy, drama and foreign language education. She obtained her doctorate from the University of California, Berkeley.

Hiroshi Fukurai is Professor of Legal Studies and Sociology at the University of California, Santa Cruz. He was born and raised in Sendai, Japan, came to the U.S. in 1976, and obtained a Ph.D. in sociology in 1985 from UC Riverside. He has published nearly 100 articles, including Op-Ed pieces and book chapters, and his research explores the potential utility of lay adjudication in an effort to create an effective deterrent and investigative mechanism against governmental abuse of power. His four books are indicative of his commitment to adjudicative justice and equality in law; *Race in the Jury Box: Affirmative Action in Jury Selection* (2003), *Anatomy of the McMartin Child Molestation Case* (2001), *Race and the Jury: Racial Disenfranchisement and the Search for Justice* (1993, Gustavus Meyers Human Rights Award), and *Common Destiny: Japan and the U.S. in the Global Age* (1990). He serves on the Law and Society Association (LSA) editorial board for *Law and Society Review,* was voted into the LSA Board of Trustees, helped co-organize the Inaugural East Asian Law and Society CRN, and was one of three organizers to hold the Inaugural East Asian Law and Society Conference in Hong Kong in February 2010, for which 160 participants gathered from the U.S., Japan, Korea, China, Taiwan, Malaysia, Australia, Canada, Iran, England, Germany, and other nations in the world. He was one of three key organizers of the Second East Asian Law and Society Conference held in Seoul, Korea in September 2011.

Hillary Geller is a graphic designer living in Chicago, Illinois. Her work was been recognized by *Communication Arts, Print Magazine, I.D. Magazine, Rebrand 100, Step Inside Design,* the *American Institute of Graphic Arts* among others. It is also in the collections of the Chicago Design Archive and The Art Institute of Chicago.

Born in Tokyo, having lived and researched extensively in Latin America and the Caribbean, **Ryuta Imafuku** is an anthropologist and cultural critic whose unique writings and voice on contemporary culture, art, history and politics are widely recognized in Japan. He is known as one of the pioneering figures in his country to demonstrate a creolist vision of culture. His recent activities include the "Archipelagic University" project in the Amami/Ryukyu/East Asian Islands, and collaborations of books and exhibitions with photographers Shomei Tomatsu and Sebastião Salgado, poet Gozo Yoshimasu, anthropologist Claude Lévi-Strauss, and filmmaker Trinh T. Minh-ha. He is the author of *Sensory Angels* (1990), *The Heterology of Culture* (1991), *Technology of the Wild* (1994), *Elsewhere: Toward the Corridor of Images* (2001), *Minima Gracia: History and Craving* (2008), and *The Archipelago-World* (2008) among others. He teaches Cultural Studies and Ethics at Tokyo University of Foreign Studies, and is a permanent visiting professor of Communication and Semiotics at the Catholic University of São Paulo, Brazil.

Setsuko Ishiguro, born in Tokyo in 1941, started modern dance at the age of sixteen and has been a Professor at Ochanomizu University in choreography for many years. She has received numerous awards and fellowships for dance and choreography, recently culminating in her selection by JAXA, the Japan Aerospace Exploration Agency, to choreograph a dance for astronauts in the International Space Station in 2009 and 2010.

Roland Nozomu Kelts is a half-Japanese American writer, editor and lecturer who divides his time between New York and Tokyo. He is the author of *Japanamerica: How Japanese Pop Culture has Invaded the U.S.* and the forthcoming novel, *Access.* He is also a contributing editor and writer for *Adbusters* magazine and *A Public Space* literary journal, and a columnist for Japan's *Daily Yomiuri* newspaper and *Paper Sky* magazine. He has taught at New York University, The University of Tokyo and Sophia University, and speaks frequently on contemporary Japanese culture and literature at numerous institutions in Japan, Australia, the

United Kingdom, and the United States, where he has appeared alongside such notables as novelist Haruki Murakami and animator/director Hayao Miyazaki. His fiction and nonfiction also appear in *Zoetrope: All Story, Psychology Today, The Wall Street Journal, Vogue Japan, The Japan Times, Animation Magazine, Bookforum, The Village Voice* and others, including the anthologies and collections *A Wild Haruki Chase, Playboy Fiction, Gamers, Kuhaku,* and *Art Space Tokyo.* He is the Editor in Chief of the *Anime Masterpieces* screening and discussion series and a frequent contributor to National Public Radio. His blog can be found at: http://japanamerica.blogspot.com/

Ikue Kina is a professor of American Literature at University of the Ryukyus, Okinawa, Japan. Born and educated in Okinawa, she did her graduate studies at Indiana University of Pennsylvania, where she completed her Ph.D. in English in 2000. She has published articles both in Japanese and in English on Native American literature, Chicana literature, and U.S. women writers. Her essay on Tami Sakiyama's short stories was published in the May/June 2008 issue of *Suisei Tsushin,* a literary magazine by *Suisei-sha* of Tokyo. Her most recent article written in English is a queer ecofeminist critique of the plays of Cherrie Moraga, which appeared in the December 2009 issue of *Tamkang Review,* a journal of Tamkang University, Taiwan.

Joel Klotz first became interested in Japan during visits to San Francisco's Japantown with his family. He studied Japanese language and history at the University of California, Santa Cruz. From 2006 to 2008, he worked in rural Japan as a member of the JET Program, teaching English and helping to coordinate cultural events. In March 2011 he again moved to Japan to teach English in a town near the Fuji Five Lakes, about ninety miles west of Tokyo. This year he will spend a month cycling through Japan, and plans to write a book about the experience.

Mari Kotani (born 1958 in Toyama), SF&Fantasy critic, has served as vice president of SFWJ (Science Fiction and Fantasy Writers of Japan) and chair of the Women Writers Committee of Japan PEN Club. Her first book, *Techno-Gynesis: The Political Unconscious of Feminist Science Fiction* (Tokyo: Keiso Publishers, 1994) won the 15th Japan SF Taisho Award. Her second book, *Evangelion as the Immaculate Virgin* (Tokyo: Magazine House, 1997) sold more than 80,000 copies and established the author as an authority on anime. She regularly publishes reviews and essays in major Japanese newspapers such as *Yomiuri Shinbun, Nihon-Keizai Shinbun,* and many magazines such as *Hayakawa's SF Magazine, S-F Studies,* and *SF Eye.* Her collaborations include *Blood Read* edited by Joan Gordon and Veronica Hollinger (Philadelphia: University of Pennsylvania Press, 1997) and *Robot Ghosts, Wired Dreams,* edited by Christopher Boton, Istvan Cscicery-Ronay and Takayuki Tatsumi (University of Minnesota Press, 2007). One of the active members of The Japanese Association of Gender Fantasy and Science Fiction, she helped found The Sense of Gender Award as the Japanese equivalent of the James Tiptree, Jr. Award.

Leza Lowitz has published over fifteen books about Japan, mostly from Stone Bridge Press and Tuttle Publishing. Her work has appeared in *Harper's,* on NPR Radio's "The Sound of Writing" and in hundreds of literary magazines internationally. Awards for her fiction, poetry and translation include a PEN Syndicated Fiction Award, grants from the National Endowment for the Arts, National Endowment for the Humanities, and the Japan–U.S. Friendship Commission Award from the Donald Keene Center at Columbia University for the Translation of Japanese Literature. She edited and co-translated a Benjamin Franklin Award-winning anthology of Japanese women's contemporary poetry. Her book, *Yoga Poems: Lines to Unfold By* received the Bay Area Independent Publisher's Association Award and the PEN/Oakland Josephine Miles Poetry Award. Leza's newest book of poems *Yoga Heart: Lines on the Six Perfections,* was published by Stone Bridge Press in 2011.

Born in 1962 in Nagasaki Prefecture, **Masataka Matsuda** is a leading Japanese playwright and theater director. He started his career in drama while a student at Ritsumeikan University in Kyoto. He formed the *Jiku Gekijo* Company in Kyoto in 1990, and wrote and directed all the works for the company until it was disbanded in 1997. He then worked as a freelancer and wrote and co-produced with Seinendan, Bungakuza and other companies. He joined the theater company Marebito "Marebito-no-Kai" in May 2004 and started to direct again as well as continuing to write for the company. He has received numerous awards, including the OMS Drama Award 1994 for *Saka no Ue no ie* (The House On the Hill), OMS Drama Award and KISHIDA Kunio Drama Award in 1996 for *Umi to Higasa* (Sea and Parasol), the Yomiuri Drama Award for *Tsuki no Misaki* (Moon Cape), the Yomiuri Literature Award in 1998 for *Natsu no Suna no ue* (On the sand of the Summer) and the Kyoto Cultural Encouragement Prize in 2000. He was selected as the most avant-garde and experimental theater artist of the year 2009 in the critical magazine *Theatre Arts*. He is a guest professor at Kyoto University of Art and Design.

Waku Miller recently published an English translation on the history of East Asian calligraphy by the avant-garde calligrapher Kyuyoh Ishikawa. He is writing a book in Japanese about the contemporary ceramic artist Anjin Abe and a book in English about the 13th-century Buddhist monk Eihei Dogen. A native of Arizona, Waku has resided in Japan since 1978.

Hitoshi Motoshima was born on February 20, 1922 in a small settlement on Shinkamigoto Island in Nagasaki Prefecture. The villagers were the descendants of the Catholic Christians who fled to the island from persecutions, becoming *Kakure Kirishitan* ("hidden" or "secret" Christians) and played a pivotal role in establishing Motoshima's mind as of a devout Christian. He entered Kyoto University Engineering Department, but due to World War II, when he was drafted and served as a soldier of the Emperor's army, he did not graduate until he was twenty-seven years old in 1949. After the war he worked as a teacher before starting his political career.

He served as a Representative for the Nagasaki Prefectural Legislature from 1959 to 1979, and then was elected Mayor of Nagasaki, a position he held from 1979 to 1995. He was a popular figure in Nagasaki with notable moral commitments to peace, but was criticized by some for paying insufficient attention to other administrative and economic municipal policies. A very strong and ambiguous reaction in the country arose after Motoshima's comments in 1988, in which he admitted that the Emperor (Hirohito, known posthumously as Showa) bore partial responsibility for the war, which is a delicate issue for Japanese cultural and historical social mentality. Motoshima refused to retract his statement after the Liberal Democratic Party Prefectural Committee requested him to do so. Furthermore, he also appealed for a rethinking of the role of Japan in WWII in light of its aggressiveness and wished Japan to offer an apology to its former victims, first of all to China and Korea. These calls were met with confusion in Japan, evoking a whole spectrum of reactions ranging from full support to wrathful denunciations. After numerous intimidations, he was shot in the back in January 1990 by a member of a right-wing group, just outside the entrance to the City Hall, but survived this attempt on his life. At present, Motoshima is retired and still of the point of view that all possible effort should be made to ensure that "Nagasaki will remain the world's last city to suffer from an atomic blast and that the 21st century will be a century of forgiveness and reconciliation." In 2002, Motoshima was awarded both the first Korea/Japan Peace and Fellowship Prize and the Order of Merit of the Federal Republic of Germany.

Janice Nakao is a Jungian analyst in private practice in Evanston, Illinois, providing psychotherapy and psychoanalysis for children, adolescents and adults. She is the Director of Social Work Services at the Japanese American Service Committee of Chicago and a faculty member of the Analyst Training Program and Clinical Training program at the CG Jung Institute of Chicago.

Carl Nommensen was born in Papua New Guinea of Australian parents. He graduated from Queensland University, Australia, majoring in computer science and psychology, and has lived in Japan since 1991. He has worked at Doshisha University, Ritsumeikan University, and other Universities in Kyoto, teaching English language and culture related subjects. His passions are literature, language, philosophy and nature.

Kyoko Nommensen was born in Osaka. She majored in American Literature at Kyoto Women's University and qualified as an English teacher. After studying business marketing in Australia for two years, she became a high school English teacher in Japan. Since having children, she has worked as a freelance translator in the commercial and literary fields.

Shogo Oketani is a writer and translator, having worked for clients from IBM to Eastman Kodak, Lucasfilm to Hitachi. A black belt in Karate and expert in Shaolinquan (Bruce Lee-style martial arts), he teaches Self-Defense for women. With his wife, Leza Lowitz, he owns a popular yoga studio in Tokyo. With Lowitz, Oketani is co-author of *Designing with Kanji* (Stone Bridge Press), and co-translator of *America and Other Poems* by Ayukawa Nobuo, for which they received the Japan–U.S. Friendship Commission Award from the Donald Keene Center at Columbia University for the Translation of Japanese Literature. Shogo's new book of fifteen interlocking short stories about a fifth grader and his friends, *J-Boys: Kazuo's World, Tokyo 1965,* has just been published by Stone Bridge Press.

Tami Sakiyama was born in 1954 on Iriomote Island, Okinawa. After living for a short time on other islands, she finally settled herself in Koza, the town located in the central part of Okinawa's main island. Neighbored by the U.S. military bases since the end of WWII, Koza has a unique history of being at the crossroads between Okinawan and other cultures. Sakiyama's experiences of moving among islands and later settlement in Koza for more than forty years have had a significant influence on her writing,

contributing to the development of her unusual sensibility about languages spoken within Okinawa and her conscious "unsettling" as an act of keeping her senses and attitude in terms of cultural and linguistic fluidity in her surroundings. Twice nominated for the Akutagawa Prize, one of the most prestigious literary prizes in Japan, Sakiyama continues to write perhaps not so much to win the prize race as out of the pure necessity for expressing her own literary subjects to artistic perfection. Her stories and novels have appeared in a number of prestigious literary magazines in Japan, and they have also been translated and included in anthologies published in the U.S., such as *More Stories by Japanese Women Writers* edited by Kyoko Selden and Noriko Mizuta (An East Gate Book, 2011) and a special issue of *Manoa* (University of Hawaii Press, 2011).

Kentaro Sasaki was born in Chiba prefecture in 1984. She is a manga artist and figure creator.

Kim Shi-Jong was born in 1929 in Wonsan, Korea, under Japanese rule, presently in the territory of North Korea. As a genuine product of the cultural "Japanization" policy during the occupation, he grew up a Japanese monolingual without any knowledge of Korean writing. After the liberation in the summer of 1945, he went to work on Jeju Island and became involved in the April 3rd popular uprising in 1948. In 1949, he settled in the Ikaino Korean neighborhood in Osaka, Japan, and began writing his poems in Japanese. He is considered a pioneer of contemporary Korean-Japanese literature, representing the voices of more than 800,000 *Zainichi* Koreans residing in Japan. His books of poetry include *Niigata, Ikaino Anthology, Gwangju Fragments, The Fosssil Summer,* and most recently *Lost Seasons,* a collection of seasonal lyric poems that won the Takami Jun Prize for Poetry in 2011.

Keijiro Suga (born 1958) is a Japanese poet, essayist, and translator. Among his nine books are *Omniphone: Poetics of World-Echoes* (2005), *Transversal Journeys* (2009, recipient of the Yomiuri Prize for Literature, 2010), and *Agend'Ars* (2010) from which the poems in this volume are taken. His translations from French, Spanish, and English into Japanese include Edouard Glissant's *Poétique de la Relation*, Isabelle Allende's *Paula*, and all of Aimee Bender's works. He is currently chair of the graduate program in Digital Content Studies, Meiji University, Tokyo.

Iona Sugihara was born and raised in Japan, and studied English Literature and Creative Writing at Royal Holloway, University of London. She currently lives and works in London.

Goro Takano (高野吾朗) was born in the city of Hiroshima. He is an assistant professor in the Faculty of Medicine at Saga University, where he teaches English and Japanese literature. He obtained his M.A. from the University of Tokyo (American Literature), and his Ph.D. from the University of Hawaii at Manoa (English/Creative Writing). His first novel, *With One More Step Ahead,* was published by BlazeVOX in 2009.

Ben Takara, born in the village of Tamagusuku, Okinawa in 1949, is one of the most influential poets in the Ryukyu archipelago. During the period of the American occupation of Okinawa, he went to Honshu, Japan's main island, for his undergraduate study of chemistry at Shizuoka University, only to become involved in the student activism of 1968 and returning to Okinawa to join the anti-revisionary cultural movement led by journalist Akira Arakawa, poet Shinichi Kawamitsu and literary critic Keitoku Okamoto. In 1979, he published his first book of poetry, *Origin of Dreams;* his second poetry collection *The Cape* (1984) won the Yamanokuchi-Baku Prize. In 1990, he received a grant to study anthropology at the University of the Philippines for a year, which resulted in *Sampaguita* (1999), his fourth book of poetry. Recently, his is the most outstanding and active voice in Okinawa's cultural movement for socio-political

autonomy. His latest book of poetry is *Gama,* published in 2009.

Takayuki Tatsumi, Ph.D. (born 1955 in Tokyo), is professor of English at Keio University, Tokyo. He is a member of the editorial board of *The Edgar Allan Poe Review, Mark Twain Studies* and *Journal of Transnational American Studies.* His major books are: *Cyberpunk America* (Tokyo: Keiso Shobo Publishers, 1988), the winner of the Japan–U.S. Friendship Commission's American Studies Book Prize; *New Americanist Poetics* (Tokyo: Seidosha Publishers,1995), winner of the Yukichi Fukuzawa Award; *Full Metal Apache: Transactions between Cyberpunk Japan and Avant-Pop America* (Durham: Duke University Press, 2006), the winner of the 2010 IAFA Distinguished Scholarship Award. Co-editor of the "New Japanese Fiction" issue of *Review of Contemporary Fiction* (Summer 2002) and the "Three Asias—Japan, S. Korea, China" issue of *PARA*DOXA* (No. 22, 2010), he has also published a variety of essays, including "Literary History on the Road: Transatlantic Crossings and Transpacific Crossovers" *(PMLA* 119.1 [January 2004]); "Race and Black Humor: From a Planetary Perspective" (*Journal of the Fantastic in the Arts* 21.3 [2010]).

Mineo Tokuda 徳田 峯夫

1942 born in Kyoto City as the second son of Noboru (father) and Shizuyo (mother) Tokuda. (The Japanese navy got a crushing defeat in the Midway sea battle this year.)

1943 father Noboru was conscripted into the Japanese navy

1947 father Noboru came back to Japan from the battlefield when Mineo was 5 years old (Mineo's first memory of seeing his father was in the JR Kyoto station to welcome him and his big bag from the internment camp in Singapore)

1962 entered Kyoto University, Department of Technology (civil engineering division)

1966 graduated from Kyoto University, Masters degree. Got a position in the Ministry of Transport (while working for the Japanese government, Mineo had many experiences of living and working in developing countries such as Pakistan, Venezuela and Thailand based on the technical cooperation program of the government)

1969 married Sanae, the daughter of Yoshio Saji, president of the Kuramaguchi Hospital

1993 retired from working for the Japanese government

1997–2007 worked in the private construction company, Fukuda-gumi Corporation

2007 retired from all workings and returned to his home town Kyoto and inherited his parents' home

---

Noboru Tokuda 徳田 昇

1910 born in the suburbs of Kyoto city, Ueba village

1914 adopted into kimono merchant family Tokuda

1929 graduated from Higashiyama middle school (now high school) and began working for his parents' kimono dealer and the famous kimono dealing company of Yoshityu

1938 married Sizuyo, the daughter of a businessman in Mineyama city

1942 second son, Mineo, was born

1943 was conscripted to the Japanese navy

1945 the end of WWII. He was restrained in the internment camp in Singapore

1947 Returned to Japan from Singapore, obtained his working place in the Shimazu Corporation, a precision instrument company, and continued to work there until 1970

1981 his wife Sizuyo died. He then lived alone in Kyoto

2007 died at the age of 97 in Kyoto city

Sizuyo Tokuda 徳田 静代

1917 born in the northern part of Kyoto Prefecture, Mineyama city

1938 married Noboru Tokuda by arranged introduction

1942 gave birth to second son, Mineo

1943 after her husband was conscripted into the navy, she opened a new store for cosmetics and kept it until 1975

1981 died at the age of 64 in Kyoto city

Shomei Tomatsu, born in Nagoya in 1930, started photography at the age of twenty, out of the burned ruins of his hometown. After working for the staff of *Iwanami Shashin Bunko* for two years, he went freelance, studying and documenting the impact of American occupation on postwar Japan, which has become a major theme throughout his career. In 1960 Tomatsu turned his camera on the aftermath of the atomic bomb in Nagasaki, and later he moved to Okinawa in order to document the lingering presence of the United States military in Japan's marginal southern archipelago. He stayed there until 1976, and during these very productive years, he published one of his most outstanding picture books, *The Pencil of the Sun (Taiyou no Enpitsu)*. In subsequent decades his lens has captured the elation of Japan's economic boom and the social changes wrought by rapid Westernization. In 1998, he moved from Chiba to Nagasaki, his personal final redemptive act for the postwar collective experience of the city of Nagasaki and its people. Ultimately, Tomatsu's body of work offers an unflinching, poetic record of the complex forces shaping contemporary Japanese identity. His comprehensive retrospective, *The Skin of the Nation,* was held at SFMOMA in 2006, and later toured all over the world. Tomatsu, still active as a photographer, now divides his time between Nagasaki and Naha, Okinawa.

Stewart Wachs, who grew up in two cultures in California and has lived in at least two more in Japan since 1984, is a non-fiction writer who enjoys crafting profiles, interviews and essays that incorporate narratives. He periodically seeks to puncture his own preconceptions and finds, in writing, a path for doing so. Stewart is also an editor, translator, teacher and photographer. He serves as Associate Editor of the international quarterly *Kyoto Journal* (www.kyotojournal.org) and as Professor of British & American Studies at Kyoto University of Foreign Studies. His writing has appeared in books, magazines and newspapers, including the Travel Section and the Op-Ed page of *The New York Times.* Stewart has also directed Shakespeare and Chekhov plays onstage and produced documentaries and video shorts. He lives with his wife Etsuko next to Lake Biwa; they have one daughter, Alisa.

Laura Williams is an artist who has created large scale props for many clients, including Ringling Brothers Circus, Saturday Night Live, MTV, and Sesame Street; she has done commissioned illustrations and design for Algonquin Books, *The Wall Street Journal,* Mary Kay Cosmetics, Viacom, and many others. It is her lifelong love of fabric that has instilled a true passion for pattern. She has recently been featured on the popular art and design blogs *Lost at E Minor, The Fox is Black,* Design.org and Poolga.com; her work has been published in *Patterns* (Mao Mao Publications, Spain), and in *Design Stars Boulevard,* a special collection publication by *dpi,* a popular design magazine from Taiwan.

Stephen Woodhams is a Californian writer and former editor of *The Short Story Review,* whose work has appeared in *Fiction Monthly* and the *San Francisco Chronicle.*

Born in Japan, **Kentaro Yamaki** trampolined from West Germany to East Berlin during childhood, lived in Yokohama through his teenage years, in Tokyo, California and India during his early twenties, then started to work at a Japan-based NGO that enabled further expeditions to other places on the globe. Recently, he set foot in Australia. Contact: kentaro.a.yamaki@gmail.com

---

Karen Tei Yamashita is a Japanese American writer from California. She lived for nine years in Brazil, the setting for her first two novels, *Through the Arc of the Rain Forest* (Coffee House Press, 1990), awarded the *American Book Award* and *The Janet Heidinger Kafka Award,* and *Brazil-Maru,* named by the *Village Voice* as one of the *25 best books of 1992.* Her third novel, set in Los Angeles, *Tropic of Orange* (1997), was a finalist for the *Paterson Fiction Prize.* A fourth book of mixed genres in fiction and nonfiction, *Circle K Cycles* (2001), is based on her research of the Brazilian community in Japan. Her most recent novel, *I Hotel* (2010), awarded the *California Book Award,* the *American Book Award,* the *Asian Pacific American Library Association Award,* and finalist for the *National Book Award,* is set in the San Francisco Bay Area and the historic backdrop of the Asian American movement from 1968 to 1977. Currently, she is Professor of Literature and Creative Writing at the University of California, Santa Cruz.

Shunichi Yamashita M.D. was born in 1952. He graduated from the Nagasaki University School of Medicine in 1978 and has been a full professor at the Atomic Bomb Disease Institute, Nagasaki University School of Medicine since October 1990. His professional fields are Endocrinology, especially Thyroidology, Molecular Biology and International Health and Radiation Research. He was dispatched from Nagasaki University to the World Health Organization (WHO) in Geneva as a Leading Scientist for two years starting in 2004. Dr. Yamashita is the Director of the WHO Collaborating Center for Research on Thyroid Disease and of the WHO-REMPAN centers in Japan. He has held the directorship of the World Albert Schweitzer Center in Japan and currently the project leadership of Global COE Program "Strategic Center for Radiation Health Risk Control in Japan." He is on the board of directors of the Japan Endocrine Society and is the president of the Japan Thyroid Association. Dr. Yamashita has received several medical academy awards and also special acknowledgements from the former USSR, such as Honorary Diploma of Franciska Skaryna from Belarus and Order of Friendship from Russia, owing to his contributions to victims of Chernobyl. As an author and co-author, he has published more than 350 peer-reviewed English papers. Currently after the quake/tsunami and the nuclear disaster at Fukushima Daiichi Nuclear Power Plants, Dr. Yamashita has been appointed an Official Advisor of radiation health risk management by the Fukushima Governor. He has also been appointed one of the governmental Special Advisors of the Nuclear Disaster Handling Team under the Cabinet.

Katsunori Yamazato received his doctorate from the University of California at Davis and is professor of American literature and culture at the University of the Ryukyus. His books include *Poetics of Place: Reading Gary Snyder* (2006), Japanese translations of Snyder's *Place in Space* (2000), *Rivers and Mountains without End* (2002), *A Narrative History of Ryudai, 1947-1972* (2010), and *Voices from Okinawa* (2010), which he co-edited with Frank Stewart. *Shaping the Land: Mobility in America Culture* (2011), the latest book that he edited, collects essays on American literature and culture in terms of mobility in American society. He won the fifth Ryukyu Shimpo short story award in 1977 and an Okinawa Times Grand Prize for literature in 2009.

Kyoko Yoshida's short stories have appeared in *Beloit Fiction Journal, Chelsea, Massachusetts Review* and others. An honorary fellow of the International Writing Program in 2005 at the University of Iowa, she presently teaches English at Keio University. Her other translations include Masataka Matsuda's *Like a Butterfly, My Nostalgia* (with Andy Bragen) and a collection of poems, *Spectacle & Pigsty,* by Kiwao Nomura (with Forrest Gander).

—
Librarians from Kyoto Sangyo
University.

About the Editor

Elizabeth McKenzie was the recipient of a Japan–U.S. Friendship Commission Fellowship in 2010. Her writing has appeared in *The Atlantic Monthly,* the Pushcart Prize anthology, *Best American Nonrequired Reading,* and *The New York Times,* among others. Her story collection *Stop That Girl* was short-listed for The Story Prize, and was a *Newsday* and *School Library Journal* Top Ten Book of the Year. Her novel *MacGregor Tells the World* was a *Chicago Tribune* Best Book of the year, a *San Francisco Chronicle* Notable Book, and a *School Library Journal* Top Ten Book of the year. McKenzie is co-editor of the *Chicago Quarterly Review* and lives in Santa Cruz, California.

Typographer's Note

The pages in this book follow classic quarto proportions: 6.75" x 9". The shape of the page however, comes from themes within the book itself: regularity suddenly halted, normalcy shifted, emptiness revealed. Margins are reversed: thin on the outside, but deep inside. The main body is off-center.

This book is set in Akkurat, a contemporary typeface designed by Laurenz Brunner. It combines humanistic proportions and features along with an impeccable sans serif clarity.